Golfing in

Washington

The *Complete* guide to Washington's golf facilities

Sixteenth Edition by: Daniel MacMillan

Published by:

MAC
Productions

Golf Guides Since 1986

Book4golf.com

WARREN MILLER

Waiver on Accuracy
We have gone to great lengths to provide the golfer with an up-to-date, accurate and comprehensive guide to golfing facilities in the state of Washington; nevertheless, we all slice it out of bounds from time to time. Each course reserves the right to change their prices and policies at any time and we will not be held liable for any inaccuracies presented in this book.

Library of Congress Cataloging-in-Publication Data in progress
MacMillan, Daniel E. ; Golfing in Washington;
The complete guide to Washington's Golf facilities (sixteenth edition)
1. Golf course guide-Washington State
2. Travel-golf related in Washington State

Printed in Canada

Cover photographs appear courtesy of:
Washington National Golf Club & Trophy Lake Golf & Casting
Photographs by Rob Perry, Rob Perry Photography ©
4466 140th Avenue NE; Bellevue, WA 98005; (425) 556-9510

1st Editon, April 1986	2nd Edition, May 1987
3rd Edition, May 1988	4th Edition, April 1989
5th Edition, March 1990	6th, Edition, March 1991
7th Edition, March 1992	8th Edition, March 1993
9th Edition, March 1994	10th Edition, March 1995
11th Edition, March 1996	12th Edition, April 1997
13th Edition, March 1998	14th Edition, March 1999
15th Edition, March 2000	16th Edition, March 2001

ISBN 1-878591-56-8 $12.95

Published by:
MAC Productions P.O. Box 84; Duvall, Washington 98019 USA
Phone: (425) 844-8406; FAX: (425) 844-9245
Web-Site: www.macproductionsgolf.com
e-mail address: mac.productions@gte.net

Preface

In this the **sixteenth edition** of "**Golfing in Washington**" I hope it will be the most complete golf guide in the state published to date. The size is designed with the idea that the book will more easily fit in your glove box or golf bag. We have also provided small map inserts along with the driving directions to help you get to the golf facilities. As always you will find new courses, par 3's, and ranges just opened or due to open later in the season. Layouts, prices and yardage have been revised to reflect any changes that have occurred since last year. I hope you enjoy the book, see you on the links!

Acknowledgements

A special thanks to all the pros, owners and course managers who have been so helpful in providing us access to their courses and current information.

Thanks to the Oregon Department of Transportation, Washington Department of Transportation and the Idaho Department of transportation for the endless supply of maps needed in doing this project.

Thanks to Bob (the big picture) Valentine and his personal touch on these projects over the years, Thanks Robert!!

Thanks to the staff at Valco Graphics for the special touch they put on every cover of our golf guides. Nadene you are the best!

Thanks to Brian and Christie Kruhlak for the endless stream of phone calls that have to be made to keep the information current.

To my children Joshua Daniel, Sarah Gene and Christian Rogers for showing me what really is important in life.

Thanks to my loving wife Kristi Gene. Words cannot express the love and support she has given me on this project. I feel blessed to have a wife whom provided a loving, caring, Christ like atmosphere in which to produce this book in. Thanks Kristi Gene. Most importantly my Lord Jesus, for his gentle hand and firm grip with my life and this company.

Daniel

GOLF COURSE LISTINGS

Daniel MacMillan has been an avid golfer for the past 16 years. He enjoys researching and playing the various golf courses of the Pacific Northwest (if it were only that easy!!). *Golfing in Washington* was the brainchild of Daniel and his previous partner Mark Fouty who, one day while playing a round at Snohomish Golf Course, discussed finding a guide to use themselves. When no such guide was available this one was written. The book has taken on many stages. It was originally called *Golfing in Western Washington*, which encompassed only the more populous half of the state. In 1988 it expanded to *Golfing in Washington* (now in it's 16th edition). Meanwhile Mark pursued a career in New York so Daniel bought out Mark's share of the company. The company has therefore become a real family operation. Daniel drags his wife Kristi and their three children throughout the west coast seeking information on new courses and facilities for upcoming publications. We hope all the thousands of miles and endless phone calls have paid off. This guide is designed to have all the information a golfer wants and needs to know about playing a course, and as a golfer Daniel has done just that.

Golfing in Oregon is the second book published by MAC Productions and written by Daniel. Now in its 11th edition it also is published on an annual basis. This book too has taken many forms it was originally called *Golfing in Oregon & Idaho*. In 1992 the book was changed to reflect the new format and now only includes the state of Oregon.

Golfing in Idaho & Montana is the third book published by MAC Productions and written by Daniel. The first edition of this book was called *Golfing In Idaho* and was published in 1994. Now in it's 2nd edition *Golfing In Idaho & Montana* was published in spring of 2000. Look for it in a pro shop or book store near you.

The Birdie Book is another one of MAC Productions titles that was first published in November of 1998. It is a coupon book that offers the golfer over $2,500.00 worth of savings at many of Oregon, Idaho and Washington's finest golf facilities and learning centers.

New territories are always being explored for writing golf course guides such as this. It takes many man hours and attention to detail to produce books of this nature. From start to finish a new book takes about two years to produce. Currently five more are in the works with many more in the initial planning stage. Look for the new publications at a pro shop or book store near you. Daniel's hope is that you will find this to be the best golf guide of its kind on the shelf. Visit us at our web site to look for new titles and the availablity of the region that you are interested in.

Our web site address is: **www.macproductionsgolf.com**

Abbreviations, Explanatory Notes and Disclaimers

Executive Course-An executive golf course is usually longer than a typical par 3 short course but shorter than a regulation course.
Private Course- A golf course that is not open to public play.
Semi-private- golf courses that are closed to the public at certain times during the week. Best to call ahead to reserve tee-times.
Tees: T-Tour; **C**-Championship; **M**-Men; **F**-Forward; **W**-Women.
W/D-Weekday; **W/E**-Weekend; **N/A**-Not available.
Course rating-This rates the degree of difficulty of course in the NorthWest and refers to the average number of shots per round a scratch golfer ought to shoot. It is figured by rating teams who factor in terrain, length and hazards of each golf course. The higher the rating the more difficult the course.
Course ratings appear courtesy of the *Pacific Northwest Golf Association* the *Oregon Golf Association* and the *Washington Golf Association.*
Slope-This is similar to the course rating but it considers other factors as well. The slope rating takes into consideration the playing difficulty of a course for handicaps above scratch. The higher the number, the more difficult the golf course. Slope ratings courtesy of the *Pacific Northwest Golf Association* and the *Oregon Golf Association.*
Greens fee- prices are subject to change at any time. Because a number of eastern Washington courses close for the winter, the prices may reflect those of last year. When two prices are given, the first refers to the 18 hole fee, the second to the 9 hole fee. "Reciprocates" refers to the practice of private courses allowing members of other private courses to play their courses. However, because some courses only reciprocate with a limited number of other courses, it's best to call first.
Trail fee- the fee a course charges an individual to use their own power cart on the course.
Reservation policy- This refers to the maximum number of days the course allows reservations to made in advance under normal circumstances.
Winter condition- Dry, damp, wet refers to the club pro's opinion of the course's condition in rainy conditions. Also whether or not the course is open.
Terrain- flat, flat some hills, relatively hilly, very hilly.
Tees- Grass or mats are the alternatives.
Spikes- many of the area golf courses are going to a soft spike policy during the peak golfing season. Be sure to check each course prior to play as the policies vary a great deal from course to course.
Course layouts/yardage- My intent is to show tees in relation to greens, obvious hazards and other holes. Some hazards may not be adequately represented, nor are trees shown. Use these layouts as a reference at the kind of golf course you are planning to visit. The more the hazards the more difficult the golf course will play.

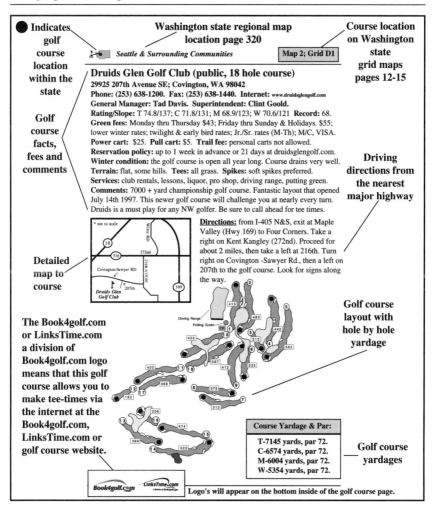

● Indicates golf course location within the state

Golf course facts, fees and comments

Detailed map to course

The Book4golf.com or LinksTime.com a division of Book4golf.com logo means that this golf course allows you to make tee-times via the internet at the Book4golf.com, LinksTime.com or golf course website.

Washington state regional map location page 320

Seattle & Surrounding Communities   Map 2; Grid D1

Course location on Washington state grid maps pages 12-15

Druids Glen Golf Club (public, 18 hole course)
29925 207th Avenue SE; Covington, WA 98042
Phone: (253) 638-1200. Fax: (253) 638-1440. Internet: www.druidsglengolf.com
General Manager: Tad Davis. Superintendent: Clint Goold.
Rating/Slope: T 74.8/137; C 71.8/131; M 68.9/123; W 70.6/121 Record: 68.
Green fees: Monday thru Thursday $43; Friday thru Sunday & Holidays. $55; lower winter rates; twilight & early bird rates; Jr./Sr. rates (M-Th); M/C, VISA.
Power cart: $25. Pull cart: $5. Trail fee: personal carts not allowed.
Reservation policy: up to 1 week in advance or 21 days at druidsglengolf.com.
Winter condition: the golf course is open all year long. Course drains very well.
Terrain: flat, some hills. Tees: all grass. Spikes: soft spikes preferred.
Services: club rentals, lessons, liquor, pro shop, driving range, putting green.
Comments: 7000 + yard championship golf course. Fantastic layout that opened July 14th 1997. This newer golf course will challenge you at nearly every turn. Druids is a must play for any NW golfer. Be sure to call ahead for tee times.

Driving directions from the nearest major highway

Directions: from I-405 N&S, exit at Maple Valley (Hwy 169) to Four Corners. Take a right on Kent Kangley (272nd). Proceed for about 2 miles, then take a left at 216th. Turn right on Covington -Sawyer Rd., then a left on 207th to the golf course. Look for signs along the way.

Golf course layout with hole by hole yardage

Course Yardage & Par:

T-7145 yards, par 72.
C-6574 yards, par 72.
M-6004 yards, par 72.
W-5354 yards, par 72.

Golf course yardages

Logo's will appear on the bottom inside of the golf course page.

All **MAC Productions** golf guides are alphabetically arranged by golf course name for easy use. You can also find the golf course locations by using our geographical index located on pages 314-319. Simply look up the nearest city or town to the location you will be visiting and the courses are listed accordingly.

In addition to this feature we also include a geographical index that is arranged by ten regions within the state of Washington. If you are visiting the Olympic Peninsula, for example, you would look in the geographical index by region on pages 321-328. Then find the Olympic Peninsula region in this section and it will tell you the names of the golf courses located in that region.

The state grid maps on pages 12-15 coincide with the map and grid numbers listed on the top right corner of each course page. These maps are intended for approximate location within the state only. The detailed map grid and driving directions are provided on the listing page for accurate course or range locations.

Map 1 ① Denotes approximate Golf Course Location.

Numbers on map correspond with golf course page numbers.

Grid→↓	1	2	3	4

British Columbia

A

N
W←↕→E
S

East Sound
Friday Harbor
197
231
159
Lopez
Island

B

Victoria
Ferry

Port
Townsend

101
Port Angeles 206
75 255
Sequim
213
53
212
104

Forks

Washington

Bremerton Area
100 121 137 145
167 225 271 283

108

C

Queets

139
16
Bremerton
3

Quinalt

140
Shelton
239

Pacific Ocean

109

D

101
Olympia

193

Aberdeen 191
12
8
105
116
101

E

Olympia Area
45 70 87 89
126 175 196 232
235 272 282

Raymond
297

Centralia
51
221
185
Chehalis
R29

257
207
103

5

F

Ilwaco
4 245

Astoria
30

157 267
103
Longview
177

101 Oregon

Woodland 152
270

Vancouver Area
36 50 84 147
198 209 227

G

Vancouver

12

Map 2

① Denotes approximate
Golf Course Location.

Numbers on map correspond
with golf course page numbers.

Grid→ ↓	1	2	3	4

A

Blaine

158 222
33 67 119 218
104 83 23
237 34 233
Bellingham

Bellingham Area
31 141 184 188
241 250

N
W←→E
S

243

22
234 Marblemount

20

B

148 242
95
295
Mt. Vernon
76 202

5
99
41 49
135
26 Everett
277 118 113
130 136 156
161 246 91 35
186 178
241 77 Monroe
300 176

Everett Area
82 110 151 285

134

C

170

Seattle
290 28
37
210 247 259
274 248 183
94 North End

2

Eastside Communities
30 47 66 98 172
201 229 260 264 298

D

163 43
96
1 8
92 Tacoma
5
273
55 86 220
174 166
143 74 63
21 78
114 132
80

Bellevue
48

90

97

90

Seattle & Surrounding Communities
38 97 106 127
128 131 133 217
232 236 275 289
293

187

261

E

7

115

12

252

Morton
129
165

F

Washington

Tacoma & Surrounding Communities
17 19 39 57 88 93
117 142 154 155 168 173
189 190 251 258 262 276
287 296

G

112

107

42

244 14 122
27

Goldendale
102
123

Oregon

Map 3

① Donotes approximate Golf Course Location.

Numbers on map correspond with golf course page numbers.

Grid→↓	1	2	3	4

A

Oroville
199
Washington
97

N
W ↔ E
S

B

20
253
29
Twisp

195 Omak

144

25 Coulee Dam

C

150 Leavenworth
18 138 162
97
72
2

281
155

D

97
182
2 291
Wenatchee 266 224
65
216

90

146
192
Moses Lake Area
124 179 180
194
Moses Lake

E

Ellensburg
46 79
82
226

12 Yakima
71
Yakima Area
20 90 256 294 301 302

228
214 Othello
200

Tri-Cities Area
40 44 60 61 120
169 204 254 269 292

395

F

181
160 Sunnyside
97
52
82

Pasco
Richland
Kennewick

G

14

Oregon
395

14

Map 4 ① Denotes approximate Golf Course Location.

Numbers on map correspond with golf course page numbers.

Grid→ ↓	1	2	3	4

Laurier

205

N
W←→E
S

A

240

Colville 62

238

IDAHO

21

54

B

395

32

68

2

69

C

2

Spokane

90

111

153 171
278

85

230

D

90

195

263

90 219

Ritzville

395

Colfax 59

E

12

288

Pullman

211

F

Washington

56
Clarkston

280

268

215

284 Walla Walla

129

IDAHO

G

125

Oregon

Spokane & Surrounding Communiies
64 73 81
109 125 149
164 203 208
249 253 286

15

Alderbrook Golf & Yacht Club (semi-private, 18 hole course)
E 300 Country Club Drive East; Union, WA 98592
Phone:(360) 898-2560, 888-898-2560. Fax: (360) 898-2492.
Pro: Mike Fields, PGA. Supt.: Dwane Ehrich. Internet: alderbrookgolf.com
Rating/Slope: C 70.3/118; M 69.0/115; W 71.5/116. **Course record:** 61.
Green fees: W/D $25/$15; W/E $30/$18; Sr. rates $18 (M-F); M/C, VISA.
Power cart: $23/$13. **Pull cart:** $3/$1.50. **Trail fee:** $8 for personal carts.
Reservation policy: yes, 3 weeks for members & guests; 1 week for the public.
Winter condition: the golf course is open all year. Dry conditions, drains well.
Terrain: flat, some hills. **Tees:** all grass. **Spikes:** no metal spikes April to Oct.
Services: club rentals, lessons, snack bar, beer, pro shop, club fitting, tennis
courts, driving range. **Comments:** Picturesque setting above Hood Canal and
the beautiful Olympic Peninsula. Well stocked pro shop that will service all
your golfing needs. The golf course has excellent drainage for winter play.

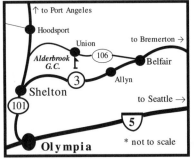

Directions: from I-5 south take Hwy
16 over the Tacoma Narrows Bridge.
Follow Hwy 16 to Hwy 3 (look for signs
to Belfair). Proceed on Hwy 3 through
Belfair and take Hwy 106 cut-off to
Union. Proceed on Hwy 106 along
Hood Canal for 15 minutes. When you
arrive in Union the golf course will be
on your left. Look for signs at your turn.

Course Yardage & Par:
C-6326 yards, par 72; M-6037 yards, par 72; W-5500 yards, par 73.

Allenmore Golf Club (public, 18 hole course)

2125 South Cedar; Tacoma, WA 98405
Phone:(253) 627-7211 or (877) 627-7211. Fax: none. Internet: none.
Pro: Don Mojean, PGA. Superintendent: Arne Smith.
Rating/Slope: C N/A; M 68.3/118; W 72.6/123. **Course record:** 60.
Green fees: W/D $22/$16; W/E $23/$17; Jr. & Sr. rates (M-F); VISA, M/C.
Power cart: $20/$10. **Pull cart:** $3/$2. **Trail fee:** $3 for personal carts.
Reservation policy: please call up to 1 week in advance for tee times.
Winter condition: the golf course is open all year long. Dry conditions.
Terrain: relatively hilly. **Tees:** all grass. **Spikes:** metal spikes permitted.
Services: club rentals, lessons, snack bar, pro shop, lockers, showers. No knob
shoes, 5-somes OK if they play fast. **Comments:** Great golf course for hosting
tournaments and special events. Good public course that gets a great deal of play
during the summer months so make your tee times well in advance for weekend
or holiday play. The course drains fairly well making this a good winter track.

Directions: from I-5 N&S exit to Hwy
16W(Gig Harbor-Bremerton). Proceed
for a short distance to the Sprague Ave.
exit. Continue on Sprague for .4 miles to
S 19th St. Take a left on S 19th. Proceed
to Cedar St. Left on Cedar Street. Golf
course entrance will be located on your
left. Look for signs marking your turn.

Course Yardage & Par:
C-6355 yards, par 71.
M-6026 yards, par 71.
W-5853 yards, par 74.

Alta Lake Golf Course (public, 18 hole course)

P.O. Box 85; Alta Lake Road; Pateros, WA 98846
Phone: (509) 923-2359. Fax: (509) 923-9467. Internet: none.
Owners: Don & Susan Barth. Pro: none.
Rating/Slope: C 71.3/125; M 69.5/121; W 69.9/118. **Course record:** 71.
Green fees: $22/$14 all week long; VISA, M/C.
Power cart: $22/$14. **Pull cart:** $3/$2. **Trail fee:** $5 for personal carts.
Reservation policy: yes, you may call ahead for a tee time, (a must in summer).
Winter condition: the golf course is closed from November to mid March.
Terrain: relatively hilly. **Tees:** all grass. **Spikes:** soft spikes only.
Services: club rentals, snack bar, beer, pro shop, motel on the 9th green.
Comments: links type course designed after the links of Scotland. Rolling terrain and the desert framing each fairway make this course a special place to play. Views of the Columbia River and Alta Lake can be seen from the course.

<u>Directions:</u> the golf course is located southwest of Pateros, Washington. From Highway 97 follow the signs to Alta Lake State Park where the course is located. (this is approximately 17 miles north of Lake Chelan).

Course Yardage & Par:
C-6659 yards, par 72.
M-6281 yards, par 72.
W-5748 yards, par 72.

American Lake VA Golf Course (private, 9 hole course)
Dept. of Veteran's Affairs, VA Medical Center; Tacoma, WA 98493
Phone: (253) 582-8440 ext. 6762. Fax: none. Internet: none.
Pro: none. Superintendent: none.
Rating/Slope: the golf course is not rated. **Course record:** none.
Green fees: private club, members & patients of the VA hospital only.
Power cart: private club. **Pull cart:** private club. **Trail fee:** private club.
Reservation policy: private club, member & guests only. No public play.
Winter condition: closed December thru January.
Terrain: flat, some steep hills. **Tees:** grass. **Spikes:** no restrictions.
Services: very limited services.
Comments: built in 1957 this 9 hole course features hilly terrain and small greens. Trees line all fairways making accuracy off the tee a must. Bunkers are in play on nearly every second shot. The golf course can get very busy during the summer months with different VA functions.

<u>Directions:</u> the golf course is located on the Fort Lewis Military Reservation. From I-5 N&S exit at the Gravelly Lake exit #124. Proceed westbound on Gravelly Lake DR SW until you reach Veterans DR SW. Turn left. Proceed on Veterans DR SW as it veers left and then right. The golf course will be located just ahead on your right hand side.

Course Yardage & Par:
M-2862 yards, par 35.
W-2706 yards, par 35.

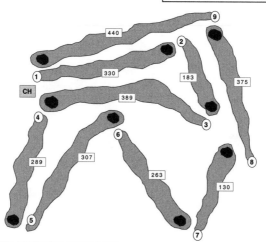

Apple Tree Golf Course (public, 18 hole course)
8804 Occidental Avenue; Yakima, WA 98903
Phone: (509) 966-5877. **Fax:** (509) 966-5537. **Internet:** www.appletreegolf.com
Mgr: Cory Groves. **Pro:** Todd Capps, PGA. **Supt.:** John Hull. **Record:** 62.
Rating/Slope: T 73.5/135; C 71.9/129; M 70.3/126; S 68.3/122; W 71.5/127.
Green fees: Monday thru Thursday $38 (+tax); Friday thru Sunday $53 (+ tax).
Power cart: $26 (plus tax). **Pull cart:** $6 (plus tax). **Trail fee:** $6 (+ tax).
Reservation policy: yes, please call ahead for your tee time info (30 days).
Winter condition: the golf course is open all year long, weather permitting.
Terrain: flat, some hills. **Tees:** all grass. **Spikes:** metal spikes not permitted.
Services: club rentals, lessons, snack bar & grill, pro shop, restaurant, banquet
facilities, beer, wine, driving range, putting & chipping greens, practice area.
Comments: Fantastic layout with an island green on the 17th hole in the shape
of a "Washington Apple". If you are looking for a course that is a pleasure to
play I highly recommend this top rate facility. This track is worth a special trip
so make sure you include Apple Tree in any eastern Washington golf vacation.

<u>Directions:</u> From I-82 take the Nob Hill
exit #34. Follow W Nob Hill westbound
to 64th Ave. Turn left on S 64th Ave.
Proceed on S 64th Ave. to Occidental
Ave. Turn right on Occidental Avenue.
Follow to 88th Avenue. Left to the
clubhouse. The golf course will be on
both sides of Occidental Avenue.

Course Yardage & Par:

T-6892 yards, par 72.
C-6618 yards, par 72.
M-6311 yards, par 72.
S-5857 yards, par 72.
F-5428 yards, par 72.

Auburn Golf Course (public, 18 hole course)
29630 Green River Road SE; Auburn, WA 98092
Phone: (253) 833-2350. Fax: none. Internet: none.
Pro: Doug Campbell, PGA. Superintendent: Kevin Van.
Rating/Slope: C 69.5/111; M 68.3/109; W 70.4/114. **Course record:** 62.
Green fees: W/D $23/$16; W/E $27/$18; Jr./Sr. rates (M-Th), twilight (M-F).
Power cart: $22/$14. **Pull cart:** $3/$2. **Trail fee:** $10 for personal carts.
Reservation policy: yes, please call ahead up to 1 week in advance for times.
Winter condition: the golf course is open all year long. Drains well.
Terrain: flat, some hills. **Tees:** grass. **Spikes:** metal spikes permitted.
Services: club rentals, lessons, snack bar, beer, pro shop, putting green.
Comments: water and sand comes into play on several holes. The front nine
is fairly wide open. The back nine is more hilly with trees coming into play
throughout. The well stocked pro shop will serve all your golfing needs.
Excellent public course that has spent 2 million dollars in improvements in the
last 10 years. Auburn is the best public golf course for the money in the area.

Directions: from I-5 N&S take exit #147
(S 272nd St.). Go east on S 272nd for 2.4
miles to Hwy 167 S. S for 2 miles to 15th
St NW exit. Go east on 15th NW for 1
mile to Harvey Rd. South for .5 miles to
8th NE. East for .4 mile to 104th SE. Go
north for .8 miles to SE 307th Pl-Green
River Road. Go for 1 mile to the course.

Course Yardage & Par:
C-6020 yards, par 71.
M-5571 yards, par 71.
W-5571 yards, par 73.

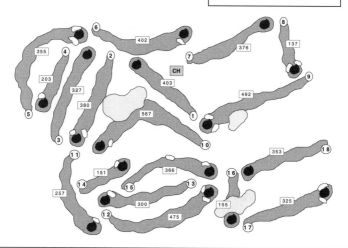

Avalon Golf Club (public, 27 hole course)

19345 Kelleher Road; Burlington, WA 98233 Internet: www.avalonlinks.com
Phone: (360) 757-1900 or 1-800-624-0202. Fax: (360) 757-2555.
Pro: Brian Kruhlak, PGA. Supt.: Rick Mooney. Course record: 69.
Rating/Slope: South/North: T 72.3/124; C 70.3/122; M 68.2/118; W 71.3/117.
Green fees: M-Th. $34; Fri. $38; Sat.-Sun. Hol. $42/$25 (all+tax); M/C, VISA.
Power cart: $25. Pull cart: $4. Trail fee: $25 for personal carts.
Reservation policy: up to 7 days or no time limit if payment is by credit card.
Winter condition: the golf course is open all year long. No temporary greens.
Terrain: flat, some hills. Tees: all grass. Spikes: no metal spikes April to Oct.
Services: club rentals, lessons, restaurant, beer, wine, pro shop, driving range,
caddy service in season, putting green. Comments: First rate golfing facility that
will not dissapoint. This 27 hole Robert Muir Graves designed course offers
spectacular views of the Skagit Valley and surrounding countryside. Avalon has
played host to the 1994 and the 2001 US Open Qualifying rounds. Great course.

Directions: from I-5 N&S take exit #232
(Cook Road).Turn east and go for 1 block
to the traffic light. Turn left and go north
on old Hwy 99. When you reach Kelleher
Road turn right. Go beyond the Humane
Society and a make a left at the sign.

Rating/Slope:
West/South: T 71.5/128; C 69.7/124; M 67.8/118; W 70.6/115.
North/West: T 71.6/126; C 69.8/121; M 67.8/115; W 69.9/115.

Course Yardage & Par:
North: T-3428 yards, C-3201 yards, M-3001 yards, W-2726 yards, par 36.
South: T-3375 yards, C-3205 yards, M-3005 yards, W-2808 yards, par 36.
West: T-3201 yards, C-3001 yards, M-2797 yards, W-2510 yards, par 36.

Baker's Edge Golf Course (public, 9 hole course)

8225 Kendall Road; Sumas, WA 98295
Phone: (360) 599-2416. Fax: (360) 599-2416. Internet: none.
Owner/Manager: Gary Lau. Superintendent: Gary Lau.
Rating/Slope: M 61/94; W 65.1/103. **Course record:** 64.
Green fees: W/D $16/$8; W/E $18/$10; Jr. & Sr. rates (M-F); VISA, M/C.
Power cart: $15/$10. **Pull cart:** $2. **Trail fee:** $3 for personal carts.
Reservation policy: please call in advance for tee-times.
Winter condition: dry conditions, the golf course is open all year long.
Terrain: flat, some hills. **Tees:** all grass. **Spikes:** metal spikes permitted.
Services: club rentals, snack bar, pro shop, club memberships, putting green.
Comments: bunkers come into play on five holes, however, the fairways are quite open. The course is very flat and easy to walk. This track has excellent views of the nearby mountains and surrounding countryside. A rustic golf course that is excellent for beginners and families. Dry winter conditions.

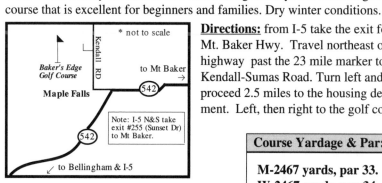

Directions: from I-5 take the exit for the Mt. Baker Hwy. Travel northeast on the highway past the 23 mile marker to the Kendall-Sumas Road. Turn left and proceed 2.5 miles to the housing development. Left, then right to the golf course.

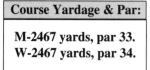

Course Yardage & Par:
M-2467 yards, par 33. **W-2467 yards, par 34.**

Ballinger Lakes Golf Course (public, 9 hole course)
23000 Lakeview Drive; Mountlake Terrace, WA 98043
Phone: (425) 775-6467. Fax: (425) 775-6468. Internet: ballingerlakesgolf.com
Owners: Jan Japar & Mimi Racicot. Superintendent: Matt Kimball.
Rating/Slope: C N/A; M 64.6/115; W 69.0/119. **Course record:** N/A.
Green fees: Mon. thru Thur. $15 (9 holes); Friday thru W/E's $16.50 (9 holes);
add'l 9 $12; Jr. & Sr. rates Monday-Thursday $13.50; VISA, MC, AMEX, DIS.
Power cart: limited/seasonal. **Pull cart:** $2.50. **Trail fee:** not allowed.
Reservation policy: yes, daily. Please call 1 week in advance year round.
Winter condition: the course is open all year long. Fair conditions in winter
Terrain: rolling hills with ponds. **Tees:** grass tees. **Spikes:** soft spikes only.
Services: beer and wine service on golf course & clubhouse. Grill, restaurant
and banquet facilities. Golf shop featuring equipment and apparel.
Comments: Ballinger Lakes Golf Course brand new layout opened for play in
May, 2000. The new Overdorf design is outstanding. The challenging layout
will be prove to be one of the best 9 hole courses in the Northwest. Improved
drainage and affordable green fees make this golf course a must play.

Directions: I-5 N take exit #178 to 236th
SW. Go west on 236th which becomes
Lakeview Dr. for .7 miles. I-5 S take
exit #179 to 220th SW. Go west on 220th
SW to 66th Ave. Go south for 1 mile to
Lakeview Dr. Go west on Lakeview Dr.
to the course.

Course Yardage & Par:
B-2564 yards, par 34.
M-2408 yards, par 34.
F-2267 yards, par 34.

Banks Lake Golf Club (public, 9 hole course)

19849 Ludolph Road NE; Electric City, WA 99123
Phone: (509) 633-0163. Fax: (509) 633-0619. Internet: none.
Manager/Pro: John W Combs Jr. Superintendent: John W Combs Jr.
Rating/Slope: M 68.1/103; W 70.2/110. **Course record:** 68.
Green fees: W/D $18/$14; W/E $20/$16; no special rates; VISA, M/C.
Power cart: $20/$12. **Pull cart:** $2. **Trail fee:** $5 for personal carts.
Reservation policy: yes, you may call in advance for a tee time, no restrictions.
Winter condition: the golf course is closed December through February.
Terrain: flat, some hills. **Tees:** grass. **Spikes:** soft spikes only.
Services: lessons, driving range, snack bar, beverages, pro shop, putting green.
Comments: rolling lush terrain situated in the midst of the "desert" in eastern
Washington. The golf course is relatively new and kept in excellent condition.
The course sports dual tees for those wanting a different look on the 2nd nine.
Good 9 hole tract that offers the golfer a very friendly atmosphere.

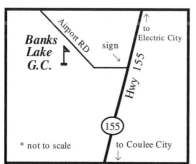

Directions: the golf course is located 2
miles south of Electric City off of Hwy
155. There is a sign on Highway 155
marking the turn to the golf course. The
golf course is located by the airport. You
will turn on Airport Road to the golf
course which will be located on the left
hand side of the road.

Course Yardage & Par:
M-3055 yards, par 36.
W-2763 yards, par 36.
Dual tees for 18 holes:
M-6127 yards, par 72.
W-5526 yards, par 72.

Battle Creek Golf Course (public 18 hole, 9 hole par 3 courses)

6006 Meridian Avenue North; Marysville, WA 98271
Phone: 800-655-7931, (360) 659-7931. Fax: (360) 659-3431.
Pro: Jim Pulliam, PGA. Supt.: Gene Connor. Internet: www.battlecreeklinks.com
Rating/Slope: C 71.2/121; M 69.3/116; W 70.5/121. **Record:** C 68; M 66.
Green fees: Weekdays $23 (+tax); Weekends & Holidays $30 (+tax);
Jr. & Sr. rates (Monday-Thursday); Winter rates (Nov.-February); VISA, MC.
Green fees for the par 3 course: W/D $12/$7.50; W/E $16/$9.50.
Power cart: $22/$13. **Pull cart:** $3/$2. **Trail fee:** $9 for personal carts.
Reservation policy: yes, call up to 7 days in advance for your tee-times.
Winter condition: the golf course is open all year long. Dry, good drainage.
Terrain: some hills. **Tees:** all grass. **Spikes:** soft spikes preferred.
Services: club rentals, lessons, cafe, beer, wine, pro shop, grass tees in practice
area, driving range, club memberships. **Comments:** excellent, scenic golf course
that wanders thru woodlands and wetlands. Greens have improved dramatically
over the last few years so be sure to add Battle Creek to your weekend outings.

Directions: from I-5 N&S take exit #199
(Tulalip-Marysville). Go west on Marine
DR for 2.75 miles. Turn right on Meridian
Avenue. Travel north for .75 miles to the
course. Note: look for a sign at your turn.

Course Yardage & Par:
C-6575 yards, par 73.
M-6153 yards, par 73.
W-5391 yards, par 73.

Beacon Rock Golf Course (public, 9 hole course)

Box 189; Highway 14; North Bonneville, WA 98639
Phone: (509) 427-5730, 800-428-5730. Fax: (509) 427-5710. Internet: none.
Owners: James & Linda Borup. Superintendent: James Borup.
Rating/Slope: M 67.5/115; W 69.7/109. **Course record:** 29.
Green fees: $22/$12 all week long; Senior rates Tuesday-Thursday; M/C, VISA.
Power cart: $10 per nine holes. **Pull cart:** $3/$2. **Trail fee:** $5.
Reservation policy: yes, you may call 7 days in advance for a tee times.
Winter condition: the golf course is open all year round. Drains very well.
Terrain: flat (easy walking). **Tees:** all grass. **Spikes:** metal spikes permitted.
Services: club rentals, restaurant, beer, beverages, pro shop, putting green.
Comments: this excellent walking golf course features tree lined fairways and
spectacular views of the Columbia Gorge. Dual tees are available for a different
look on your second nine. The course is playable throughout the entire year.

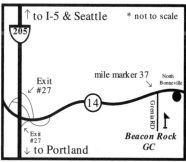

<u>Directions:</u> the golf course is located
west of North Bonneville off of Hwy 14.
Exit at Grenia Street to the course. Watch
for a sign on the highway marking your
way to the course. If coming from I-205
N&S be sure to exit to Hwy 14 (exit #27)
going eastbound (Lewis & Clark Hwy).

Course Yardage & Par:
M-2753 yards, par 36.
W-2555 yards, par 36.
<u>Dual tees for 18 holes:</u>
M-5594 yards, par 72.
W-4984 yards, par 72.

Bear Creek Country Club (private, 18 hole course)

13737 202nd Avenue NE; Woodinville, WA 98072
Phone: (425) 881-1350. Fax: (425) 869-0894. Internet: www.bearcreekcc.com
Pro: Rex Fullerton, PGA. **Supt.:** P. J. Patuzak. **Course record:** 68.
Rating/Slope: T 75.0/139; C 72.5/132; M 69.3/128; W 71.7/124.
Green fees: private club, members & guests only; Jr. rates; VISA, M/C.
Power cart: private club, members & guests only. **Pull cart:** members only.
Reservation policy: private club, members & guests of members only.
Winter condition: the golf course is open all year long. Dry conditions.
Terrain: relatively hilly. **Tees:** all grass. **Spikes:** soft spikes May-September.
Services: club rentals, lessons, snack bar, beer, wine, liquor, pro shop, lockers,
showers, driving range, putting green. **Comments:** very difficult course where
shot placement is a must. Hilly terrain gives the golfer a wide variety of lies.
Out of bounds comes into play a nearly every hole. Excellent private course.

Directions: from I-405 N&S take exit
#20B (NE 124th) to NE 124th. Travel
eastbound for 4.25 miles to Avondale
Road. Go North for .1 miles (your turn
will come up quickly, veer left) to NE
132nd. Go east for .3 miles to NE 133rd.
Go eastbound on 133rd until you reach
202ND Ave NE, take a left to the course.

Course Yardage & Par:		
T-6964 yards, par 72; C-6422 yards, par 72.		
M-5822 yards, par 72; W-5240 yards, par 72.		

Bear Creek Golf Course (public, 9 hole course)

8 A Bear Creek Golf Course Road; Winthrop, WA 98862
Phone: (509) 996-2284. Fax: (509) 996-3243. Internet: www.bearcreekgolfcourse.com
Managers: Ashley & Linda Court. Superintendent: Ashley Court.
Rating/Slope: M 69.4/117; W 70.1/112. **Course record:** 65.
Green fees: W/D $22/$14; W/E $25/$16; M/C, VISA.
Power cart: $20/$10. **Pull cart:** $2. **Trail fee:** $2.50 for personal carts.
Reservation policy: yes, recommended for weekends and holidays only.
Winter condition: the golf course is closed from November thru March.
Terrain: relatively hilly. **Tees:** all grass. **Spikes:** soft spikes preferred.
Services: club rentals, snack bar, beer, beverages, practice green, pro shop.
Comments: the course has beautiful views of the North Cascades. Fairways are well-kept, lush and green. Water, and trees are the primary hazard from the tee and on your approach shots. Versatility of placement on the back set of tees makes you feel like you've played 18 holes. If you are looking for nice 9 hole course in a great area of Washington try Bear Creek it will not disappoint you.

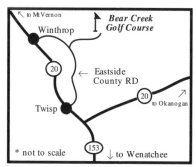

Directions: the golf course is located north of Twisp and east of Winthrop. From Hwy 20 go 7 miles north on Eastside County Road. The golf course is located 3/4 of a mile up the first paved road on the right hand side. Look for signs marking your way to the course.

Course Yardage & Par:
M-3168 yards, par 36.
W-2760 yards, par 37.
Dual tees for 18 holes:
M-6271 yards, par 72.
W-5322 yards, par 73.

Bellevue Golf Course (public, 18 hole course)
5500 140th NE; Bellevue, WA 98005
Phone: (425) 452-7250. **Fax:** (425) 869-3857. **Internet:** none.
Director of Golf: K. C. Anderson, PGA. **Course record:** 60.
Head Professional: Steve Hubbard, PGA. **Superintendent:** Tom Robinson.
Rating/Slope: M 66.3/105; W 67.5/109.   (*fee prices subject to change).
Green fees: W/D $22*; W/E $25*; Jr./Sr. rates (M-Th $16*); M/C, VISA.
Power cart: $25/$15. **Pull cart:** $4. **Trail fee:** to be determined.
Reservation policy: please call Monday for the entire weeks tee-times.
Winter condition: the golf course is open all year long. Excellent drainage.
Terrain: flat, some hills. **Tees:** grass. **Spikes:** metal spikes permitted.
Services: club rentals, lessons, snack bar, beer, wine, pro shop, driving range.
Comments: starting times suggested. For being such a busy municipal course it can be found to be in excellent condition. Greens are generally in great shape during the peak season. Covered range for those wanting to practice.

Directions: from I-405 N&S take exit #17 to NE 70th St. Proceed to 140th Ave. NE and turn left. Follow 140th Ave. NE until you reach the course, which will be on your left. From I-5 N&S take exit to Hwy 520 eastbound. Go east to 148th Ave. NE. Go north on 148th for .8 miles to NE 40th. West for .5 miles to 140th NE. Travel north for 1 mile to the course.

Course Yardage & Par:
M-5535 yards, par 71; W-5081 yards, par 71.

Bellingham Golf & Country Club　(private, 18 hole course)
3729 Meridian; Bellingham, WA 98225
Phone: (360) 733-5381. **Fax:** (360) 676-9073. **Internet:** www.bellinghamgcc.com
Pro: Dean Russell, PGA. **Superintendent:** Dave Bocci.
Rating/Slope: C 71.0/123; M 69.8/120; W 72.7/124. **Course record:** 65.
Green fees: private club, member & guests only; reciprocates; no credit cards.
Power cart: private club. **Pull cart:** private club. **Trail fee:** private club.
Reservation policy: private club, member & guests only. No public play.
Winter condition: the golf course is open all year long. Dry conditions.
Terrain: flat, some hills. **Tees:** grass. **Spikes:** soft spikes March thru October.
Services: lessons, lounge, beer, wine, liquor, pro shop, lockers, showers, range.
Comments: Built in 1925 Bellingham Country Club is one of the oldest golf
courses in Whatcom County. The course drains well in the winter months and is
very walkable for the golfer. The course features tree lined fairways, small well
bunkered greens and lush conditions throughout the golfing season.

Directions: from I-5 N&S take exit #256
(Meridian St.) to Meridian St. Travel west
on Meridian Street for .2 miles to the
course which will be on the right side.

Course Yardage & Par:
C-6473 yards, par 72.
M-6220 yards, par 72.
W-5781 yards, par 73.

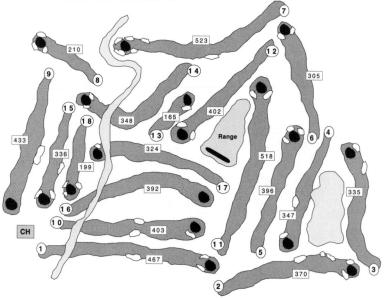

Big Bend Golf & Country Club (semi-private, 9 hole course)

P.O. Box 162; Golf Course Road; Wilbur, WA 99185
Phone: (509) 647-5664. Fax: (509) 647-5664. Internet: linwicks@excite.com
Pro: Lin Wicks, PGA. Superintendent: Lin Wicks.
Rating/Slope: C 68.5/109; M 67.4/107; W 72.5/115. **Course record:** 30.
Green fees: W/D $14/$10; W/E $18/$14; All day $20, W/E's $25. VISA, MC.
Power cart: $18/$12. **Pull cart:** $3.50/$2. **Trail fee:** $10 for personal carts.
Reservation policy: yes, please call in advance for your tee times.
Winter condition: the golf course is open until the snow flies.
Terrain: flat, some hills. **Tees:** all grass. **Spikes:** metal spikes permitted.
Services: club rentals, snack bar, lounge, beer, wine, liquor, driving range,
pro shop, showers. **Comments:** the best greens in the basin highlight this
challenging course that is fun for all levels of players. Lush fairways, strategically placed bunkers and water hazards will make you think about shot placement from the tee or fairway. You can always get a tee time at Big Bend.

Directions: the course is located south
of the junctions of Hwys 2 and 174, just
northwest of Wilbur. The golf course is
on the east side of Hwy 2. Look for a
sign on the highway marking the way to
the course. If traveling from Spokane
take Highway 2 to Wilbur.

Course Yardage & Par:
M-2985 yards, par 36.
W-2875 yards, par 37.
<u>**Dual tees for 18 holes:**</u>
M-6100 yards, par 72.
W-5705 yards, par 74.

Birch Bay Golf Club (public, 18 hole executive course)

7878 Birch Bay Drive; Blaine, WA 98230
Phone: (360) 371-7933. Fax: (360) 371-5643. Internet: wwwbirchbaygolfclub.com
Manager: Jim Trull. Superintendent: Jon Cline.
Rating/Slope: M 50.7/67; W 50.7/67. **Course record:** 47.
Green fees: W/D $15/$11; W/E $18/$13; Jr./Sr. (M-Th); M/C, VISA, DIS.
Power cart: $15. **Pull cart:** $2. **Trail fee:** N/A.
Reservation policy: yes, call up to 1 week in advance for tee times.
Winter condition: the golf course is open all year. Dry conditions.
Terrain: flat, some hills. **Tees:** grass. **Spikes:** soft spikes only.
Services: club rentals, lessons, restaurant, beer, wine, pro shop, liquor.
Comments: historical waterfront course, established in 1929, in beautiful Birch
Bay. This 18 hole executive course will challenge golfers of any caliber with its
8 water crossings and 32 sand bunkers. Undulating terrain and many natural
features create a spectacular setting for any tournament or regular golf play.

Directions: from I-5 N&S take exit
270 to Lynden-Birch Bay Road.
Travel westbound for 3.7 miles to
Harborview. Turn south. Proceed .2
miles to the bay. Turn left and travel 1/2
mile to the golf course. Look for signs
marking your turn to the facility.

Course Yardage & Par:
C-3135 yards, par 57.
M-2358 yards, par 54.
W-2075 yards, par 54.

Birch Bay Village Golf Course (private, 9 hole course)

8169 Cowichan Road; Blaine, WA 98230
Phone: (360) 371-2026. Fax: (360) 371-3254. Internet: none.
Manager/Pro: Grant Wilson. Superintendent: Craig Swanson.
Rating/Slope: C 59.6/84; M N/A; W N/A. **Course record:** 59 (18 holes).
Green fees: private golf course, members & guests only; no credit cards.
Power cart: members & guests only. **Pull cart:** private. **Trail fee:** not allowed.
Reservation policy: yes, 1 week in advance. Must be a property owner or guest.
Winter condition: the golf course is closed during inclement weather.
Terrain: flat, some hills. **Tees:** all grass. **Spikes:** metal spikes permitted.
Services: club rentals, lessons, small pro shop, putting & chipping green.
Comments: the course reciprocates for club professionals. Adjacent to Birch Bay in Whatcom County, the course houses three ponds which are in play for the majority of the round. Greens are large with dual pin placements.

Directions: from I-5 N&S take exit 270 (Lynden-Birch Bay Road), to Lynden-Birch Bay Road. Travel west for 3.7 miles to Harbor View Road. Go south for .2 miles to the road paralleling the bay. Go north for 1.3 miles to the course entrance. Look for a sign marking your turn to the private entrance.

Course Yardage & Par:
C-2120 yards, par 33.
M-1785 yards, par 30/32.
W-1605 yards, par 30.

Blue Boy West (public, 9 hole course)

27927 Florence Acres Road; Monroe, WA 98272
Phone: (360) 793-2378. **Fax:** none. **Internet:** none.
Managers: Ernie & Doug Smith. **Superintendents:** Ernie & Doug Smith.
Rating/Slope: M 61.2/98; W 64.2/109. **Course record:** 29.
Green fees: W/D $16/$11; W/E $17/$12; Jr. & Sr. rates (M thru F $14/$10).
Power cart: $10. **Pull cart:** $3/$2. **Trail fee:** no charge.
Reservation policy: yes, please call ahead 1 day for tee times.
Winter condition: the golf course is open all year long. Dry conditions.
Terrain: flat, some rolling hills. **Tees:** grass. **Spikes:** metal spikes permitted.
Services: lessons (at the Iron Eagle Sports Center in Monroe (360) 794-0933),
snack bar, beverages, pro shop, full service clubhouse to serve all your needs.
Comments: beautiful scenery, many views of the mountains and flowers. This
short golf course is very challenging. Water comes into play on eight holes. If
you are looking for a course to take the whole family to, try Blue Boy West.

Directions: from Hwy 2 in Monroe, turn
up Old Owens Road. When you come to
a "Y" in the road veer to your left. This
will be Florence Acres Road. Proceed
for approximately 4 miles to the course.
The golf course will be located on the
left hand side of the road. Look for signs
that are posted indicating your turns.

Course Yardage & Par:
M-2199 yards, par 33.
W-1938 yards, par 33.

Bowyer's Par 3 Golf, Inc. (public, 9 hole par 3 course)

11608 NE 119th; Vancouver, WA 98662
Phone: (360) 892-3808. Fax: none. Internet: none
Owners: Mike & Kim Bowyer. Superintendent: Mike Bowyer.
Rating/Slope: the golf course is not rated. **Course record:** 21.
Green fees: W/D $14/$7; W/E $15/$7.50; Jr. & Sr. rates $12/$6.50
(Monday thru Friday only); M/C, VISA, AMEX, DISCOVER.
Power cart: not available. **Pull cart:** $1.50. **Trail fee:** not allowed.
Reservation policy: none. Tee-times are on a first come first served basis.
Winter condition: the golf course is open all year long. Damp conditions.
Terrain: flat (easy walking). **Tees:** mats. **Spikes:** metal spikes permitted.
Services: club rentals, snack bar, club memberships, small, limited pro shop.
Comments: this short par 3 course is well maintained with many fir trees
towering above the fairways. Greens are of medium size and can challenge you
at every turn. If you are looking for a course that challenges your iron play, try
Bowyer's Par 3 Golf.

Directions: From I-205 N&S exit at NE 119th and travel eastbound on 119th to the golf course which will be located on your left hand side. Look for signs indicating your turn to the golf course.

Course Yardage & Par:
M-1015 yards, par 27.
W-1015 yards, par 27.

Brae Burn Golf & Country Club (private, 9 hole course)
2409 182nd Avenue NE; Redmond, WA 98052
Phone: (425) 881-0274. Fax: none. Internet: none.
Pro: none. Superintendent: Todd Tibke.
Rating/Slope: the golf course is not rated. **Course record:** 25.
Green fees: private club, members & guests only.
Power cart: none. **Pull cart:** none. **Trail fee:** not allowed.
Reservation policy: none. Private club, members & guests only.
Winter condition: the golf course is open all year long. Damp conditions.
Terrain: flat, some hills. **Tees:** grass. **Spikes:** metal spikes permitted.
Services: very limited services. Pool is for the property owners only.
Comments: a scenic executive golf course which is situated in a very attractive housing development . One creek and a few sand traps come into play through-out this short yet challenging track. Excellent greens during the peak season.

Directions: from I-405 N&S take exit #14 (northbound) 14A (southbound) to Hwy 520E. Take the 148th Avenue NE exit and turn left on NE 24th St. (It is the first light). Proceed on 24th St. to 182nd. Clubhouse is on your immediate left. There is a sign at the entrance to the golf course.

Course Yardage & Par:
M-1283 yards, par 28.
W-1216 yards, par 29.

Broadmoor Golf Club (private, 18 hole course)
2340 Broadmoor Drive East; Seattle, WA 98112
Phone: (206) 325-8444. **Fax:** (206) 324-5403. **Internet:** www.broadmoorgolfclub.com
Pro: Dan Hill, PGA. **Superintendent:** Jerry Hilperts.
Rating/Slope: M 70.2/123; W 74.7/131. **Course Record:** 60.
Green fees: private club members & guests only; reciprocates, very limited.
Power cart: private club. **Pull cart:** complimentary. **Trail fee:** not allowed.
Reservations policy: private club, members & guests only.
Winter condition: the golf course is open all year long. Dry conditions.
Terrain: flat, some hills. **Tees:** grass. **Spikes:** no metal spikes April-October.
Services: lessons, snack bar, lounge, restaurant, beer, wine, liquor, pro shop,
lockers, showers, driving range. **Comments:** course built in 1926. One of the
finest courses in the state. It is set among tree lined fairways and stately homes.
Greens are very fast, well bunkered, small and hard to hold. Great golf course.

Directions: from I-5 N&S take exit 168B
to Hwy 520E. Exit at Montlake Blvd.
Travel east through the light to E Lake
Washington Blvd. Travel east for .5 miles
to Foster Island Road. Go left on Foster
Island Road to the course entrance which
will be on your right. **Note:** the course is
located near the arboretum. If coming
from Hwy 520 westbound take Montlake
Blvd exit and follow the above directions.

Course Yardage & Par:
M-6241 yards, par 70; W-5873 yards, par 74.

Brookdale Golf Course (public, 18 hole course)
1802 Brookdale Road E; Tacoma, WA 98445
Phone: 800-281-2428; (253) 537-4400. Internet: none.
General Manager: Christine Jones. Director of Golf: Doug Jones.
Pro: Rob Powers, PGA. Supt.: Steve Newman. Course record: 60.
Rating/Slope: C 70.3/119; M 69.2/117; W 73.1/120.
Green fees: $23/$15 every day; Sr. rates (M-F only $16/$10); M/C, VISA.
Power cart: $20/$12. **Pull cart:** $3. **Trail fee:** $5 for personal carts.
Reservation policy: yes, call up to 1 month in advance for your tee times.
Winter condition: the golf course is open all year long. Dry conditions.
Terrain: flat, some slight hills. **Tees:** all grass. **Spikes:** metal spikes preferred.
Services: club rentals, lessons, restaurant, beer, pro shop, lockers, showers.
Comments: the golf course's excellent drainage system provides dry play during the dead of winter. Good greens and excellent fairways make this golf course a local favorite. Outside tournaments are welcome so be sure to call.

Directions: from I-5 N&S take exit #127 to Hwy 512E. Travel eastbound on Hwy 512 to Hwy 7. Exit at Hwy 7. Proceed southbound on Hwy 7 for 1.3 miles to 131st Street. Go eastbound on 131st Street for 1.3 miles to the golf course. **Note:** 131st Street will be become Brookdale Road. Look for signs marking your way to the course.

Course Yardage & Par:
C-6466 yards, par 71.
M-6203 yards, par 71.
W-5833 yards, par 74.

Buckskin Golf Club (public, 9 hole course)

2549 Aileron Street; P.O. Box 661; Richland,WA 99352
Phone: (509) 942-0888. Fax: same as phone #, call first. Internet: none.
Pro: Jeff Marcum, PGA. Superintendent: Jeff Marcum.
Rating/Slope: 63.6/97; C 62.4/89; M 61.2/87; W 60.6/85. **Record:** 30 (9 holes).
Green fees: $8 for 9 holes every day; M/C, VISA.
Power cart: $20/$10. **Pull cart:** $2. **Trail fee:** $5 for personal carts.
Reservation policy: walk-ons are welcome at any time.
Winter condition: the golf course is open all year long. Damp conditions.
Terrain: flat, easy walking. **Tees:** all grass. **Spikes:** soft spikes preferred.
Services: club rentals, lessons, pro shop, driving range, vending machine.
Comments: this new 9 hole executive course opened for play in late 1998. The
course features flat terrain medium size greens with few hazards. The resident
pro Jeff Marcum states that his course is playable and affordable for everyone.

Directions: from Hwy 240 exit on Van
Giesen at the Van Giesen intersection.
Head westbound on Van Giesen to your
second right hand turn (this will be
Buckskin Street). Turn right on Buckskin. The pro shop is located 1000 yards
straight ahead. Look for signs.

Course Yardage & Par:
M-2600 yards, par 35.
W-2600 yards, par 35.
<u>Dual tees for 18 holes:</u>
M-4932 yards, par 67.
W-4932 yards, par 67.

Camaloch Golf Club (public, 18 hole course, driving range)

326 NE Camano Drive; Camano Island, WA 98292
Phone: (360) 387-3084, 800-628-0469. Fax: (360) 387-9277. Internet: none.
PGA Director of Golf: Gary Schopf, PGA. Superintendent: Felix Rivera.
Rating/Slope: C 70.0/118; M 68.5/114; W 70.0/114. **Course record:** 65.
Green fees: W/D $21.50/$16; W/E & Holidays $29/$19; Jr/Sr rates (M-F).
Power cart: $23/$14. **Pull cart:** $3.50. **Trail fee:** $10 (add tax).
Reservation policy: reservations recommended, walk-ons are always welcome.
Winter condition: the course is open all year long. Dry, excellent drainage.
Terrain: 2 hills, very walkable. **Tees:** grass. **Spikes:** soft spikes recommended.
Services: club rentals, lessons, cafe, beer/wine, pro shop, driving range.
Comments: this well maintained golf course lies in the sun belt of Washington State. The area receives less rainfall than many places in western Washington. If you want a dry course in winter, try Camaloch. Greens are well maintained and putt very true. Great course that is worth the trip if in the area.

Directions: from I-5 N&S take exit #212 (Stanwood Hwy 532). Go west on Hwy 532 through Stanwood. Continue to the golf course which will be on your left hand side of the road. (The golf course is located about 12 miles from I-5). The course is very easy to find.

Course Yardage & Par:

C-6200 yards, par 72.
M-5809 yards, par 72.
W-5234 yards, par 72.

Camas Meadows Golf Club (public, 18 hole course)
4105 NW Camas Meadows Drive; Camas, WA 98607
Phone: (360) 833-2000. Fax: (360) 834-7075. Internet: www.camasmeadows.com
Pro: Jenny Duce. GM: Chet Knapp. Superintendent: Rod Nelson.
Rating/Slope: T 71.3/130; C 69.3/126; M 67.2/123; W 68.9/126. **Record:** 71.
Green fees: Monday thru Thursday $42; Friday-Sunday $50; Jr. & Sr. rates.
Power cart: included in fee. **Pull cart:** N/A. **Trail fee:** not allowed.
Reservation policy: please call 10 days in advance for your tee-times.
Winter condition: the course is open all year long. Dry, excellent drainage.
Terrain: flat, green to tees spread out. **Tees:** grass. **Spikes:** soft spikes required.
Services: club rentals, lessons, lounge, restaurant, beer, wine, liquor, pro shop.
Comments: this brand new golf course features narrow, tight fairways with
scenic views of the natural wetlands and Lacamas Lake. Wonderful views of Mt.
Hood abound from nearly every tee on the course. All golf carts include a
Parview GPS computer, which gives a player pin locations and potential hazards.

Directions: from the north. Southbound
on I-205. Left on SE Mill Plain Blvd. Left
on SE 164th Ave. Right on SE 1st St. Left
on 192nd Ave. Right on NE 13th St.
Right on Camas Meadows Drive to the
course. From the south. Northbound on
I-205. East on Hwy 14. Left on SE 164th
Street. Right on SE 1st St. Left on 192nd
Ave. Right on NE 13th St. Right on
Camas Meadows Drive to the golf course.

Course Yardage & Par:

T-6518 yards, par 72.
C-6137 yards, par 72.
M-5743 yards, par 72.
W-4859 yards, par 72.

Canterwood Golf & Country -Club (private, 18 hole course)
4026 Canterwood Drive NW; Gig Harbor, WA 98335
Phone: (253) 851-1745. Fax: (253) 853-3652. Internet: cwgcc@earthlink.net
Pro: Mike Drake, PGA. Superintendent: Scott Young. Record: 64.
Rating/Slope: T 76.5/141; C 74.4/138; M 72.1/134; W 74.5/130.
Green fees: private club, members & guests only, reciprocates; VISA, MC.
Power cart: private club. **Pull cart:** private club. **Trail fee:** monthly basis.
Reservation policy: yes, members can call up to 1 week in advance.
Winter condition: the golf course is open all year long. Dry conditions.
Terrain: relatively hilly. **Tees:** all grass. **Spikes:** no metal spikes permitted.
Services: lessons, snack bar, restaurant, lounge, beer, wine, liquor, pro shop,
lockers, showers, driving range, putting & chipping greens, banquet facilities.
Comments: very scenic, difficult golf course that has large undulating greens,
bunkers and water hazards everywhere. This Robert Muir Graves designed track
is nothing short of spectacular. Rated as one of the toughest courses in the state.

Directions: from I-5 N&S take exit #132
for Hwy 16W (Gig Harbor-Bremerton)
Proceed to the Purdy exit and to 144th
NW. Travel east for 1 mile to 54th. Turn
south to the entrance to the Golf &
Country Club. **Note:** look for signs to
Canterwood G&CC indicating your turn.

Course Yardage & Par:
T-7175 yards, par 72.
C-6705 yards, par 72.
M-6245 yards, par 72.
W-5538 yards, par 73.

Canyon Lakes Golf Course (public, 18 hole course)

3700 West Canyon Lakes Drive; Kennewick, WA 99337
Phone: (509) 582-3736. **Fax:** (509) 585-0914. **Internet:** www.canyonlakesgolfcourse.com
Director of Golf: Terry Graff, PGA. **Pros:** Wendy Rash PGA, Matt Mandell PGA.
Manager: Mike Lundgren. **Superintendent:** Kim Brock.
Rating/Slope: T 73.4/127; C 71.2/124; M 69.2/120; W 72.0/124. **Record:** 63.
Green fees: Mon.-Thur. $24; Fri. $29; W/E & Hol. $34. M/C, VISA, AMEX.
Power cart: $26/$13. **Pull cart:** $2. **Trail fee:** $8 for personal carts.
Reservation policy: please call up to 1 week in advance for your tee times.
Winter condition: course is open all year weather permitting. Dry conditions.
Terrain: relatively hilly. **Tees:** all grass. **Spikes:** no metal spikes permitted.
Services: club rentals, lessons, snack bar, restaurant, liquor, wine, beer, pro
shop, driving range, putting green. **Comments:** a links style course, Canyon
Lakes is set in the desert area of Eastern Washington. A challenging course
where water comes into play on many of the holes. One of the top ten public
golf courses in the Northwest that features an 18 hole putting course.
Be sure to make a special trip to Canyon Lakes, its simply a great golf course.

Directions: from Hwy 395S exit south
of Kennewick take 27th Street exit.
Proceed east to your second right and
the entrance to the golf course.

Course Yardage & Par:
T-6973 yards, par 72.
C-6505 yards, par 72.
M-6034 yards, par 72.
W-5565 yards, par 72.

Capitol City Golf Club (public, 18 hole course)

5225 Yelm Highway SE; Lacey, WA 98513
Phone: (360) 491-5111. Fax: (360) 493-6067. Internet: www.americangolf.com
Manager: Darin Safford. Superintendent: Mark Biscay.
Rating/Slope: C 70.6/121; M 69.2/118; W 71.2/116. **Course record:** 62.
Green fees: W/D $18; W/E $25; Jr./Sr. rates, (M-F). VISA, MC, AMEX, DIS.
Power cart: $22. **Pull cart:** $3. **Trail fee:** $8 for personal carts.
Reservation policy: yes, call up to 1 week in advance for all your tee-times.
Winter condition: the golf course is open all year long. Dry conditions.
Terrain: flat (easy walking). **Tees:** all grass. **Spikes:** metal spikes permitted.
Services: club rentals, lessons, lounge, beer, wine, pro shop, lockers, showers,
driving range, putting green. **Comments:** "One of the state's finest and driest
courses year round," beautiful view's of Mt. Rainier. Greens are kept in excel-
lent condition throughout the season. Fantastic facility that is worth the trip.

Directions: from I-5N exit #108 College
St. Proceed to College St. and take a right.
Follow College St. for 3 miles to the Yelm
Hwy. Take a left and follow for .4 miles
to the course which will be on your right.
From I-5S take exit #109. Take left on
College St. and follow the same directions.

Course Yardage & Par:
C-6536 yards, par 72.
M-6224 yards, par 72.
W-5510 yards, par 72.

Carey Lakes Golf Course (public, 18 hole course)
1201 Umptanum Road; Ellensburg, WA 98926
Phone: (509) 962-5256. Fax: none. Internet: none
Manager: John W. Carey. Superintendent: John W. Carey.
Rating/Slope: the course has not been rated yet. **Course record:** 55.
Green fees: W/D $15/$9; W/E $15/$9; no credit cards.
Power cart: $10/$7.50. **Pull cart:** $2/$2. **Trail fee:** N/A.
Reservation policy: you may call ahead up to 7 days in advance.
Winter condition: the course is closed during the winter months.
Terrain: flat (easy walking). **Tees:** all grass. **Spikes:** soft spikes only.
Services: club rentals, lessons, snack bar, pro shop, driving range, state of the art practice facility. **Comments:** a friendly new course which promises to be a fast favorite with the locals. If you are making a quick trip through Ellensburg be sure to stop in at Carey Lakes for a quick round!

Directions: from I-90 take exit number 106. Proceed north 1/2 mile and turn left on Umptanum Road (road next to McDonalds). Travel west 1/2 mile to the course. Look for signs along the way.

Course Yardage & Par:

M-3785 yards, par 59.
W-3785 yards, par 67.

Carnation Golf Course (public, 18 hole course)

1810 West Snoqualmie River Road NE; Carnation, WA 98014
Phone: (425)-333-4151, (206) 583-0314. Internet: www.carnationgolf.com
Director of Golf: Dan Tachell, PGA. Pro: Chad Tachell, PGA.
Tournament Director: Heidi Tachell. GM: Stephanie Tachell.
Rating/Slope: C 67.7/111; M 65.3/107; W 65.0/102. **Course record:** 64.
Green fees: W/D $25/$15; W/E $29; twilight $15; early bird $16; VISA, MC.
Power cart: $24/$14. **Pull cart:** $3. **Trail fee.** $5 for personal carts.
Reservation policy: yes, no time limit. Please call in advance for tee-times
Winter condition: the golf course is open all year long. Damp conditions.
Terrain: flat (easy walking). **Tees:** all grass. **Spikes:** soft spikes preferred.
Services: club rentals, lessons, all grass practice facility, restaurant, beer, wine,
pro shop, memberships. **Comments:** the course is flat, easy to walk and in good
condition. It sits in a peaceful setting along the Snoqualmie River. Very friendly.

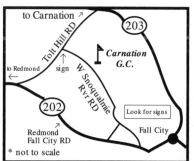

<u>Directions:</u> from I-5 N&S exit to 168B (Hwy 520E). Proceed eastbound on Hwy 520 to Hwy 202 in Redmond (Redmond-Fall City RD). Go east on Hwy 202 for 8 miles to Tolt Hill RD. Turn left on Tolt Hill RD. Proceed for 2.5 miles. Take a right on W Snoqualmie River Road NE. The golf course will be located on your left. Look for signs that are posted.

Course Yardage & Par:
C-6019 yards, par 71. M-5503 yards, par 72.
W-5503 yards, par 71. W-4623 yards, par 72.

Cascade Golf Course (public, 9 hole course)
14303 436th Avenue SE; North Bend, WA 98045
Phone: (425) 888-0227. Fax: (425) 888-6600. Internet: www.cascade.com
Owner/Manager/Superintendent: LeRoy Jorgenson.
Rating/Slope: M 63/94; W 67.2/103. **Course record:** M 69; W 84.
Green fees: Monday thru Friday $24/$15; Saturday, Sunday and Holidays $26/$17; Senior rates $20/$12 age 62+ (M-F); M/C, VISA.
Power cart: $20/$12. **Pull cart:** $3. **Trail fee:** no charge personal carts.
Reservation policy: tee-times required March to October. Walk-ons welcome.
Winter condition: the course is open all year with extremely dry conditions.
Terrain: flat (easy walking). **Tees:** all grass. **Spikes:** metal spikes permitted.
Services: club rentals, restaurant, beer, snacks, beverages, espresso.
Comments: Excellent drainage provides dry fairways and greens for winter play. A friendly golf course where you can usually walk on during the week. Home of the "Tony Burger." Great place to bring the whole family to golf.

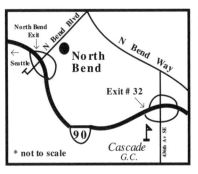

Directions: from I-90 E&W take exit #32 to 436th SE. Proceed for .1 mile to the course which will be on your right. The golf course is located 2 miles east of the city of the North Bend.

Course Yardage & Par:
Red Tees-2331 yards, par 36.
White Tees-2595 yards, par 36.
Blue Tees-2712 yards, par 36.
Dual tees for 18 holes:
Red Tees-4662 yards, par 72.
White Tees-5190 yards, par 72.
Blue Tees-5424 yards, par 72.

Cedarcrest Municipal Golf Course (public, 18 hole course)

6810 84th Street NE; Marysville, WA 98270
Phone: (360) 659-3566. **Fax:** (360) 659-0586. **Internet:** none.
Pro: Rob Lindsey, PGA. **Superintendent:** Monty Mechling.
Rating/Slope: C 67.0/114; M 65.0/109; W 66.6/112 **Course record:** 63.
Green fees: $22/$16; Sr. rates $16/$12 (M-F); Jr. rates $10 (M-F).
Power cart: $20. **Pull cart:** $4. **Trail fee:** $7 for personal carts.
Reservation policy: yes, please call up to 1 week in advance for your tee-times. Call Saturday for next Saturday & Sunday tee-times. A must during the summer.
Winter condition: the golf course is open all year long. Dry conditions.
Terrain: flat, some hills. **Tees:** all grass. **Spikes:** soft spikes in summer.
Services: club rentals, lessons, lockers, showers, pro shop, restaurant.
Comments: well conditioned course that can offer a wide variety of fairway lies and approach shots to greens. The golf course has been remodeled and is much improved over the previous design. Great public track that is enjoyable to play.

Directions: from I-5 N&S take exit #199 (Marysville-Tulalip) to Hwy 528E (4th St.). Continue on 4th St which becomes 64th St. NE. Proceed to 67th Avenue NE. Turn left on 67th Ave. Travel north on 67th until you reach 84th St NE. Turn right on 84th. The golf course will be on your right.

Course Yardage & Par:

C-5811 yards, par 70.
M-5381 yards, par 70.
W-4846 yards, par 70.

Cedars Golf Club (public, 18 hole course)

15001 NE 181 Street; Brush Prairie, WA 98606
Phone: (360) 687-4233. **Fax:** (360) 687-1554. **Internet:** none.
Pro: Bob Evans, PGA. **Superintendent:** Steve Brown.
Rating/Slope: C 71.3/127; M 69.9/125; W 71.7/117. **Course record:** 64.
Green fees: W/D $26/$14; W/E $28/$15; M/C, VISA.
Power cart: $22/$12. **Pull cart:** $2/$1.50. **Trail fee:** not allowed.
Reservation policy: yes, call up to 1 week in advance for your tee-times.
Winter condition: the golf course is open all year long. Drains well in winter.
Terrain: flat, some slight hills. **Tees:** all grass. **Spikes:** soft spikes encouraged.
Services: club rentals, lessons, restaurant, bar, lockers, showers, pro shop,
driving range, putting & chipping greens. **Comments:** picturesque setting, cedar
trees, lakes and trout stream surround challenging golf. Greens are well bunkered
and can putt very tough at times. Good course that can get very busy in summer.

Directions: from **I-5 N&S** *1).* take exit #2
"Orchards" to WA-500 East. *2).* Merge onto
WA-500 East and proceed 5.4 miles until you
reach ORCHARDS. Jump down to instruction
#3 below. From **I-205 N&S** *1).* take exit #30
"Orchards"-Vancouver to WA-500 East.
2). Merge onto WA-500 East and proceed 0.7
miles until you reach ORCHARDS. *3).* At
ORCHARDS, WA-500 East curves to the left
(north), crosses Fourth Plain Blvd. and
becomes 117th Ave. (WA-503). *4).* Continue
north on 117th Ave. for 4.3 miles until you
reach Caples Rd. on the right. *5).* Turn right
and continue NE on Caples Rd. for 0.7 miles
until you reach 159th St. on the right. *6).* Turn
right and continue east on 159th St. for 1.3
miles until you reach the 4-way stop at the
intersection with 152nd Ave. *7).* Turn left and
continue on 152nd Ave. for 1.1 miles until the
road ends. Turn left across the railroad tracks
and immediately turn left again to the course.

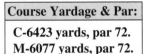

Course Yardage & Par:
C-6423 yards, par 72.
M-6077 yards, par 72.
W-5216 yards, par 73.

Centralia Public Golf Course (public, 9 hole course)
1012 Duffy Street; Centralia, WA 98531
Phone: (360) 736-5967. **Fax:** (360) 736-6909. **Internet:** none.
Owners: Michel & Renee Rey. **Superintendent:** Pete Holmstedt.
Rating/Slope: M 67.4/118; W 71.9/125. **Course record:** 32 (9 holes).
Green fees: W/D $10/$7; W/E $13/$10; Jr. rates $5; M/C, VISA.
Power cart: $16/$10. **Pull cart:** $2. **Trail fee:** $4 for personal carts.
Reservation policy: please call ahead for your tee-times. No time limit.
Winter condition: the golf course is open all year long. Dry conditions.
Terrain: relatively hilly, walkable. **Tees:** grass. **Spikes:** soft spikes preferred.
Services: club rentals, beer, wine, liquor, restaurant, snack bar, limited pro shop.
Comments: tight fairways puts an emphasis on your shot placement. The golf course offers a dual tee layout for 18 hole play. Creeks come into play on several holes throughout the course which features a pond on the 6th hole.

Directions: from I-5 N&S take the Centralia/Harrison Ave/Mellen Street. (exit #82) Follow the city center signs. Proceed to Tower Street and turn left (east). When you reach E Maple Street turn right. Go up the hill on Seminary Road, thru the intersection at the Armory, and down the hill to the golf course. Look for signs that are posted along the way.

Course Yardage & Par:
M-2826 yards, par 36.
W-2897 yards, par 37.
Dual tees for 18 holes:
M-5728 yards, par 72.
W-5405 yards, par 74.

Cherry Hill Golf Club (public, 9 hole executive course)
530 Cherry Hill Road; Granger, WA 98932
Phone: (360) 854-1800. **Fax: same as phone number. Internet: none.**
Pro: Randy Duford, PGA. Superintendent: Randy Duford.
Rating/Slope: the golf course is not rated. **Course record:** N/A.
Green fees: $8 for 9 holes; $10 for all day; Jr.'s 14 and under $6, $8 all day.
Power cart: not available. **Pull cart:** $2. **Trail fee:** not available.
Reservation policy: tee-times are made on a first come first served basis.
Winter condition: the golf course is open all year long. Dry conditions.
Terrain: flat, easy walking. **Tees:** all grass. **Spikes:** soft spikes in summer.
Services: club rentals, lessons, pro shop, putting green, driving range.
Comments: new golf course that is a great place to learn the game of golf.
Holes range in yardage from 78 yards to over 270. If you are a beginner golfer
or an advanced player who wants to practice be sure to visit Cherry Hill.

Directions: from I-82 E&W take exit
#58 (Hwy 223). Proceed westbound on
Hwy 223 for .7 miles to Cherry Hill
Road. Turn left onto local roads and then
turn left again onto Cherry Hill Road.
The golf course is located on the left.

Course Yardage & Par:
M-1430 yards, par 30.
W-1430 yards, par 30.

Chevy Chase Golf Club (public, 18 hole course)

7401 Cape George Road; Port Townsend, WA 98368
Phone: (360) 385-0704, 1-800-385-8722. Fax: (360) 379-9362.
Pro: Shawn Yim, PGA. Supt.: Scott Westwood. Internet: www.chevychasegolf.com
Rating/Slope: C 71.5/120; M 68.1/113; W 69.2/111. **Record:** 68.
Green fees: W/D $24/$17; W/E $27/$19; twilight rates, Jr. & Sr. rates.
Power cart: $24/$18. **Pull cart:** $3/$2. **Trail fee:** $10. VISA, M/C is honored.
Reservation policy: yes, you may call 7 days in advance for your tee time.
Winter condition: the golf course is open all year long. Dry conditions.
Terrain: flat, some hills. **Tees:** all grass. **Spikes:** soft spikes in summer.
Services: club rentals, lessons, snack bar, beer, banquet room, pro shop, lockers,
waterfront rental cabins, driving range. **Comments:** "one of the oldest courses in
the state". The course recently opened its "Forest Nine" in May of 1997 to
complement its "Farm Nine" and provides you with a challenging but user
friendly course that is located in one of the most beautiful and peaceful settings
in the "Sun Belt" of the Olympic Peninsula. With the historic Pt. Townsend and
all of its victorian homes located just 7 miles away it is a perfect weekend spot.

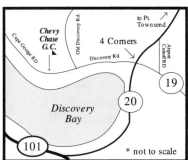

Directions: from the Hood Canal Bridge,
go 5 miles. Turn right off Route 104 onto
Route 19 at signs to Chimacum, Port
Ludlow and Pt. Townsend. Go through
Chimacum to Four Corners Rd. Take left
on Four Corners Rd. Go straight to stop
sign & Junction with Route 20 (Four
Corners Store) Proceed straight ahead for
1 mile and take left at Cape George Rd. to
the Chevy Chase Complex.

Course Yardage & Par:
C-6642 yards, par 72.
M-5925 yards, par 72.
W-5185 yards, par 72.

Chewelah Golf & Country Club (semi-private, 27 hole course)

P.O. Box 407; Sand Canyon Road; Chewelah, WA 99109
Phone: (509) 935-6807. Fax: (509) 935-8522. Internet: none.
Pro: Kim Walker, PGA. Superintendent: Tim Rowe.
Rating/Slope: C 70.9/125; M 69.9/123; W 72.7/120. **Course record:** 64.
Green fees: $20/$14 all week long; Jr & Sr rates; M/C, VISA.
Power cart: $22/$12. **Pull cart:** $3. **Trail fee:** $8 for personal carts.
Reservation policy: call up to 30 days in advance for your tee times.
Winter condition: the golf course is closed from mid November to March.
Terrain: flat, some hills. **Tees:** all grass. **Spikes:** no metal spikes permitted.
Services: club rentals, lessons, snack bar, pro shop, beverage cart, driving range putting & putting greens, tennis courts, RV park, 3800' lighted airstrip.
Comments: narrow fairways, numerous sand traps trees, and five ponds make this course play difficult. Well run golf course that offers a real challenge for every caliber of golfer. The new 9 holes is now open for play. Worth a trip.

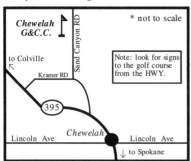

Directions: from Spokane travel on Hwy 395N for approximately 45 miles to Chewelah Washington. When in Chewelah look for and follow signs to the golf course.

Course Yardage & Par:
C-6531 yards, par 72.
M-6161 yards, par 72.
W-5637 yards, par 74.

Christy's Golf Range & Par 3 (public, 9 hole par 3 course)
37712 28th Avenue South; Federal Way, WA 98003
Phone: (253) 927-0644. Fax: none. Internet: none.
Pro: Dave Christy. Superintendent: George Christy.
Rating/Slope: the golf course is not rated. **Course record:** 24.
Green fees: W/D $13/$7; W/E $15/$8; Sr. rates W/D's $12/$6; W/E's $14/$7.
Jr. golfers 10-15 years old W/D's $12/$6; W/E's $14/$7.
Power cart: not available. **Pull cart:** $1.50. **Trail fee:** not allowed.
Reservation policy: tee times are on a first come first served basis.
Terrain: flat, some hills. **Tees:** grass and mats. **Spikes:** metal spikes permitted.
Services: club rentals, lessons, full service pro shop, excellent driving range.
Comments: challenging par 3 golf course that is great for the whole family.
Great course to practice your short irons on. Excellent on course pro shop that
will service all your golfing needs. The facility also includes a lighted and
covered driving range that is open seven days a week.

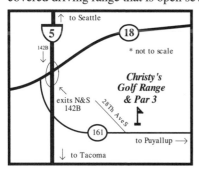

Directions: from I-5 N&S take exit 142B.
Proceed westbound for .2 miles to Hwy
161S. Turn south for 1.6 miles to 28th
Avenue South. Turn left on 28th Avenue
South to the golf course. Look for a sign.

Course Yardage & Par:
M-905 yards, par 27.
W-905 yards, par 27.

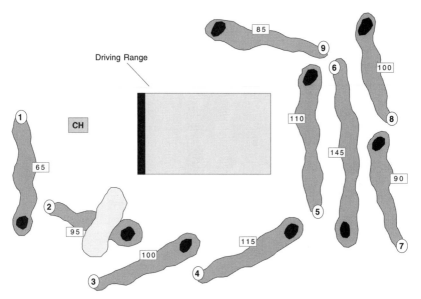

Clarkston Golf & Country Club (private, 18 hole course)
1676 Elm Street; Clarkston, WA 99403
Phone: (509) 758-7911. **Fax:** (509) 751-9229. **Internet:** cgcc@clarkston.com
Pro: Doug Phares, PGA. **Supt.:** Mike Waisanen. **GM:** Steve Prine.
Rating/Slope: C 72.0/120; M 71.3/118; W 71.1/120. **Course record:** 63.
Green fees: $20 accompanied/$45 un-accompanied; VISA, M/C.
Power cart: $25. **Pull cart:** private club. **Trail fee:** $6 for private carts.
Reservation policy: yes, please call up to 1 week in advance for members.
Winter condition: the golf course is open weather permitting. Dry conditions.
Terrain: flat, some hills. **Tees:** all grass. **Spikes:** metal spikes not permitted.
Services: club rentals, lessons, restaurant, lounge, beer, wine, liquor, lockers,
showers, driving range. **Comments:** beautiful setting along the Snake River
with the Palouse Mountains nearby. Water, trees and well bunkered greens
abound. This well kept private facility will test your skill at every turn.

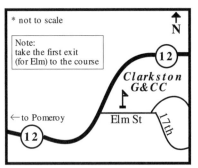

Directions: travel to Clarkston via
Hwy 12. The golf course is located
north of Clarkston near Hwy 12 which
parallels the golf course. Take the first
exit (for Elm Street) to the golf course.

Course Yardage & Par:
T-6680 yards, par 72.
C-6444 yards, par 72.
M-5920 yards, par 72.
W-5436 yards, par 72.

Classic Country Club (public, 18 hole course, driving range)
4908 208th Street East; Spanaway, WA 98387
Phone: (253) 847-4440; (206) 622-4653. Fax: (206) 846-9868.
Manager: Kelly Beymer. Superintendent: Matthew Weaver.
Rating/Slope: C 72.8/135; M 71.2/131; W 72.7/128. **Course record:** 67.
Green fees: April 1st to Sep. 30th W/D $30/$15, W/E & Holidays $45;
October to March 31st W/D $22/$15; W/E & Holidays $30/$15; Twilight $15,
Jr. & Sr. rates $15 (Monday through Friday), AMEX, MC, VISA, DIS.
Power cart: $22. **Pull cart:** $5/$3. **Trail fee:** $8 for personal carts.
Reservation policy: yes, please call 7 days in advance for your tee times.
Winter condition: the golf course is open all year long. Dry conditions.
Terrain: flat, some hills. **Tees:** all grass. **Spikes:** soft spikes preferred.
Services: club rentals, lessons, snack bar, restaurant, beer, wine, pop, pro shop,
excellent driving range, putting green & chipping green, beverage cart in season.
Comments: *Golf Digest* magazine rated the Classic Country Club #7 in the state
of Washington on their list of America's best 500 places to play in 1996. This
course is worth a special trip at anytime during the year. Excellent golf course.

Directions: from I-5 N&S take exit #127
to Hwy 512. Follow Hwy 512 to Hwy 7.
Exit to Hwy 7 southbound. Follow Hwy 7
south until you reach 208th St. E go left.
The course is located 2 miles ahead on the
right.

Course Yardage & Par:
C-6793 yards, par 72.
M-6387 yards, par 72.
M-6008 yards, par 72.
W-5580 yards, par 72.

Club Green Meadows (private, 18 hole course)

7703 NE 72nd Avenue; Vancouver, WA 98661
Phone: (360) 256-1510, (503) 230-1461. Fax: (360) 256-1596.
Pro: Ross Thurik, PGA. Superintendent: Phil Taylor.
Rating/Slope: C 70.4/118; M 69.2/116; W 71.8/120. **Course record:** 63.
Green fees: private club, members & guests only; reciprocates.
Power cart: private club. **Pull cart:** private club. **Trail fee:** private club.
Reservation policy: private club, reservations for members & guests only.
Winter condition: the golf course is open all year long. Damp conditions.
Terrain: flat (easy walking). **Tees:** all grass. **Spikes:** soft spikes only.
Services: lessons, snack bar, lounge, restaurant, beer, wine, liquor, pro shop.
Comments: course has narrow tree lined fairways with ponds and greenside
bunkers coming into play on nearly every hole. Athletic club is on site.

Directions: from I-5 N&S take exit #4
to NE 78th. Go east on NE 78th to NE
72nd Ave. Go south on NE 72nd Ave.
While on NE 72nd Ave. turn east to the
golf course. From I-205 N&S take exit
#32. Go west on NE 83rd. Take a left on
Andersen RD. When you reach NE 78th
St. turn left. Proceed to 72nd Avenue NE
turn right.

Course Yardage & Par:
C-6486 yards, par 72.
M-6246 yards, par 72.
W-5831 yards, par 76.

Colfax Golf Club (public, 9 hole course)
2402 North Cedar Street; Route 1, Box 46-A; Colfax, WA 99111
Phone: (509) 397-2122. Fax: none. Internet: none.
Pro: Craig Gronning. Superintendent: Mark Black.
Rating/Slope: M 67.8/117; W 70.9/115. **Course record:** M/63; W/73.
Green fees: $18/$12 all week long; $12 Mondays (all day); no credit cards.
Power cart: $20/$12. **Pull cart:** $1.50. **Trail fee:** $5 for personal carts.
Reservation policy: yes, for weekend play only. Call 1 week in advance.
Winter condition: the golf course is open all year long, dry conditions.
Terrain: flat (easy walking). **Tees:** grass. **Spikes:** no metal spikes permitted.
Services: club rentals, lessons, pro shop, driving range net, putting green.
Comments: easily walked golf course. The atmosphere at this rural golf
course is friendly and casual. Dual tees are available for those wanting to play
a full18 hole round. The Palouse River borders the golf course. Be straight off
the tee as out of bounds borders nearly every hole on this golf course.

Directions: from Hwy 195 take the Cedar Street exit and travel east bound to the golf course. The golf course is located slightly north of the city of Colfax, Washington. **Note:** look for signs from the Highway indicating your turn to the golf course.

Course Yardage & Par:

M-3010 yards, par 35.
W-2817 yards, par 36.
Dual tees for 18 holes:
M-5907 yards, par 70.
W-5556 yards, par 72.

Columbia Park Golf Course (public, 18 hole course)

Physical address: 2701 Columbia Park Trail; Kennewick, WA 99336
Mailing address: 7422 West Clearwater; Kennewick, WA 99336
Phone: (509) 586-2800. **Fax:** (509) 735-1923. **Internet:** none.
Pro: Jerry Asher, PGA. **Superintendent:** Marc Richey.
Rating/Slope: M 51.1/079; W 51.1/079. **Course record:** 47.
Green fees: $12/$8 everyday; Jr. & Sr. rates; VISA, M/C, DIS, AMEX.
Power cart: $12/$8. **Pull cart:** $2. **Trail fee:** not allowed.
Reservation policy: tee time reservations are not required.
Winter condition: the golf course is open weather permitting. Dry conditions.
Terrain: very flat. **Tees:** grass and mats. **Spikes:** soft spikes only.
Services: club rentals, driving range, pro shop, lessons, snack bar.
Comments: the course is on the Columbia River which can be seen from every tee. A sporty iron course with lots of trees and small greens, requiring accurate iron shots. The golf course is flat & easy to walk. Great course for beginners, women, seniors and juniors or to practice your iron play. Great on course range.

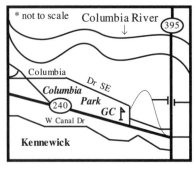

Directions: from Hwy 395 take Hwy 240 West to Columbia Park exit. Go to Columbia Park Trail and turn left. Course is a short distance on your left. If you are going east I-182 take the Hwy 240 East/Kennewick exit to Edison St. exit, turn left to Columbia Park then a right on Columbia Park Trail, proceed to the golf course.

Course Yardage & Par:

M-2682 yards, par 55.
W-2682 yards, par 55.

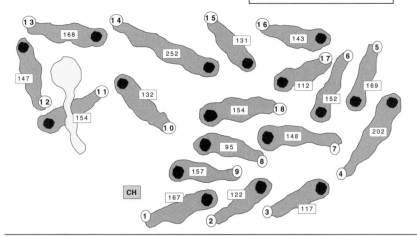

Columbia Point Golf Course (public, 18 hole course)
225 Columbia Point Drive; Richland, WA 99352
Phone: (509) 946-0710. **Fax:** (509) 946-1930. **Internet:** www.columbiapointgolf.com
Pro: Joe Creager, PGA. **Superintendent:** Gary Elliott.
Rating/Slope: T 70.0/121; C 67.1/114; M 64.2/105; W 65.9/107. **Record:** 65.
Green fees: Monday-Thur. $22; Fri. $27; W/E & Hol. $32; W/D 9/twilight $15;
W/E 9/twilight $22; Jr.'s $14/$8 (M-Th); Sr.'s $17/$11 (M-Th); after 3pm W/E.
Power cart: $12/$8. **Pull cart:** $3/$2. **Trail fee:** $8 for personal carts.
Reservation policy: please call up to 10 days in advance for your tee time.
Winter condition: the golf course is open weather permitting. Dry conditions.
Terrain: flat some hills. **Tees:** grass. **Spikes:** metal spikes not permitted.
Services: club rentals, lessons, lounge, restaurant, beer, wine, liquor, pro shop,
lockers, driving range, putting green. **Comments:** Columbia Point features
beautifully manicured fairways and greens. With a staff dedicated to player
satisfaction this course is sure to please. This championship 18 hole course,
beautiful clubhouse, and practice facility is a perfect setting to enjoy great golf
and nearly 300 days of sunshine a year. Worth a trip if in the Tri-City area.

Directions: When in Richland exit off
of either Hwy 182 or Hwy 240 on to
George Washington Way. At the first
stop light turn right on Columbia Point
Drive. The clubhouse is 1 mile up on
your right. From I-82 take exit #5-B and
head north on George Washington Way.
Then follow the above directions

Course Yardage & Par:
T-6555 yards, par 72.
C-6038 yards, par 72.
M-5365 yards, par 72.
W-4651 yards, par 72.

Colville Elks Golf Course (public, 9 hole course)
1861 East Hawthorne; P. O. Box 367; Colville, WA 99114
Phone: (509) 684-5508. Fax: (509) 684-2526. Internet: none.
Pro: Andy Hite, PGA. Superintendent: Ron Arnold.
Rating/Slope: M 69.3/115; W 73.6/122. **Course record:** 62.
Green fees: $16/$10 all week long; no special rates; no credit cards.
Power cart: $20/$10. **Pull cart:** $2.50. **Trail fee:** $2 for personal carts.
Reservation policy: tee-times are on a first come first served basis.
Winter condition: the golf course is closed from November 1st until thaw.
Terrain: flat, some hills. **Tees:** all grass. **Spikes:** metal spikes permitted.
Services: club rentals, lessons, snack bar, beer, restaurant, lounge, pro shop, lockers, showers, driving range. **Comments:** This eastern Washington course is well conditioned and plays much tougher than the yardage would indicate. The golf course will be expanding to 18 holes in the future. Alternating tees.

Directions: from Spokane travel N on Hwy 395 through Chewelah to Colville. Go east on Hawthorne Avenue. While traveling on Hawthorne Avenue you will go up a hill then you will proceed to the golf course. Look for signs marking your way to the golf course.

Course Yardage & Par:
M-3125 yards, par 36.
W-2865 yards, par 36.
Dual tees for 18 holes:
M-6330 yards, par 72.
W-5990 yards, par 73.

Course at Taylor Creek, The (public, 9 hole course)

21401 244th Avenue SE; Maple Valley, WA 98038
Phone: (425) 413-1900. **Fax:** (425) 413-1456. **Internet:** none.
Manager: Brad Habenicht. **Superintendent:** Rich O'Connell.
Rating/Slope: C 67.4/117; M 65.6/114; W 70.2/115. **Course record:** 63.
Green fees: W/D $22/$14; W/E $28/$16; Jr. & Sr. $18/$12; twilight $10.
Power cart: $10/$5 per person. **Pull cart:** $3. **Trail fee:** $5 for personal carts.
Reservation policy: please call in advance for a tee time. Walk-ons welcome.
Winter condition: the course is open all year long. Very dry conditions.
Terrain: rolling hills. **Tees:** all grass. **Spikes:** no spike restrictions.
Services: restaurant, pro shop, 12 stall driving range.
Comments: This 9-hole Scottish-links designed course plays exceptionally dry all year round. This unique layout features picturesque grass mounding and requires a variety of different shots. The golf course surrounds the Olson Mansion, a King County Historical Landmark built in 1908, which is available for receptions and business meeting functions. Excellent newer golf course.

Directions: from Hwy 18 northbound (toward North Bend) or southbound (toward Auburn) turn eastbound on 244th Avenue SE. Proceed to the golf course entrance that will be located on your right hand side. Look for signs.

Course Yardage & Par:
C-2705 yards, par 35.
M-2437 yards, par 35.
W-2130 yards, par 35.

Creek at Qualchan, The (public, 18 hole course)

301 East Meadow Lane Road; Spokane, WA 99204
Phone: (509) 448-9317. Fax: (509) 448-2240. Internet: none.
Pro: Mark Gardner, PGA. Superintendent: Mark Nord.
Rating/Slope: C 71.6/127; M 69.9/123; W 72.3/126. **Course record:** 65.
Green fees: $23.50/$16.50 all week; $16.50 with discount card; Jr/Sr rates M-F.
Power cart: $24. **Pull cart:** $3. **Trail fee:** $9 for personal carts.
Reservation policy: W/D call 1 day in advance. W/E call 1 week in advance.
Winter condition: the course is closed during winter. November to March.
Terrain: very hilly. **Tees:** all grass. **Spikes:** soft spikes preferred.
Services: club rentals, lessons, restaurant, beer, wine, pro shop, driving range.
Comments: the facility opened in spring of 1993. The golf course features
bunkers, 5 ponds, and a creek wandering through. Excellent newer golf course
that will challenge you at every turn. Worth a trip if in the Spokane area.

Directions: From I-90 E&W (#279) exit
to Hwy 195 and proceed southbound.
Turn eastbound on Meadow Lane Road.
Follow this to the golf course. Look for
signs that are posted along the way. The
route to the golf course is well marked.

Course Yardage & Par:
C-6599 yards, par 72.
M-6180 yards, par 72.
W-5533 yards, par 72.

Crescent Bar Resort (public, 9 hole course)

8894 Crescent Bar Road NW; Suite 1; Quincy, WA 98848
Phone: (509) 787-1511, 1-800-824-7090. Fax: (509) 787-3125.
Manager: Gil Stewart. Superintendent: unavailable. Internet: none.
Rating/Slope: C 68.8/108; M 68.4/107; W 72.4/118. **Course record:** 67.
Green fees: $22/$18 all week long; Sr rates (Mondays only); VISA, M/C.
Power cart: $21/$16. **Pull cart:** $4/$3. **Trail fee:** $5; seasonal rates available.
Reservation policy: please call up to 1 week in advance for tee times.
Winter condition: the golf course is open all year long weather permitting.
Terrain: flat, easy walking. **Tees:** all grass. **Spikes:** soft spikes only.
Services: club rentals, lessons, restaurant, cafe, lounge, store, pro shop, driving range, tennis courts, marina, campground. **Comments:** well-designed course with bunkers, water and rough. Accommodates both low and high handicappers. Good eastern Washington course set on an island in the Columbia River.

Directions: from I-90 E&W take exit #149 to Hwy 281 to Quincy. When you reach Hwy 28 turn left and go west on Hwy 28. Proceed on Hwy 28 for 7.1 miles to Crescent Bar RD and turn left. **Note:** look for the sign on the highway marking your turn to the course.

Course Yardage & Par:
C-3034 yards, par 35.
M-2944 yards, par 35.
W-2844 yards, par 36.
Dual tees for 18 holes:
C-6068 yards, par 70.
M-5978 yards, par 70.
W-5788 yards, par 72.

Crossroads Park Golf Course (public, 9 hole par 3 course)
16000 NE 10th; Bellevue, WA 98008
Phone: (425) 452-4875. **Fax:** (425) 452-7221. **Internet:** none.
Manager: Ted Mittelstaedt.
Rating/Slope: the golf course is not rated. **Course record:** 21.
Green fees: $6 for 9 holes all week long; Jr & Sr rates $5.
Power cart: not available. **Pull cart:** not available. **Trail fee:** not available.
Reservation policy: none needed, all times are on a first come first served basis.
Winter condition: the golf course is closed November 1st through March 1st.
Terrain: flat, some slight hills. **Tees:** all mats. **Spikes:** metal spikes permitted.
Services: club rentals, lessons, snack machines, beverages.
Comments: good golf course to take a young family member to learn the game of golf. The atmoshpere is very casual with no pressure on having to play fast. Holes range from 64 to 107 yards and is not overly difficult.

Directions: from I-405 N&S take the NE 8th exit eastbound. Follow NE 8th to 160th Avenue NE and turn left. The pro shop is located inside of the Community Center at the end of 160th Avenue NE, just east of the Crossroads Mall. Look for signs indicating your turn to the course.

Course Yardage & Par:

M-837 yards, par 27.
W-837 yards, par 27.

Dakota Creek Golf & Country Club (public, 18 hole course)

3258 Haynie Road; Custer, WA 98240
Phone: (360) 366-3131. **Fax:** unavailable. **Internet:** none.
Owner: Pam Foster. **Superintendent:** James Boyer.
Rating/Slope: M 64.3/103; W 67.5/112. **Course record:** 67.
Green fees: W/D $18/$10; W/E $24/$12; M/C, VISA.
Power cart: $22/$11. **Pull cart:** $2. **Trail fee:** not allowed.
Reservation policy: you may call up to 2 weeks in advance.
Winter condition: the golf course is open all year long. Dry conditions.
Terrain: relatively hilly. **Tees:** all grass. **Spikes:** soft spikes in summer.
Services: snack bar, pro shop, chipping green. **Comments:** tough, challenging and fun, all holes different. Good, well kept golf course that is worth the trip if you are in the area. Great views of the surrounding countryside can be seen from nearly every tee. Good tournament course, free BBQ party area for parties.

Directions: from I-5 N&S exit #270 to Birch Bay-Lynden Road turn right go for 100' and turn left on Valley View. Follow Valley View until you reach Haynie Road. Turn right on Haynie Road and proceed to the golf course.

Course Yardage & Par:
M-5185 yards, par 71.
W-4803 yards, par 71.

Deer Meadows Golf Course (public, 9 hole course)
Route 1; Box 203; Davenport, WA 99122
Phone: (509) 725-8488. **Fax:** none. **Internet:** none.
Manager: Vanessa Hollis. **Superintendent:** none.
Rating/Slope: M 68.8/112; W 68.1/113.
Green fees: W/D $16/$10; W/E $16/$10; call for special green fee rates.
Power cart: $20/$15. **Pull cart:** $5. **Trail fee:** not allowed.
Reservation policy: please call up to 1 day in advance for tee times.
Winter Condition: the golf course is closed from November to March.
Terrain: flat, some hills. **Tees:** grass. **Spikes:** metal spikes permitted.
Services: club rentals, pro shop, driving range. **Comments:** newer 9 hole course that opened the 1st 9 in April of 1995. The course offers the golfer modest length and challenging terrain. Plans include an additional 9 holes (due to open sometime in 2001) a clubhouse and other services in the future. Very friendly.

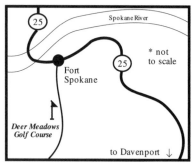

Directions: the golf course is located south of Fort Spokane off of Hwy 25. From Davenport follow Hwy 25 north toward Fort Spokane. When in Fort Spokane turn southbound on Miles Creston Road. The course will be located on your right hand side. Look for a sign marking your turn to the golf course.

Course Yardage & Par:
M-3082 yards, par 36.
W-3000 yards, par 36.

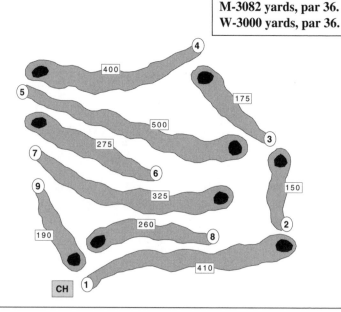

Deer Park Golf Club (semi-private, 18 hole course)

N 1201 Country Club Drive; Deer Park, WA 99006
Phone: (509) 276-5912. Fax: (509) 276-5806. Internet: www.deerparkgc.com
Pro: Craig Schuh. Superintendent: Jim Jenson. Course record: 61.
Rating/Slope: C 71.2/114; M 69.0/110; W 69.9/110.
Green fees: Monday-Thur. $16/$10; Friday & W/E's $21/$14.
Power cart: $23/$12. **Pull cart:** $2. **Trail fee:** $7 for personal carts.
Reservation policy: call Saturday to make your T-time for the following week.
Winter Condition: golf course is closed from November to February or March.
Terrain: flat, some hills. **Tees:** all grass. **Spikes:** soft spikes preferred.
Services: club rentals, lessons, lounge, restuarant, snack bar, beer, wine, liquor,
pro shop, driving range. **Comments:** new desert design with 4 lakes, ponds and
streams. Waste bunkers and other traps are in play on nearly every hole. Very
scenic course that will be enjoyable for all. Great course, worth a special trip.

Directions: from I-90 take the exit for Hwy 395 (Division Street) Proceed north on Hwy 395 toward Deer Park. When you get to Crawford turn east. Proceed to Country Club Drive where you will turn north to the course. Look for signs.

Course Yardage & Par:

C-6750 yards, par 72.
M-6340 yards, par 72.
W-5615 yards, par 72.

Delphi Golf Course (public, 9 hole course)
6340 Neylon Drive SW; Olympia, WA 98512
Phone: (360) 357-6437. Fax: none. Internet: none.
Manager: Rich Williams. Superintendent: Bernie Shey.
Rating/Slope: M 60.4/100; W 60.4/100. **Course record:** 27 (9 holes).
Green fees: W/D $16/$11; W/E $18/$12; Jr. & Sr. rates are available, twilight rates are available; VISA, M/C, AMEX, Discover.
Power cart: $18/$12. **Pull cart:** $2.50. **Trail fee:** $5 for personal carts.
Reservation policy: yes, reservations are taken, no time limit.
Winter Condition: the golf course is open all year long, drains very well.
Terrain: a few hills, but the course is very walkable. **Tees:** all grass.
Spikes: metal spikes permitted. **Services:** club rentals, pro shop.
Comments: residential course. Beautiful setting with narrow tree-lined fairways on every hole. This track is in excellent condition throughout the season. Lots of new drainage adds to the playability during the winter months. Fun course.

Directions: from I-5 N&S exit to Hwy 101 (exit #104) in Olympia. Follow 101 and exit at Black Lake Blvd. (which becomes 62nd Ave. SW). Go south on Black Lake Blvd to Delphi Road. Turn left on Delphi Road to Alpine Dr. SW, right to the golf course. Look for signs.

Course Yardage & Par:
M-1937 yards, par 32.
W-1789 yards, par 34.

Desert Aire Golf Course (semi-private, 18 hole course)

505 Clubhouse Way West; Desert Aire, WA 99349
Phone: (509) 932-4439. Fax: (509) 932-5844. Internet: none.
Pro: Gary Momberg, PGA. Superintendent: James Crudy.
Rating/Slope: M 69.0/111; W 71.9/111. **Course record:** M 65/ W 75.
Green fees: W/D $20/$16; W/E $24/$16; Sr. & twilight rates (May-September).
Power cart: W/D $24/$14; W/E $24/$14. **Pull cart:** $3/$2. **Trail fee:** $5.
Reservation policy: yes, please call 7 days in advance for tee-times.
Winter condition: dry conditions. The course is usually open during the winter.
Terrain: flat, some hills. **Tees:** all grass. **Spikes:** soft spikes only.
Services: club rentals, snack bar, pro shop, driving range, beer, wine, lessons,
RV spots, memberships are available. **Comments:** the course is fairly wide
open with a beautiful view of the Columbia River and surrounding countryside.
The golf course can play very difficult if the wind picks up. Fair golf course.

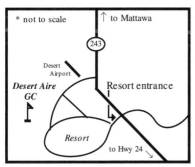

Directions: from I-90 E&W take exit
to Hwy 243S towards Mattawa. The
course is located 5 miles south of
Mattawa off of Hwy 243. Go through
the resort to Clubhouse Way. Turn
right on Clubhouse Way and proceed
to the clubhouse and the golf course.
Look for signs marking your way.

Course Yardage & Par:
M-6501 yards, par 72.
W-5786 yards, par 73.

Desert Canyon Golf Resort (public, resort 18 hole course)

1201 Desert Canyon Boulevard; Orondo, WA 98843
Phone:(509) 784-1111, 800-258-4173. **Fax:** (509) 784-2701.
Dir. of Golf: Jack Frei. Pro: Von Smith, PGA. Internet: www.desertcanyon.com
Rating/Slope: T 74.0/127; C 72.4/121; M 68.2/108; W 67.5/104. **Record:** 65.
Green fees: July 1st to Oct.14th M-Th. $75, Fri.-Sun. $85; M/C, VISA, AMEX.
Power cart: included in green fee. **Pull cart:** none. **Trail fee:** not allowed.
Reservation policy: yes, please call 7 days in advance for all your tee-times.
30 days in advance with pre payment made by a major credit card.
Winter condition: the golf course is open, weather permitting.
Terrain: rolling hills. **Tees:** all grass tees. **Spikes:** soft spikes required.
Services: club rentals, full service resort facilities, driving range, pro shop.
Comments: This is a desert style, links course with spectacular views of the
Columbia River. The facilty was recently ranked #2 in the state of Washington
by *Golf Digest*. It was also ranked #35 in Americas top 75 upscale golf courses
to play. This is simply a must play and is well worth the price of admission.

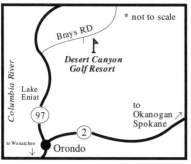

Directions: the course is located on the
east side of the Columbia River off of
Hwy 97 (not Alt. Hwy 97 on the
westside), 6.5 miles north of Orondo.
From Hwy 97 turn eastbound on Brays
Road. Go 3/4 of a mile to the entrance.

Course Yardage & Par:
T-6923 yards, par 72.
C-6894 yards, par 72.
M-6181 yards, par 72.
W-5515 yards, par 72.

Downriver Golf Course (public, 18 hole course)
3225 Columbia Circle; Spokane, WA 99205
Phone: (509) 327-5269. Fax: none. Internet: none.
Pro: Steve Conner, PGA. Superintendent: Bob Mielke.
Rating/Slope: M 68.8/115; W 72.8/118. **Course record:** 60.
Green fees: $18.50/$13.50 all week long; Green fees with discount
card $13.50/$11.50 all week long; Jr.'s $8; VISA, M/C.
Power cart: $24. **Pull cart:** $3. **Trail fee:** $7 for personal carts.
Reservation policy: weekdays call 1 day in advance, weekends-previous Sat.
Winter condition: the golf course is closed during the winter months.
Terrain: flat, some hills. **Tees:** all grass. **Spikes:** soft spikes preferred.
Services: club rentals, lessons, restaurant, snack bar, beer, wine, beverages,
pro shop, lockers, showers, driving range, putting & chipping greens.
Comments: tree-lined fairways are a challenge on this course. If you are
looking for a good public golf course at a very affordable price try Downriver.

Directions: from I-90 eastbound take exit #280 (westbound #280A) to Maple Street Bridge. Go north on Maple St. until you reach Northwest Blvd. Turn left on Northwest Blvd. and follow to Euclid St. Turn left on Euclid. Follow this to the golf course. The course is located about 1 mile off NW Blvd.

Course Yardage & Par:
M-6021 yards, par 71.
W-5992 yards, par 73.

Druids Glen Golf Club (public, 18 hole course)
29925 207th Avenue SE; Covington, WA 98042
Phone: (253) 638-1200. Fax: (253) 638-1440. Internet: www.druidsglengolf.com
General Manager: Tad Davis. Superintendent: Clint Goold.
Rating/Slope: T 74.8/137; C 71.8/131; M 68.9/123; W 70.6/121 **Record:** 68.
Green fees: Monday thru Thursday $43; Friday thru Sunday & Holidays. $55;
lower winter rates; twilight & early bird rates; Jr./Sr. rates (M-Th); M/C, VISA.
Power cart: $25. **Pull cart:** $5. **Trail fee:** personal carts not allowed.
Reservation policy: up to 1 week in advance or 21 days at druidsglengolf.com.
Winter condition: the golf course is open all year long. Course drains very well.
Terrain: flat, some hills. **Tees:** all grass. **Spikes:** soft spikes preferred.
Services: club rentals, lessons, liquor, pro shop, driving range, putting green.
Comments: 7000 + yard championship golf course. Fantastic layout that opened
July 14th 1997. This newer golf course will challenge you at nearly every turn.
Druids is a must play for any NW golfer. Be sure to call ahead for tee times.

Directions: from I-405 N&S, exit at
Maple Valley (Hwy 169) to Four Corners.
Take a right on Kent Kangley (272nd).
Proceed for about 2 miles, then take a
left at 216th. Turn right on Covington -
Sawyer Rd., then a left on 207th to the
golf course. Look for signs along the way.

Course Yardage & Par:
T-7145 yards, par 72.
C-6574 yards, par 72.
M-6004 yards, par 72.
W-5354 yards, par 72.

Dungeness Golf & Country Club (public, 18 hole course)

1965 Woodcock Road: Sequim, WA 98382 Internet: www.dungenessgcc.com
Phone: (360) 683-6344; 1-800-447-6826. Fax: (360) 683-1709.
Pro: Robert Bourns, PGA. Superintendent: Robert Schoessler.
Rating/Slope: C 70.1/123; M 68.3/120; W 70.3/119. **Course record:** 63.
Green fees: M-Th. $26.50/$17; Fri.-Sun. $29.50/$19; winter rates; M/C, VISA.
Power cart: $23/$14.50. **Pull cart:** $3/$2. **Trail fee:** $11/$6 (all prices + tax).
Reservation policy: call up to 60 days in advance for your tee-times.
Winter condition: the golf course is open all year long. Very dry conditions.
Terrain: flat, some hills. **Tees:** all grass. **Spikes:** soft spikes March-September.
Services: pro shop, driving range, club rentals, lessons, restaurant and lounge,
beer, wine, liquor, showers, putting & chipping greens, banquet facility.
Comments: One of the finest and friendliest golf courses in Washington. The
course features well bunkered greens, wide fairways and spectacular views from
nearly every tee on the course. Condos that border the golf course are available
for rent all year round. This course is worth a special trip to Olympic Peninsula.

Directions: from Seattle take the
Edmonds or Winslow ferry. Follow signs
to the Hood Canal Bridge and Hwy 104.
From Hwy 104 follow to Hwy 101.
Proceed on Hwy 101 through Sequim for
3 miles. Turn right on Kitchen-Dick Road.
Go for 3 miles to Woodcock Road. Turn
right on Woodcock Road. Proceed for
1/2 mile. The course will be on your left.
Note signs marking your turns.

Course Yardage & Par:
C-6456 yards, par 72.
M-6034 yards, par 72.
W-5347 yards, par 72.

Eaglemont (public, 18 hole course)

4127 Eaglemont Drive; Mount Vernon, WA 98273 Internet: www.eaglemont.com
Phone: (360) 424-0800; 1-800-368-8876. Fax: (360) 424-0790.
Pro: Mike O'Laughlin, PGA. Superintendent: Charles Fisher.
Rating/Slope: T 73.4/134; C 71.6/129; M 70.5/126; M 69.4/124; W 70.7/124.
Green fees: W/D $43; W/E $56; w/ cart; earlybird $35; M/C, VISA, AMEX.
Power cart: included. **Pull cart:** not available. **Trail fee:** not allowed.
Reservation policy: yes, please call in advance for all your reservations.
Winter condition: the golf course is open all year long. Dry conditions.
Terrain: very hilly. **Tees:** all grass. **Spikes:** soft spikes preferred.
Services: the golf course offers a full service clubhouse and pro shop, range.
Comments: This John Steidel designed golf course is of championship caliber, featuring ponds, tree lined fairways and bunkers galore. Excellent newer course that can play very tough. Shot placement off the tee is a must at Eaglemont.

Directions: From I-5 N&S take exit #227 (College Way). Proceed eastbound on College Way until you reach Waugh Road. Turn right on Waugh Road. Proceed on Waugh Road to Eaglemont Drive. Continue until you see the parking lot on your left hand side.

Course Yardage & Par:

T-7006 yards, par 72.
C-6659 yards, par 72.
M-6445 yards, par 72.
M-6187 yards, par 72.
W-5307 yards, par 72.

LinksTime.com
a division of BookGolf.com

Echo Falls Golf Club (semi-private, 18 hole course)

20414 121st Avenue SE; Snohomish, WA 98296
Phone: (206) 362-3000 or (360) 668-3030. Fax: (360) 668-3733
Pro: Kevin LeDuc, PGA. Supt.: Rob Daily. Internet: www.echofallsgolf.com
Rating/Slope: C 69.4/132; M 67.4/120; W 64.6/118. **Course record:** 61.
Green fees: Mon.-Th. $37*; Fri.-Sun. 49*; twilight rates; VISA, M/C, AMEX.
Power cart: $13* per person. **Pull cart:** $3*. **Trail fee:** not allowed. *Add tax.
Reservation policy: please call 7 days in advance for your tee-times.
Winter condition: the golf course is open all year long. Good winter drainage.
Terrain: relatively hilly. **Tees:** all grass. **Spikes:** soft spikes required.
Services: club rentals, lessons, full service pro shop, clubhouse, restuarant, beer,
wine, driving range, putting & chipping greens. **Comments:**18th hole is an
island green that is spectacular. Shot placement is a must in order to score well.
Greens are large, undulating and well bunkered. The staff at Echo Falls wants
you to feel that this facility is "The Public's Country Club". Excellent track.

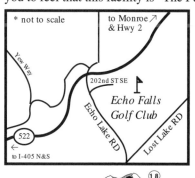

Directions: If traveling on I-405 N&S
exit to Hwy 522 eastbound. Proceed for
7.1 miles to Echo Lake Road. Turn right
on Echo Lake Road. Proceed to your first
left (202nd Ave SE) and turn left. Proceed
for 1/4 of a mile to the course entrance on
your right hand side. Look for signs to
mark your way to the golf course.

Course Yardage & Par:
C-6123 yards, par 70.
M-5626 yards, par 70.
W-4357 yards, par 70.

Elk Run Golf Course (public, 18 hole course)

22500 SE 275th Place; Maple Valley, WA 98038
Phone: (425) 432-8800. Fax: (425) 432-1907. Internet: none.
Director of Golf: Steve Dubsky, PGA. Head Golf Pro: Doug Eisele, PGA.
Manager: Roy Humphreys. Superintendent: Tony Bubenas.
Rating/Slope: C 66.2/118; M 63.5/113; W 67.9/112. **Course record:** 62.
Green fees: Monday thru Thursday $30/$19; Fridays $33/$21.
W/E's & Holidays $35/$23; Jr & Sr.'s $27/$18 (Monday-Thursday); M/C, VISA.
Power cart: $24. **Pull cart:** $3. **Trail fee:** $7 for personal carts.
Reservation policy: yes, please call 5 days in advance for your tee-times.
Winter condition: the golf course is open all year long. Dry conditions.
Terrain: flat, some slight hills. **Tees:** grass. **Spikes:** soft spikes optional.
Services: club rentals, lessons, restaurant, coffee shop, pro shop, driving range.
Comments: excellent drainage keeps Elk Run as one of the driest golf courses
in the Northwest. The newer 9 is a real challenge with fairways that are narrow
and tree-lined. Numerous bunkers and ponds guard tricky undulating greens.

Directions: from I-405 N&S take exit
#4 (southbound) #4A (northbound) to
Hwy 169 (Maple Valley-Black Diamond
Road). Proceed to the Kent-Kangley
Road and turn right. Proceed for 1 mile
to 228th SE. Turn left on 228th SE and
follow to the golf course. Look for signs
marking your turn to the course the way
is well marked.

Course Yardage & Par:
M-5724 yards, par 71.
W-5189 yards, par 71.

Ellensburg Golf Club (semi-private, 9 hole course)

3231 Thorp Road South; Ellensburg, WA 98926
Phone: (509) 962-2984. Fax: (509) 962-5171. Internet: none.
Pro: Rich Farrell, PGA. Superintendent: Frank Crimp.
Rating/Slope: M 69.4/115; W 72.3/120. **Course record:** 29/62.
Green fees: W/D $16/$9; W/E $18/$10; M/C, VISA.
Power cart: $20/$10. **Pull cart:** $3/$1.50. **Trail fee:** $5 for personal carts.
Reservation policy: you may call ahead to make a tee time.
Winter condition: golf course is closed from mid November to March.
Terrain: flat (easy walking). **Tees:** grass. **Spikes:** soft spikes preferred.
Services: club rentals, lessons, restaurant, snack bar, lounge, beer, wine, liquor, pro shop, lockers, showers, driving range, putting green. **Comments:** sand traps and water make this 9 hole course a real challenge. Fairways are fairly wide giving you ample room off the tee. Dual tees available for 18 hole play. Course does limit outside play at certain times so be sure call ahead for your tee time.

Directions: from I-90 eastbound take Thorp Hwy exit #101 and go for 2 miles to the golf course. From westbound I-90 take exit #106 the West Interchange by the KOA campground. Cross the bridge over the Yakima River onto Thorp Road and proceed for 2 miles to the golf course.

Course Yardage & Par:
M-2988 yards, par 35.
W-2807 yards, par 36.
Dual tees for 18 holes:
M-5974 yards, par 70.
W-5597 yards, par 73.

Enumclaw Golf Course (public, 18 hole course)
45220 288th SE; Enumclaw, WA 98002
Phone: (360) 825-2827. **Fax:** none. **Internet:** none.
Pro: John McGregor, PGA. **Superintendent:** Chad Chevalier.
Rating/Slope: M 66.0/105; W 68.6/109. **Course record:** 61.
Greens fee: $19/$14; Jr. & Sr. rates (Monday thru Friday only); M/C, VISA.
Power cart: $22/$11. **Pull cart:** $3. **Trail fee:** no charge for personal carts.
Reservation policy: yes, call up to one week in advance for tee-times.
Winter condition: the golf course is open all year long. Wet conditions.
Terrain: relatively hilly. **Tees:** grass & mats. **Spikes:** metal spikes permitted.
Services: club rentals, lessons, snack bar, restaurant, beer, wine, chipping &
putting greens. **Comments:** The golf course has beautiful views of the sur-
rounding countryside. Boise Creek winds through the golf course and is a factor
on many of the holes. The course itself can play much longer than the yardage
would indicate. Be sure to call ahead for tee times during the summer.

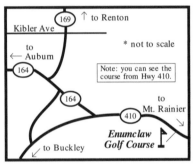

Directions: from I-5 N&S take exit 142
to Hwy 18E. East to Auburn Way S/Hwy
164 E exit. Go east on Hwy 164 for 13.8
miles to Hwy 410 (SE 448th). Proceed
eastbound for 1 mile to the golf course.
Note: You can see the golf course when
driving on Hwy 410. Look for signs
indicating your turn to the golf course.

Course Yardage & Par:
M-5561 yards, par 70.
W-5211 yards, par 71.

Esmeralda Golf Course (public, 18 hole course)
East 3933 Courtland; Spokane, WA 99207
Phone: (509) 487-6291. Fax: none. Internet: none.
Pro: Bill Warner, PGA. Superintendent: Morgan Boyce.
Rating/Slope: C 68.7/108; M 67.7/106; W 70.8/113. **Course record:** 62.
Green fees: $18.50/$13.50 all week long; Jr. rates W/D's $8; VISA, M/C.
Power cart: $22/$11. **Pull cart:** $2. **Trail fee:** $7 for personal carts.
Reservation policy: yes, 1 day for weekdays, 1 week for the weekends.
Winter condition: the course open weather permitting. Dry conditions.
Terrain: flat, some hills. **Tees:** all grass. **Spikes:** soft spikes preferred.
Services: club rentals, lessons, restaurant, beer, wine, pro shop, driving range,
putting green. **Comments:** large, quick greens and fairly flat terrain make for
a pleasant round. Fairways are wide giving the golfer ample room off the tee.
Excellent public course with tree lined fairways and few hazards.

Directions: from I-90 E&W take the
Freya/Thor exit #283B. Go northbound
for 3 miles to Euclid Avenue. Go right on
Euclid Avenue for 3 blocks to Freya. Turn
left on Freya to the golf course. Look for
signs indicating your turn to the course.

Course Yardage & Par:
C-6249 yards, par 70.
M-6015 yards, par 70.
W-5594 yards, par 72.

Everett Golf & Country Club (private, 18 hole course)
1500 52nd Street; P.O. Box 2300; Everett, WA 98203
Phone: (425) 259-1214. Fax: (425) 355-4570. Internet: www.everettgcc.com
Pro: Bob Borup, PGA. Superintendent: Randy White.
Rating/Slope: C 70.0/126; M 69.1/125; W 73.1/126. **Course record:** 62.
Green fees: private course, members & guests only; reciprocates.
Power cart: private club. **Pull cart:** private club. **Trail fee:** not allowed.
Reservation policy: private club, members only. No public play allowed
Winter condition: The golf course is open all year long. Dry conditions.
Terrain: flat, some hills. **Tees:** grass. **Spikes:** soft spikes required in summer.
Services: lessons, lounge, restaurant, beer, wine, liquor, lockers, showers,
pro shop, driving range. **Comments:** the golf course is fairly flat with tree lined
fairways with small well bunkered greens. This private track was built in 1910
and gives the golfer many outstanding views of the surrounding countryside.

Directions: from I-5 N&S take exit #189
to Hwy 526E for .5 miles to Evergreen
Way. Turn right (north) on Evergreen
Way and proceed for 2 miles to 52nd
Street. Turn right (east) on 52nd Street.
Proceed to the golf course.

Course Yardage & Par:
C-6188 yards, par 72.
M-6005 yards, par 72.
W-5741 yards, par 72.

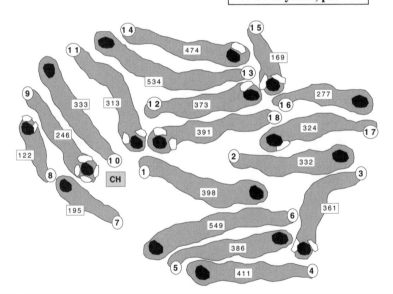

Evergreen Golf Course (public, 9 hole course)
P.O. Box 156; 413 East Main Street; Everson, WA 98247
Phone: (360) 966-5417. Fax: none. Internet: none.
Owner: Jerry McBeth. Superintendent: none.
Rating/Slope: the golf course is not rated. **Course record:** 28, 9 holes.
Green fees: $13/$9 all week long; Jr. & Sr. rates $11/$7; no credit cards.
Power cart: none available for use. **Pull cart:** $2. **Trail fee:** no charge.
Reservation policy: none. Tee-times are on a first come first served basis.
Winter condition: the golf course is closed during the winter months.
Terrain: flat, some slight hills. **Tees:** grass. **Spikes:** metal spikes permitted.
Services: club rentals, snack bar, beer, wine, limited pro shop, putting green.
Comments: family owned executive course with narrow tree lined fairways.
A creek which wanders throughout the course comes into play on a number
of holes. Fairly rustic course that is very friendly and has a laid back feel.

Directions: from I-5 N&S take exit #256
to Guide Meridian St. Go northbound on
Meridian (Hwy 539) for 7.7 miles to Hwy
544E. Turn eastbound on Hwy 544 for 8.4
miles to the golf course. Look for signs
marking your way to the entrance of the
golf course.

Course Yardage & Par:
M-2145 yards, par 31.
W-2145 yards, par 31.

Fairway Village Golf Course (public, 9 hole course)

15503 SE Fernwood Drive; Vancouver, WA 98684
Phone: (360) 254-9325. Fax: (360) 253-5525. Internet: none.
Manager: Robert Hardner. Superintendent: Chris Carley.
Rating/Slope: M 64.5/107; W 64.3/106. **Course record:** 29.
Green fees: $20/$12 all week long; Sr. rates M-Th $17/$10; M/C, VISA.
Power cart: $18/$12. **Pull cart:** $3. **Trail fee:** $5 for personal carts.
Reservation policy: yes, call up to 1 week in advance for your tee-times.
Winter condition: the golf course is open all year long. Dry conditions.
Terrain: flat, some hills. **Tees:** grass. **Spikes:** soft spikes preferred.
Services: club rentals, lessons, pro shop, vending machines, putting green.
Comments: this well bunkered short and narrow golf course was designed by
Bunny Mason and dedicated by Sam Snead. Greens and fairways are kept in
excellent condition with the course playing tight in certain area's. Great course if
you are looking for a change of pace from the 6500 yard back breaker.

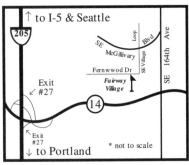

Directions: from I-5 N&S exit to I-205
N&S. Exit from I-205 to Hwy 14 going
eastbound. Proceed east to exit #8 (SE
164th). Turn left on SE 164th and
proceed for 1 mile to SE McGillivary
(2nd light). Turn left for .2 miles to SE
Village Loop. At SE Village Loop turn
left and then follow this to the course.

Course Yardage & Par:
M-2500 yards, par 34.
W-2311 yards, par 34.
<u>Dual tees for 18 holes:</u>
M-5133 yards, par 68.
W-4797 yards, par 68.

Fairways at West Terrace, The   (public, 18 holes)

W 9810 Melville Road; Cheney, WA 99004
Phone: (509) 747-8418. Fax: (509) 455-8403. Internet: none.
Pro: Jerry Zink, PGA. Superintendent: Chris Becker.
Rating/Slope: C 69.0/117; M 67.5/114; W 71.4/125; W 68.9/120. **Record:** 61.
Green fees: W/D $17/$13; W/E $20; Jr & Sr rates $13; M/C, VISA.
Power cart: $23/$12. **Pull cart:** $2. **Trail fee:** $8 for personal carts.
Reservation policy: yes. Call up to 1 week in advance for tee-times.
Winter condition: the golf course is open weather permitting. Drains well.
Terrain: flat, some hills. **Tees:** all grass. **Spikes:** metal spikes permitted.
Services: club rentals, lessons, snack bar, restaurant, beer, wine, liquor, driving
range, pro shop, putting & chipping greens. **Comments:** home of the "Lilac
City Invitational Tournament." The course has numerous sand traps and 6 ponds
which come in to play. Great golf course that can play very tough.

Directions: from I-90 E&W take exit
#272 (Medical Lake). Go south to 4-way
stop (West Bow Road). Turn right. Go to
Hayford Road. Turn left. Go to Melville
Road turn left. The course will be on your
left side of the road.

Course Yardage & Par:
C-6459 yards, par 72.
M-6138 yards, par 72.
W-5650 yards, par 72.
W-5142 yards, par 72.

Fairwood Golf & Country Club (private, 18 hole course)

17070 140th SE; Renton, WA 98055
Phone: (425) 226-7890. Fax: (425) 226-1737. Internet: none.
Pro: Chris Johnson, PGA. Superintendent: Greg Hall.
Rating/Slope: C 71.1/127; M 69.5/124; W 72.4/123. **Course record:** 61.
Green fees: private club, members and guests only, limited reciprocation.
Power cart: private club. **Pull cart:** private club. **Trail fee:** not allowed.
Reservation policy: yes, call on Thursday for the following week.
Winter condition: the golf course is open all year long. Dry conditions.
Terrain: relatively hilly. **Tees:** all grass. **Spikes:** soft spikes preferred.
Services: lessons, lounge, beer, wine, liquor, lockers, showers, sauna, pro shop, driving range, chipping & putting green. **Comments:** OB on both sides of each hole puts a premium on accuracy off the tee. Undulating greens, bunkers and length make this golf course difficult. Excellent private facility built in 1972.

Directions: from I-5 N&S exit to I-405 N&S. From I-405 N&S take exit #4 to Hwy 169S. Proceed on Hwy 169 until you reach 140th PL SE. Turn right on 140th PL SE. Travel up the hill until 140th PL SE turns into 140th St SE. The golf course will be on your left. Note the clubhouse is beyond the main entrance.

Course Yardage & Par:
C-6306 yards, par 71.
M-5944 yards, par 71.
W-5396 yards, par 71.

Map 1; Grid E4

Family Golf Center @ Tumwater (public, 9 hole course)
8080 Center Street SW; Tumwater, WA 98501
Phone: (360) 786-8626. **Fax:** (360) 786-1848. **Internet:** www.familygolf.com
Pro: LeAnne Hine, LPGA. **Supt.:** Neil Lupkes. **Manager:** Eric Rowe.
Rating/Slope: M 28.9/85. **Course record:** 27.
Green fees: W/D \$14/\$9; W/E \$15/\$10 all week long; winter rates.
Power cart: not allowed. **Pull cart:** \$2. **Trail fee:** personal carts not allowed.
Reservation policy: call ahead up to 7 days in advance for a tee time.
Winter condition: the golf course is open all year around. Dry conditions.
Terrain: flat (easy walking). **Tees:** grass. **Spikes:** soft spikes preferred.
Services: club rentals, lessons, club repair, pro shop, driving range that is
covered and has heated stalls, club memberships, putting & chipping green.
Comments: Very challenging executive golf course. Great place to sharpen
your scoring iron play. The course layout facilitates using all the clubs in your
bag. The driving range is open 8am- 9pm during the winter and from dawn to
dusk during the summer months. Be sure to give Family Golf Center a try.

Directions: from I-5 N&S take exit #101
(Airdustrial). Proceed eastbound to the
first stoplight. Right on Center Street.
Proceed for 1/2 mile, the course is on
the left side of the street. Look for signs.

Course Yardage & Par:
M-1737 yards, par 29.
W-1401 yards, par 30.

Driving Range

Fircrest Golf Club (private, 18 hole course)
1500 Regents Boulevard; Fircrest, WA 98466
Phone: (253) 564-5792, 564-6756. **Fax:** (253) 565-1880. **Internet: none.**
Pro: Greg Talley, PGA. **Superintendent:** Eric Thompson.
Rating/Slope: C 72.6/131; M 71.8/128; W 74.8/131. **Course record:** 62.
Green fees: private, members only; very limited reciprocation; no credit cards.
Power cart: private club. **Pull cart:** private club. **Trail fee:** not allowed.
Reservation policy: none. Private club members only no outside play allowed.
Winter condition: the golf course is open all year long. Dry conditions.
Terrain: relatively hilly. **Tees:** all grass. **Spikes:** soft spikes preferred.
Services: lessons, snack bar, lounge, restaurant, beer, wine, liquor, lockers, showers, pro shop, practice range, club memberships, dress code, putting green.
Comments: Established in 1923, this course's fairways are surrounded by trees which makes the course play tight. Greens are very fast and well bunkered. This older private club is rich in golf tradition and feel. Excellent, demanding course.

Directions: from I-5 N&S take exit #132 to SR16 Westbound. Take the Fircrest-Center Street exit off of SR16. Turn right onto Center Street. Center Street becomes Regents Blvd. in Fircrest. Look for your turn to the facility.

Course Yardage & Par:
C-6685 yards, par 71.
M-6440 yards, par 71.
W-5985 yards, par 75.

First Tee of Olympia, The (public, 3 hole course)
8000 72nd Lane SE; Olympia, WA 98513
Phone: (360) 493-1000. **Fax:** none. **Internet:** none.
Pro: Kevin Bishop, PGA. **Superintendent:** unavailable.
Rating/Slope: the golf course is not rated. **Course record:** 62.
Green fees: prices of fees are determined by various factors. It is best to call the course and confirm fees. The course is used as a golf learing center.
Power cart: N/A. **Pull cart:** call for prices. **Trail fee:** N/A.
Reservation policy: golf learning center. Please call for policy.
Winter condition: the golf course is open all year long. Dry conditions.
Terrain: flat. **Tees:** all grass. **Spikes:** soft spikes are required.
Services: lessons, pro shop, practice range, putting green & chipping green.
Comments: this three hole learning center is one of the best in the state of Washington. Run by the PGA of America it features an excellent driving range and a course that is used as teaching aid for players. Great for the young golfer.

Directions: from I-5 N&S exit at Martin Way. Proceed 3.4 miles east on College St. to Yelm Hwy. Turn left. Proceed to Spurgeon Creek Rd. turn right. Look for a sign at the course.

Course Yardage & Par:
C-unavailable.
M-unavailable.
W-unavailable.

Fisher Park Golf Course (public, 9 hole par 3 course)
2301 40th Avenue; Yakima, WA 98908
Phone: (509) 575-6075. **Fax:** none. **Internet:** none.
Manager: Dottie Hodgson. **Teaching Pro:** Bob Hoag.
Rating/Slope: the golf course has not been rated. **Course record:** 23.
Green fees: W/D $12/$7; W/E & Holidays $10/$6; Jr & Sr rates $8/$5.
Power cart: none available. **Pull cart:** $2.50. **Trail fee:** no personal carts.
Reservation policy: tee-times are on a first come first served basis.
Winter condition: the course is closed from November 15th to March 1st.
Terrain: flat, some slight hills. **Tees:** grass. **Spikes:** soft spikes only.
Services: club rentals, lessons, snack bar, beverages, putting green.
Comments: Economical course golf course run by the City of Yakima Parks
Department. This par 3 golf course can play long at times with holes ranging
from 118 to 191 yards. You will use every iron in your bag.

Directions: From I-82 take the Nob
Hill exit #34 and proceed westbound.
At 40th Avenue turn right and proceed
to the golf course. The golf course will
be located on your right hand side.
Look for signs.

Course Yardage & Par:
M-1354 yards, par 27.
W-1354 yards, par 27.

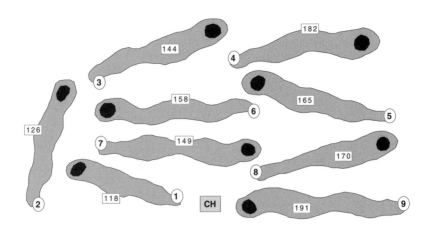

Flowing Lake Golf Course (public, 18 hole course)

5001 Weber Road; Snohomish, WA 98290
Phone: (360) 568-2753. Fax: (360) 658-1418. Internet: none.
Manager: Gary Laz. Superintendent: Gary Laz.
Rating/Slope: M 60.0/100; W 61.2/101. **Course record:** 63.
Green fees: W/D $17/$11; W/E $21/$15; M/C, VISA, DISC.
Power cart: $25/$12.50. **Pull cart:** $3/$1.50. **Trail fee:** $5.
Reservation policy: yes, please call 1 week in advance for a tee time.
Winter condition: course closed from November 15th to February 15th.
Terrain: flat, some hills. **Tees:** all grass. **Spikes:** soft spikes preferred.
Services: club rentals, snack bar, putting green, small pro shop.
Comments: newer family run golf course that can play very tight in spots.
This is a beautiful country course with spectacular views of the Cascades from
many of the tees and fairways. The track has improved every year as the layout
and greens have had a chance to mature. Water is a major factor on many holes.

Directions: from Hwy 2 exit at 100th St.
SE (which is east of Snohomish). Follow
to Spada Road. Right on Spada. Proceed
to Storm Lake Road. Right on Storm Lake
Road to Weber Road where you will turn
left. The golf course entrance is located
ahead on your right. Look for signs.

Course Yardage & Par:
M-4265 yards, par 66.
W-4265 yards, par 66.

Fort Lewis Golf Course (public & military, 27 hole course)

P.O. Box 33175; Fort Lewis, WA 98433

Phone: (253) 967-6522. **Fax:** (253) 964-2789. **Internet:** none.

Pro: James Barnhouse, PGA. **Supt.:** John Ford. **Course record:** 64.

Rating/Slope: Red/Blue C 72.6/125; M 70.4/121; W 73.3/120.

Green fees: daily, unlimited play fees-civilian & military. Call for rates.

Power cart: available. **Pull cart:** available. **Trail fee:** allowed.

Reservation policy: please call ahead the day prior to play at 2:30pm.

Winter condition: the golf course is open all year long. Dry conditions.

Terrain: relatively hilly. **Tees:** grass. **Spikes:** spikeless only.

Services: club rentals, lessons, snack bar, beer, lockers, showers, two driving ranges, pro shop, putting green. **Comments:** Mature trees, ponds and sand traps make this 27 hole layout a very difficult course to score on. Most tees are elevated leaving the golfer very little room off the tee. Excellent military track.

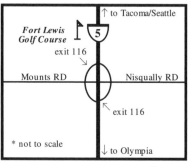

Directions: from I-5 N&S take exit #116 (Mounts Rd.-Nisqually). Proceed west for .1 miles to the golf course. **Note:** the golf course is adjacent to I-5.

Course Yardage & Par:
Red/Blue: C-6855 yards, par 72.
Red/Blue: M-6388 yards, par 72.
Red/Blue: W-5822 yards, par 74.

Fort Steilacoom Golf Course (public, 9 hole course)
Box 97325; 8202 87th SW; Tacoma, WA 98498
Phone: (253) 588-0613. Fax: (253) 588-0613. Internet: none.
Pro: Keith Johnson. Superintendent: Scott Tyson.
Rating/Slope: M 62.8/098; W 66.8/105. **Course record:** 54.
Green fees: $16.50/$10.75; Jr & Sr rates $11.50/$7.50; twilite rate; M/C, VISA.
Power cart: $16/$10. **Pull cart:** $3. **Trail fee:** $5 for personal carts.
Reservation policy: yes, please call in advance for your tee times.
Winter condition: golf course is open all year long. Dry conditions.
Terrain: very flat. **Tees:** grass & mats. **Spikes:** soft spikes preferred.
Services: club rentals, lessons, pro shop, pop, vending machines, hot & cold
sandwiches, snacks, putting & chipping green, club memberships available.
Comments: golf course is not overly long so its an excellent course to practice
your short irons on. Dual tees are available for those wanting to play a full 18
hole round. Fairways are tree lined and fairly wide leaving room off the tee.

Directions: from I-5 N&S take exit
#129 to S 74th. Turn west on S 74th
and proceed 2.2 miles to Custer Road
W. Go south for 1 mile to Steilacoom
Blvd. Turn west on Steilacoom Blvd.
for 1.1 miles to 87th Ave. SW. Turn
north on 87th Ave. SW for .2 miles to
the golf course driveway. Look for
signs marking your turn to the course.

Course Yardage & Par:
M-2520 yards, par 34; W-2410 yards, par 34.
Dual tees for 18 holes:
M-5040 yards, par 68; W-4820 yards, par 68.

Foster Golf Links (public, 18 hole course)

13500 Interurban Avenue; Tukwila, WA 98168
Phone: (206) 242-4221. Fax: (206) 246-4064. Internet: none.
Pro: Marty O'Brien, PGA. Superintendent: Chuck Morris.
Rating/Slope: M 62.3/94; W 66.6/101. **Course record:** 59.
Green fees: W/D $21/$16; W/E $23/$18; Senior rates W/D's $16.50/$13.75;
Junior rates $13/$9; Winter rates $18/$14.50, Sr. rates $13.50/$12; VISA, MC.
Power cart: $22/$13. **Pull cart:** $3/$1.50. **Trail fee:** $8 for personal carts.
Reservation policy: yes, call up to 1 week in advance for tee times.
Winter condition: the golf course is open all year long. Dry conditions.
Terrain: flat, some hills. **Tees:** grass & mats. **Spikes:** soft spikes optional.
Services: club rentals, restaurant, beer, wine, pop, liquor, pro shop.
Comments: the course is easy to walk and a favorite of seniors. This track has
been undergoing changes the last two years to enhance its playability. If you are
looking for a change of pace from the 6000+ yards golf course, give Foster a try.

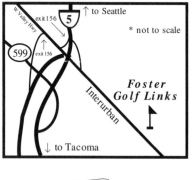

Directions: from I-5 N&S take exit
#156 (Tukwila) to Interurban South.
Proceed south for .4 miles to the golf
course which will be on your left hand
side. Look for a sign indicating your
turn into the parking lot.

Course Yardage & Par:
M-4930 yards, par 68.
W-4695 yards, par 70.

Gallery Golf Course (military, open to public, 18 hole course)

MWR Golf; NAS Whidbey Island; Oak Harbor, WA 98278
Phone: (360) 257-2178. Fax: (360) 257-6585. Internet: none.
Golf Course General Manager: Christopher M. Braun.
Rating/Slope: C 70.1/121; M 69.0/120; W 70.7/123. **Course record:** 66.
Green fees: Monday-Thursday $20; Friday-Sunday & Holidays $22;
sliding fee scale for military based on rank; VISA, M/C, DIS, AMEX.
Power cart: $14. **Pull cart:** $3. **Trail fee:** not allowed.
Reservation policy: yes, please call in advance for all tee-times.
Winter condition: the golf course is open all year long. Dry conditions.
Terrain: flat, some hills. **Tees:** grass. **Spikes:** soft spikes preferred.
Services: club rentals, lessons, restaurant, lounge, beer, wine, beverages, liquor,
lockers, pro shop, driving range, short practice chipping green, putting green.
Comments: a very scenic and demanding layout located at the Whidbey Island
Naval Air Station. Gallery Golf Course features well bunkered greens that can
get very fast in the summer months. The golf course is now open for public play.

Directions: from I-5 N&S take exit 230 to Hwy 20 W. Travel west to Whidbey Island and exit at Ault Field Road. Continue beyond NAS to Clover Valley Road to the golf course. **Note:** the golf course is located right outside the military base. Look for signs indicating your way to the base.

Course Yardage & Par:
C-6351 yards, par 72.
M-6101 yards, par 72.
W-5454 yards, par 74.

Gig Harbor Golf & Country Club (private, 9 hole course)
6909 Artondale Drive. NW; Gig Harbor, WA 98335
Phone: (253) 851-2378. Fax: (253) 858-2917. Internet: none.
Pro: to be determined. Superintendent: Todd Lupkes.
Rating/Slope: M 65.6/109; W 68.8/114. **Course record:** 64.
Green fees: private club, members & guests only; limited reciprocation.
Power cart: private club. **Pull cart:** private club. **Trail fee:** private club.
Reservation policy: please call in advance for your tee times.
Winter condition: the golf course is open all year long. Dry conditions.
Terrain: relatively hilly. **Tees:** all grass. **Spikes:** soft spikes preferred.
Services: club rentals, lessons, snack bar, beer, wine, lounge (members only), lockers, pro shop, driving range, custom built clubs-Zevo Fitting System.
Comments: beautiful views of Mount Rainier and the surrounding countryside from many holes. A friendly staff and some of the best greens in the northwest can be found at Gig Harbor Golf & Country Club. Good private course.

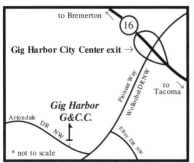

Directions: from I-5 N&S take exit #132 to Highway 16 West. Proceed on Highway 16 West to the Gig Harbor City Center exit. Turn south off exit onto Pioneer Way. Proceed for 2 miles to Artondale Road where you will turn right. Proceed for .3 miles to the golf course located on your right hand side.

Course Yardage & Par:

M-2702 yards, par 35.
W-2614 yards, par 35.
<u>Dual tees for 18 holes:</u>
M-5420 yards, par 70.
W-5095 yards, par 70.

Glen Acres Golf & Country Club (private, 9 hole course)
1000 South 112th Street; Seattle, WA 98168
Phone: (206) 244-3786. **Fax:** (206) 439-9952. **Internet:** www.cybergolf.com/glenacres
Pro: Bart Turchin, PGA. **Supt.:** Daniel Kukla. **GM:** Eric Forrer.
Rating/Slope: M 69.4/127; W 72.2/126. **Course record:** 61.
Green fees: private club, members & guests only; limited reciprocation.
Power cart: private club. **Pull cart:** private club. **Trail fee:** private club.
Reservation policy: yes, call up to 1 week for tee-times. No public play.
Winter condition: the golf course is open all year long. Wet conditions.
Terrain: flat to hilly terrain. **Tees:** grass. **Spikes:** soft spikes preferred.
Services: club rentals, lessons, snack bar, lounge, restaurant, beer, wine, liquor, pro shop, lockers, showers, social memberships, driving range, putting green.
Comments: the fairways are narrow and tree lined leaving very little room off the tee. All greens are well bunkered, elevated and have huge undulations. Good, older private club that is kept in excellent condition throughout the golfing year. Be sure to call and inquire about what memberships they offer. This is Glen Acres Homeowners Assoc. Facility managed by G. R. NW.

Directions: from I-5 N&S take exit 158B. Go west on Boeing Access Road for .4 miles to Pacific Hwy S. Travel south for 1.2 miles to S 128th. West for 1 mile to Des Moines Way. Go north for .5 miles and veer left to Glendale Way S. Proceed north for .7 miles to the course.

Course Yardage & Par:
M-3060 yards, par 36.
W-2828 yards, par 36.
Dual tees for 18 holes:
M-6088 yards, par 72.
W-5652 yards, par 72.

Glendale Golf & Country Club (private, 18 hole course)
13440 Main Street; Bellevue, WA 98005
Phone: (425) 746-7377. **Fax:** (425) 746-7660. **Internet:** none.
Pro: Stan Hyatt, PGA. **Superintendent:** Stephen Kealy.
Rating/Slope: C 71.5/135; M 70.2/132; W 73.1/131. **Course record:** 65.
Green fees: private club, members only; limited reciprocation; no credit cards.
Power cart: private club. **Pull cart:** private club. **Trail fee:** not allowed.
Reservation policy: yes, call up to 1 week in advance for weekends only.
Winter condition: the golf course is open all year long. Dry (drains well).
Terrain: relatively hilly. **Tees:** all grass. **Spikes:** soft spikes preferred.
Services: lessons, snack bar, lounge, restaurant, beer, wine, liquor, pro shop,
lockers, showers, club memberships, driving range, putting & chipping greens.
Comments: tough, well-trapped, woodsy layout that has fast greens and trouble
off the tees. This private facility has hosted the Washington State Open
Championship. A well maintained track that will challenge any level of golfer.

Directions: from I-405 N&S take exit #13 to NE 8th St eastbound. Travel east for 1.6 miles to 140th Ave. Turn south (right) and proceed for 1 mile to Main St. When you reach Main St. turn west (right) on Main St. and proceed to the golf course. **Note:** small sign just before the entrance to the facility.

Course Yardage & Par:
C-6568 yards, par 72.
M-6274 yards, par 72.
W-5706 yards, par 72.

Gleneagle Golf Course (public, 18 hole course)

7619 Country Club Drive; Arlington, WA 98223
Phone: (360) 435-6713. Fax: (360) 425-4769. Internet: www.americangolf.com
General Manager: Todd Ganglehoff Superintendent: Paul Peterson.
Rating/Slope: C 69.8/129; B 67.0/123; M 65.6/121; F 64.2/118. **Record:** 66.
Green fees: W/D $23; W/E $29; twilight rates; M/C, VISA, AMEX, DIS.
Power cart: W/D $18, W/E $24, Sr. $13. **Pull cart:** $3. **Trail fee:** $10.
Reservation policy: please call 7 days in advance for your tee times.
Winter condition: the golf course is open all year long, weather permitting.
Terrain: flat, some hills. **Tees:** all grass. **Spikes:** metal spikes permitted.
Services: club rentals, pro shop, driving range, snack bar, full service clubhouse
with restaurant. **Comments:** The course features tree lined fairways, ponds and
well bunkered greens. Homes line most of the fairways as Gleneagle is part of a
master planned development. The 1st 9 holes have been open for play since
1993, with the 2nd nine opening up 2 years later. Good course that is very tight.

Directions: From I-5 N&S take exit
#206 and proceed eastbound on 172nd
ST NE until you reach 67th Ave. NE. At
67th Ave. proceed straight through up
the hill to Gleneagle Dr. where you will
turn left. Proceed on Gleneagle Dr. to the
course. Look for signs along the way.

Course Yardage & Par:
C-6010 yards, par 70.
B-5498 yards, par 70.
M-4828 yards, par 70.
F-4318 yards, par 70.

Gold Mountain Golf Complex (public, 36 hole course)

Physical address: 7263 West Belfair Valley Road; Gorst, WA 98337
Mailing address: P.O. Box 4130; Bremerton, WA 98312
Phone number: Seattle (206) 464-1175; Tacoma (253) 627-8904
Fax number: (360) 415-6880. **Internet:** www.goldmt.com
Director of Golf: Scott Alexander, PGA. **Superintendent:** Edward Faulk.
Pros: Cascade: Daryl Matheny, PGA. Olympic: Daryl Matheny, PGA
Rating/Slope: T 73.5/131; C 70.9/125; M 68.9/122; W 69.5/120 (Olympic).
Rating/Slope: T 72.1/120; C 70.2/119; M 68.9/117; W 70.0/116 (Cascade).
Green fees: Cascade Course: W/D $23/$17; W/E $29/$20; M/C, VISA.
Jr. rates $8.50; Sr. rates $18 W/D's only. Twilight rates are available.
Green fees: Olympic Course: W/D $33/$19; W/E $40/$24; M/C, VISA.
Jr. $19 & Sr. $29 rates are available weekdays only. Twilight rates available.
Power cart: $24/$15. **Pull cart:** $3. **Trail fee:** $15 for personal carts.
Reservation policy (both): 1 month in advance w/credit card. No discounts.
Winter condition: the golf course is open all year long. Dry conditions.
Terrain: flat, some steep hills. **Tees:** grass. **Spikes:** spikeless April-September.
Services: club rentals, lessons, snack bar, lounge, restaurant, beer, wine, pop,
lockers, well stocked pro shop, driving range, putting & chipping greens.
Comments: the course is well manicured, bunkered and long. The newer course
(Olympic) features extensive mounding, varied terrain and tree-lined fairways.
Water comes into play on some holes leaving the golfer many challenges from
the fairway. The Olympic Course has received great reviews from many national
golf magazines and is worth a special trip. Gold Mountain is a must play.

Directions: from I-5 N&S take exit 132
to Hwy 16W. Travel west to Hwy 3S. Go
straight ahead on Sam Christopherson Ave. to
W. Belfair Valley Rd. Turn left and go for 2.3
miles to the course on your left. From the
Bremerton Ferry veer left to 1st for 1 block to
Burwell (Hwy 304W). Follow signs to
Shelton and to Hwy 3S. Turn south on 3S to
Sam Christopherson Ave. Turn right to W.
Belfair Valley Rd. Turn left and go 2.3 miles.

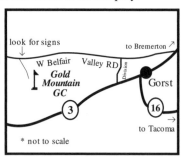

The Olympic Course
Course Yardage & Par:
T-7003 yards, par 72.
C-6474 yards, par 72.
M-6003 yards, par 72.
W-5220 yards, par 72.

The Cascade Course
Course Yardage & Par:
T-6708 yards, par 72.
C-6351 yards, par 72.
M-6059 yards, par 72.
W-5306 yards, par 72.

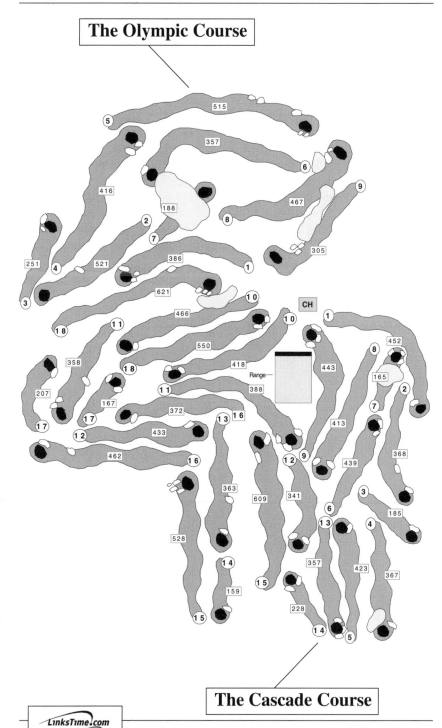

The Olympic Course

The Cascade Course

Goldendale Country Club (semi-private, 9 hole course)
1901 North Columbus; P.O. Box 1026; Goldendale, WA 98620
Phone: (509) 773-4705. **Fax:** none. **Internet:** none.
Pro: Steve Welker, PGA. **Superintendent:** N/A.
Rating/Slope: M 66.2/107; W 69.4/114. **Course record:** 66.
Green fees: W/D $18/$13; W/E $20/$15; winter rates; no credit cards.
Power cart: $20/$11. **Pull cart:** $2. **Trail fee:** $5 for personal carts.
Reservation policy: please call up to 1 week in advance for tee times.
Winter condition: the course is sometimes closed in December and February.
Terrain: flat, some hills. **Tees:** grass tees. **Spikes:** soft spikes preferred.
Services: club rentals, lessons, pro shop, putting green, chipping area.
Comments: the course is open to men only after 1 pm on Wednesday. This track offers dual tees for those wanting to play a full 18 hole round. Beautiful mountain and territorial views abound from this golf course. A creek comes into play on two holes with sand bunkers dotting some fairways. Good 9 hole course.

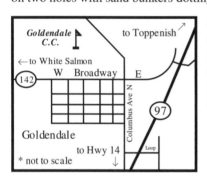

Directions: from Hwy 97 N&S follow to city center to Columbus St. (flashing light). Turn right and travel 1.5 miles to the golf course. **Note:** the golf course is located on the north edge of the city. Look for signs indicating your turn.

Course Yardage & Par:
M-2789 yards, par 36.
W-2546 yards, par 37.
Dual tees for 18 holes:
M-5610 yards, par 72.
W-5217 yards, par 74.

Golfgreen Golf Center (public, 9 hole par 3 course)

P.O. Box 1123; 561 7th Avenue; Longview, WA 98632
Phone: (360) 425-0450, 800-424-0450. Fax: (360) 501-4045.
Manager: Skip Manke. Superintendent: none. Internet: none.
Rating/Slope: the golf course is not rated. **Course record:** 21.
Green fees: W/D $10/$5.25; W/E's & Holdays $10.50/$5.50; no credit cards.
Power cart: not available. **Pull cart:** $1. **Trail fee:** not allowed.
Reservation policy: none, tee times are on a first come first served basis.
Winter condition: the golf course is open all year long.
Terrain: flat, very walkable. **Tees:** grass. **Spikes:** metal spikes permitted.
Services: club rentals $3, coffee shop, full service pro shop, miniature golf.
Comments: good hole variation. Yardage ranges from 55 yards to almost 200.
A great course to practice your short and long iron game on. Good golf course
for family golf or the first time golfer. Very easy course to walk so it is great for
the senior golfer. If you are looking for a change of pace try Golfgreen.

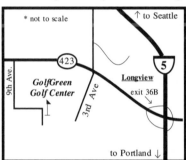

Directions: From I-5 N&S take exit #36
(Hwy 423) and travel westbound on Hwy
432 for .7 mile. Turn left at your first
available left at 9th Avenue to the golf
course. Look for signs indicating your
turn to the golf course. (The course is
located across from the drive in theater).

Course Yardage & Par:
M-1175 yards, par 27.
W-1175 yards, par 27.

Grandview Golf Course (public, 18 hole course)
7738 Portal Way; Custer, WA 98240
Phone: (360) 366-3947. **Fax:** (360) 366-3948. **Internet:** none.
Manager: Thomas Okuma. **Superintendent:** Paul Booterbaugh.
Rating/Slope: C 69.9/117; M 68.2/113; W 71.2/120. **Course record:** 67.
Green fees: W/D $21/$15; W/E $24/$17; Jr/Sr rates (M-F); VISA, M/C, DIS.
Power cart: $22/$16. **Pull cart:** $3. **Trail fee:** $8 for personal carts.
Reservation policy: yes, please call 7 days in advance for your tee times.
Winter condition: the golf course is open all year long. Dry conditions.
Terrain: flat (easy walking). **Tees:** all grass. **Spikes:** soft spikes preferred.
Services: club rentals, snack bar, beer, wine, pro shop, lockers, putting green.
Comments: a very flat easy to walk course where water comes into play on
numerous holes. Bunkers guard medium size greens on many of your approach
shots. The golf course is fast becoming a top rate facility with added upgrades
to enhance its playability. The golf course has great freeway access.

Directions: from I-5 N&S take exit #270
(Lynden-Birch Bay) to the west. Travel
west for .2 miles to Portal Way. Turn
south for 1.4 miles to the golf course.
Note: the golf course can be seen from
Interstate 5. Look for signs marking your
way to the golf course.

Course Yardage & Par:
C-6425 yards, par 72.
M-6119 yards, par 72.
F-5422 yards, par 72.

Grays Harbor Country Club (private, 9 hole course)

5300 Central Park Drive; Aberdeen, WA 98520
Phone: (360) 532-1931. **Fax:** (360) 533-3252. **Internet:** none.
Pro: Keith Liedes, PGA. **Supertindent/General Manger:** Don Scott.
Rating/Slope: M 67.6/114; W 71.9/117. **Course record:** 61.
Green fees: private club, members & guest only; reciprocates.
Power cart: private club. **Pull cart:** private club. **Trail fee:** private club.
Reservation policy: yes, minimum call 1 day in advance for tee times.
Winter condition: the golf course is open all year long. Dry (drains well).
Terrain: flat, some hills. **Tees:** grass. **Spikes:** soft spikes required.
Services: club rentals, lessons, snack bar, lounge, restaurant, beer, wine, liquor, lockers, pro shop, showers, club memberships, driving range, putting green.
Comments: a variety of shots are required on this course. Greens are medium to large in size and have few hazards fronting them. Challenging holes abound from this 9 holer. Great course that plays much longer and harder than it looks.

Directions: from I-5 N&S take exit #104 (Ocean Beaches) to Hwy 12 to Aberdeen/Hoquiam. Exit (left) in Central Park on Central Park Drive. Travel .75 miles to the golf course.

Course Yardage & Par:
M-2915 yards, par 35.
W-2884 yards, par 36.
Dual tees for 18 holes:
M-5779 yards, par 70.
W-5644 yards, par 72.

Green Lake Golf Course (public, 9 hole par 3 course)

5701 West Greenlake Way North; Seattle, WA 98103
Phone: (206) 632-2280. **Fax:** none. **Internet:** none.
Manager: Marlene Taitch. **Pro:** none. **Superintendent:** none.
Rating/Slope: the golf course is not rated. **Course record:** 22.
Green fees: $5/$3 additional 9 holes (all week long); Jr. & Sr. rates.
Power cart: none. **Pull cart:** none. **Trail fee:** no personal carts allowed.
Reservation policy: tee times are on a first come first served basis.
Winter condition: the golf course is closed during the winter months.
Terrain: very, flat. **Tees:** all mats. **Spikes:** metal spikes permitted.
Services: club rentals, vending machines.
Comments: the course is located at Green Lake in north Seattle. Excellent for practice on your short iron play. If you are looking for a course for the first time golfer Green Lake is sure to fit the bill.

Directions: From I-5 N&S take exit 159 to NE 50th. Go westbound for 1.3 miles to Green Lake Way N. North for .8 miles to the golf course (located at the southern tip of Green Lake).

Course Yardage & Par:
M-705 yards, par 27.
W-705 yards, par 27.

Green Mountain Resort (public, 18 hole course)

2817 NE Ingle Road; Vancouver, WA 98682
Phone: (360) 833-8463, 800-443-6612. Fax: (360) 833-9924. Internet: none.
Pro: Kevin Coombs, PGA. GM: Paul DeBoni. Supt.: M. Scott Coogan.
Rating/Slope: C 69.8/122; M 68.7/119; W 70.1/123. **Course record:** N/A.
Green fees: Weekdays $25; Weekends & Holidays $30.
Power cart: $22/$11. **Pull cart:** $4. **Trail fee:** not allowed.
Reservation policy: you may call up to 10 days in advance for tee-times.
Winter condition: the golf course is open all year long. Weather permitting.
Terrain: flat some hills. **Tees:** all grass. **Spikes:** soft spikes required.
Services: club rentals, lessons, snack bar, beer, pro shop, driving range.
Comments: this new course requires good course management to score well.
The layout has a good mix of holes giving the golfer a feeling a never playing
the same hole twice. Good test of golf for any level of golfer. Worth a trip.

Directions: From I-205 N&S take the
Orchards exit to Hwy 500. Proceed east
on Hwy 500 (Fourth Plain Road) until
you reach 199th Ave. (just beyond the
Green Mtn. Airport) turn right on 199th
Ave. which becomes Ingle Road. The
course entrance will be on your left.

Course Yardage & Par:

C-6170 yards, par 72.
M-5754 yards, par 72.
W-5187 yards, par 72.

Grow's Vineyard Greens (public, 18 hole course)
5180 Country Club Way SE; Port Orchard, WA 98366
Phone: (360) 871-2236. Fax: (360) 871-6344. Internet: none.
Pro: to be determined. Superintendent: to be determined.
Rating/Slope: M 64.9/102; W 66.8/106. **Course record:** 63.
Green fees: W/D $12.50/$9; W/E $16/$11; Jr. and Sr. rates; VISA, MC.
Power Cart: $18/$10. **Pull Cart:** $3. **Trail fee:** none.
Reservation policy: yes, call in advance for a tee time (no restrictions).
Winter Condition: the golf course is open all year long. Wet conditions.
Terrain: flat with some hills. **Tees:** grass. **Spikes:** metal spikes permitted.
Services: banquet hall, snack bar, beer, pro shop, driving range, putting green.
Comments: located near Bremerton in Port Orchard on the Olympic Peninsula.
Water comes into play on several holes throughout the course. Very friendly
course that has improved every year. The facility now sports an on course range.
The 9th hole, a 228 yard par 3 is one of the toughest par 3's you will ever find.

Directions: from Hwy 16 take the Port
Orchard-Sedgewick Road (Hwy 160)
exit. Proceed 3 miles on Sedgwick Road
until you reach Long Lake Road then
turn right. While on Long Lake Road
take your first right onto Country Club
Way to the golf course. **Note:** look for
signs from Hwy 16 indicating the exit to
the golf course.

Course Yardage & Par:

M-5341 yards, par 69.
W-4824 yards, par 70.

Hangman Valley Golf Club (public, 18 hole course)

2210 E Hangman Valley Road; Spokane, WA 99223
Phone: (509) 448-1212. **Fax:** (509) 448-7612. **Internet:** none.
Pro: Steve Nelke, PGA. **Superintendent:** Mike Barber.
Rating/Slope: C 71.9/126; M 69.4/119; W 72.2/124. **Course record:** 64.
Green fees: $22/$16 all week long; Jr. & Sr. rates (M-F); M/C, VISA.
Power cart: $24/$12. **Pull cart:** $3. **Trail fee:** $6 for personal carts.
Reservation policy: call ahead up to 1 week in advance for times.
Winter condition: the golf course is closed from November until mid March.
Terrain: relatively hilly. **Tees:** all grass. **Spikes:** metal spikes permitted.
Services: club rentals, lessons, restaurant, snack bar, beer, wine, beverages, pro shop, driving range, putting green, club memberships, handicapping service.
Comments: a challenging course featuring elevated tees, many trees, and well bunkered greens. Hangman Creek comes into play on seven holes and is a major factor. Excellent public golf course that is well maintained throughout the year.

Directions: from I-90 east and west, take the exit for Hwy 195 S. Proceed for 4.5 miles to the Hatch Road exit. Turn left on Hatch Road for .2 miles to Hangman Valley Road. Turn right on Hangman Valley Road. The golf course will be located five miles ahead. Look for signs.

Course Yardage & Par:
C-6951 yards, par 72.
M-6409 yards, par 72.
W-5603 yards, par 72.

Harbour Pointe Golf Club (public, 18 hole course)

11817 Harbour Point Boulevard; Mukilteo, WA 98275
Phone: 800-233-3128, (425) 355-6060. Fax: (425) 347-2200.
Pro: Mark Rhodes, PGA. Supt.: Keith Coleman. Internet: www.harbourpt.com
Rating/Slope: T 73.0/137; C 71.9/129; M 70.0/118; W 71.5/123. **Record:** 64.
Green fees: Monday-Th. $49; Fri.- Sun. $65 the golf course offers lower rates during the off season; twilight, early bird rates; M/C, VISA, AMEX.
Power cart: $15/$10 per player. **Pull cart:** $4.50. **Trail fee:** not allowed.
Reservation policy: yes, call up to 7 days in advance for tee-times.
Winter condition: the golf course is open all year long. Dry conditions.
Terrain: flat, some hills. **Tees:** all grass. **Spikes:** soft spikes preferred.
Services: club rentals, lessons, restaurant, lounge, beer, wine, liquor, pro shop, driving range, practice area. **Comments:** outstanding layout with water and sand coming into play on nearly every hole. This track is challenging and demanding. Breathtaking view of Puget Sound from the 11th hole. Excellent golf course.

Directions: from I-5 or I-405 exit to Mukilteo and to Hwy 99. Turn right on Hwy 99. At the first stop light turn left onto the Mukilteo Spdwy. Once on the Mukilteo Spdwy go to the second light and turn left onto Harbour Pointe Blvd. Proceed to the course on the right side. I-5 south should exit at 164th St. and proceed to 99 northbound and proceed to the Mukilteo Speedway. Follow the above directions.

Course Yardage & Par:
T-6862 yards, par 72.
C-6598 yards, par 72.
M-6138 yards, par 72.
M-5321 yards, par 72.
W-4836 yards, par 72.

LinksTime.com
a division of Book4golf.com

Harrington Golf & Country Club (semi-private, 9 hole course)

700 South 2nd; P. O. Box 191; Harrington, WA 99134
Phone: (509) 253-4308. Fax: (509) 253-4286. Internet: none.
Pro: Bud Drake, PGA. Superintendent: Jim Gilliland.
Rating/Slope: M 70.4/119; W 72.6/126. **Course record:** 66.
Green fees: W/D $15/$11; W/E $18/$12; Sr rates (weekdays); M/C, VISA.
Power cart: $20/$12. **Pull cart:** $3.00. **Trail fee:** not available.
Reservation policy: please call in advance for your starting times.
Winter condition: the golf course is open all year long, if playable.
Terrain: relatively hilly. **Tees:** grass. **Spikes:** soft spikes preferred.
Services: club rentals, restaurant, snack bar, lounge (members and guests), beer, wine, liquor, pro shop, driving range, putting green. **Comments:** the course is one of the finest 9 holers in the state. This course is situated in the midst of rolling, beautiful wheat fields. Excellent golf course that has wide open fairways and large, well bunkered greens. You will truly enjoy your round at Harrington.

Directions: from I-90 east & west exit to Hwy 231, #245 and head northbound. Hwy 231 will intersect with Hwy 23. Follow Hwy 23 to Harrington. When in Harrington exit to Hwy 28. From Hwy 28 exit on Main Street and proceed south to the golf course.

Course Yardage & Par:
M-3166 yards, par 36.
W-2983 yards, par 36.
<u>Dual tees for 18 holes:</u>
M-6348 yards, par 72.
W-5988 yards, par 72.

Hartwood Golf Course (public, 9 hole executive course)
12506 NE 152nd Avenue; Brush Prairie, WA 98606
Phone: (360) 896-6041. **Fax:** none. **Internet:** none.
Manager: Sue Hart. **Superintendent:** James Hart.
Rating/Slope: golf course is not rated. **Course record:** 25.
Green fees: W/D $9.50; W/E $10; Sr. rates $7.50; M/C, VISA, AMEX, DIS.
Power cart: not available. **Pull cart:** $2. **Trail fee:** not allowed.
Reservation policy: tee times are on a first come first served basis.
Winter condition: the golf course is closed December thru January.
Terrain: flat. **Tees:** grass & mats. **Spikes:** soft spikes only.
Services: club rentals, pro shop, snack bar, putting green.
Comments: beautiful views of Mt. St. Helens and Mt. Hood are seen from the mostly open fairways. Picturesque natural ponds and sand traps add a challenge to golfers of all ablities. Fun, executive course that is enjoyable for all.

Directions: from I-5 N&S take SR/500 Orchards exit. Follow SR500 until it intersects with 4th Plain. Continue straight across 4th Plain onto 117th Avenue headed north. Turn right (east) onto 119th Street. Proceed 2 miles then turn left (north) onto 152nd Ave. Course is 1/4 mile on the west side of 152nd.

Course Yardage & Par:
M-1588 yards, par 29.
W-1464 yards, par 29.

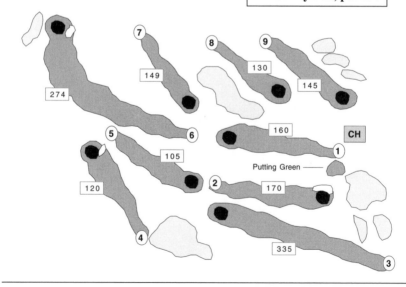

Hat Island Golf Course (private, 9 hole course)

Hat Island; Everett, WA 98201
Phone: no phone listing. Fax: none. Internet: none.
Manager: Jan Coleman. Superintendent: none.
Rating/Slope: golf course is not rated. **Course record:** 32.
Green fees: private club, property owners and their guests $10/$5.
Power cart: private club. **Pull cart:** private club. **Trail fee:** private club.
Reservation policy: private club, members & guests only.
Winter condition: the golf course is open for play open, weather permitting.
Terrain: very flat. **Tees:** all grass. **Spikes:** metal spikes permitted.
Services: private club, members and guests only.
Comments: the golf course is very flat and easy to walk. Holes are very narrow
with many trees surrounding fairways and greens. Tight golf course.

Directions: Hat Island golf course is
located in Puget Sound just west of
Everett and southeast of Camano Island.

Course Yardage & Par:
M-2335 yards, par 35.
W-2335 yards, par 35.
Dual tees for 18 holes:
M-4805 yards, par 70.
W-4805 yards, par 70.

High Cedars Golf Club (public 18 & 9 hole course)

14604 149th Court East; Box 490; Orting, WA 98360
Phone: (253) 845-1853. Fax: (253) 848-6849. Internet: none
Manager: Ron Shurtz. Superintendent: Greg Williams.
Rating/Slope: C 69.7/114; M 68.6/111; W 70.7/115. **Course record:** 64.
Green fees: W/D $24/$18; W/E $32/$22; M/C, VISA, AMEX.
Power cart: $22$15. **Pull cart:** $4/$2.50. **Trail fee:** $15 for personal carts.
Reservation policy: call ahead up to 1 week in advance for tee-times.
Winter condition: the golf course is open all year long weather permitting.
Terrain: flat (easy walking). **Tees** all grass. **Spikes:** soft spikes preferred.
Services: club rentals, lessons, snack bar, beer, pro shop, large driving range, outdoor barbecue. **Comments:** towering cedar trees, great restaurant, and beautiful flowers make for a fantastic day of golf. This one is a favorite with the locals. Great views of Mount Rainier abound from nearly every tee.

Directions: From I-5 S exit to I-405 N to Hwy 167S. Proceed southbound on Hwy 167 and exit at Hwy 410E. Proceed east on Hwy 410E to the Orting exit (Hwy 162). Turn right on Hwy 162 and proceed for 5 miles to the golf course. From I-5 N take exit #127 to Hwy 512E. Travel east to the Pioneer Ave exit. Turn right on Hwy 162 and travel 4 miles to the golf course. **Note:** Sign on Hwy 410.

Executive Course Yardage & Par:
C-1566 yards, par 28.
M-1538 yards, par 28.
W-1326 yards, par 28.

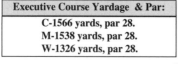

Course Yardage & Par:
C-6303 yards, par 71.
M-5971 yards, par 72.
W-5503 yards, par 72.

High Valley Golf Course (private, 9 hole course)

633 Cannon Road, Box 427; Packwood, WA 98361
Phone: (360) 494-8431. Fax: none. Internet: none.
Manager: Carol Beaty. Superintendent: Wright VanderWegen.
Rating/Slope: M 58.2/83; W 59.1/87. **Course record:** 29.
Green fees: guests fees W/D $5 all day rate; W/E $10 all day rate.
Power cart: limited. **Pull cart:** limited. **Trail fee:** none.
Reservation policy: none, private club members and guests only.
Winter condition: closed November to February depending on the weather.
Terrain: flat (easy walking). **Tees:** all grass. **Spikes:** soft spikes preferred.
Services: club rentals, limited pro shop, vending machines, pool, putting green.
Comments: a very scenic private club near Mount Rainier and right on the
Cowlitz River. Fairways are tree lined with few other hazards coming into play.
The course can play tough if the wind begins to blow. Good private course.

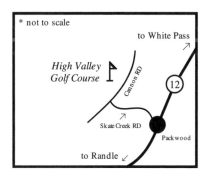

Directions: from Hwy 12 exit on Skate
Creek Road (north in Packwood). Travel
east, just over the river (.5 miles). Turn
right on Cannon Road. Proceed 2 miles
to the golf course.

Course Yardage & Par:
M-1728 yards, par 31.
W-1728 yards, par 33.

Highland Golf Course (public, 18 hole course)
300 Yard Drive; P.O. Box 542; Cosmopolis, WA 98537
Phone: (360) 533-2455. Fax: same as phone number. Internet: none.
Pro: Joe Golia, PGA. Superintendent: Mike Strada.
Rating/Slope: C 67.4/108; M 65.7/105; W 63.0/100. **Course record:** 62.
Green fees: W/D $15/$10; W/E & Holidays $17/$12; credit cards accepted.
Power cart: $20/$10. **Pull cart:** $1.50. **Trail fee:** $5 for personal carts.
Reservation policy: please call in advance for all your tee times.
Winter condition: the golf course is open all year long. Dry conditions.
Terrain: relatively hilly. **Tees:** grass. **Spikes:** metal spikes permitted.
Services: club rentals, lessons, snack bar, beer, wine, pro shop, driving range.
Comments: established in 1929 this course has many mature trees with which
one must contend to score well. Greens are large and well bunkered. This good
public track is worth a try when visiting the Grays Harbor area.

Directions: from I-5 north & south take
exit #104 and follow Hwy 12 to Aberdeen. Proceed to Hwy 101. The golf
course is located 2 miles south of the
Aberdeen city limits. Turn westbound to
the golf course. Look for signs marking
your way to the golf course.

Course Yardage & Par:

C-6112 yards, par 70.
M-5830 yards, par 70.
W-5165 yards, par 71.

Highlands Golf Course (public, 9 hole course)

1400 Highlands Parkway North; Tacoma, WA 98406

Phone: (253) 759-3622. Fax: none. Internet: none.

Manager: Jerry Brugler. Superintendent: Clyde Strampher.

Rating/Slope: golf course is not rated. **Course record:** 9 holes 23, 18 holes 52.

Green fees: W/E $15/$9; W/D $14/$8.50; Jr. & Sr. rates $12/$7.50 (Monday thru Friday); punch cards & yearly rates available; M/C, VISA.

Power cart: not allowed. **Pull cart:** $2. **Trail fee:** not allowed.

Reservation policy: call up 3 days in advance for tee times (summer is a must).

Winter condition: the golf course is open all year long, dry, excellent drainage.

Terrain: flat, some hills. **Tees:** grass. **Spikes:** soft spikes preferred.

Services: club rentals, pro shop, club memberships, putting green.

Comments: kept in good condition, two water holes, lots of bunkers, and challenging golf is what you will find at Highlands. Excellent executive length golf course that will be worth the trip if you are looking for a change of pace.

Directions: from I-5 N&S take exit #132 to Hwy 16W. From Hwy 16W exit at the Jackson Avenue exit. Turn north to N 17th. Turn right on N 17th. Proceed to Highlands Parkway where you will turn right. **Note:** You can see the golf course from Hwy 16. Look for signs.

Course Yardage & Par:
M-1279 yards, par 28.
W-1279 yards, par 28.

Holmes Harbor Golf Club (public, 18 hole course)
5023 Harbor Hills Drive; Freeland, WA 98249
Phone: (360) 331-2363. **Fax:** (360) 331-2366. **Internet:** www.hhgc@whidbey.com
Pro: Rich Kirk. Superintendent: unavailable.
Rating/Slope: C 64.8/114; M 62.9/110; W 60.3/104. **Course record:** 57.
Green fees: Monday-Thursday $20; Friday thru Sunday & holidays $27;
Jr. & Sr. rates available; twilight rates available; M/C, VISA.
Power cart: $8 per player. **Pull cart:** $2. **Trail fee:** $16 for personal carts.
Reservation policy: please call ahead for tee times. No time limit.
Winter condition: the golf course is open all year long. Dry conditions.
Terrain: flat, some hills. **Tees:** all grass. **Spikes:** soft spikes preferred.
Services: club rentals, lessons, lounge, restaurant, snack bar, beer, wine, liquor,
pro shop. **Comments:** very scenic newer course with views of the Cascades,
Olympics, and Holmes Harbor from many of the tees and greens. The golf
course has rolling fairways well bunkered greens and excellent conditions.

Directions: take the Mukilteo ferry to
Clinton. Travel 10.1 miles on Hwy 525.
Turn right on Honeymoon Bay Road.
Travel 1.3 miles. Turn right on Harbor
Hills Dr. and follow directly to the
parking lot of the golf course (this is
where the road ends). Look for signs.

Course Yardage & Par:
C-4371 yards, par 64.
M-4035 yards, par 64.
W-3565 yards, par 64.

Homestead Farms Golf Resort (semi-private, 18 hole course)

115 E Homestead Boulevard; P.O. Box 707; Lynden, WA 98264
Phone: 800-354-1196. Fax: (360) 354-5614. Internet: www.cybergolf.com/homestead
Pro: Bill Chrysler, PGA. Superintendent: Mick O'Brien.
Rating/Slope: T 73.6/129; C 71.9/125; M 69.9/117; W 72.9/123. **Record:** 66.
Green fees: January-March W/D $30, W/E $40; April-June W/D $34, W/E $45;
July-September W/D $37.50, W/E $50; October-December W/D $34, W/E $45.
Power cart: $12 per person. **Pull cart:** $3/$2. **Trail fee:** not allowed.
Reservation policy: please call up to 1 week in advance for tee-times.
Winter condition: the golf course is open all year long. Dry conditions.
Terrain: flat, some mounds. **Tees:** all grass. **Spikes:** soft spikes required.
Services: club rentals, lessons, driving range, full service clubhouse with
restaurant, beer, wine, beverages, pro shop. **Comments:** this Bill Overdorf
design is a challenge to all golfers. The signature hole is the par 5 eighteenth
that features and island green that will test your nerve. Worth a special trip.

Directions: from I-5 northbound take exit
#256, Hwy 539 (Guide Meridian) to
Lynden (10 miles). Turn eastbound on
Hwy 546 for 1.5 miles to Depot RD. Turn
south on Depot RD for 1/4 mile to the
course. From I-5 southbound exit off of
I-5 at Birch Bay-Lynden #270 and follow
to Lynden. Turn northbound on Hwy 539
and follow the above directions to the golf
course. Look for signs along the way.

Course Yardage & Par:
T-6927 yards, par 72; C-6504 yards, par 72. M-6033 yards, par 72; W-5570 yards, par 72.

Horn Rapids Golf & Country Club (public, 18 hole course)

2800 Clubhouse Lane; P. O. Box 840; Richland, WA 98352
Phone: (509) 375-4714. Fax: (509) 375-7494. Internet: cybergolf.com/hornrapids
Manager: Nick Rodrigues. Superintendent: Shane Rodrigues.
Rating/Slope: C 73.6/130; M 71.0/122; W 70.4/117; F 69.0/118. **Record:** 62.
Green fees: Mon.-Th. $20/$15; Fri. $25/$18; W/E & Hol. $30/$18; M/C, VISA.
Power cart: $26/$16. **Pull cart:** $4/$2. **Trail fee:** $7 for personal carts.
Reservation policy: you may call 1 week in advance for tee times.
Winter condition: dry, the golf course open all year weather permitting.
Terrain: flat, some rolling hills. **Tees:** grass. **Spikes:** soft spikes only.
Services: club rentals, lessons, snack bar, beer, wine, pro shop, driving range.
Comments: the golf course is a desert style track emphasizing shot placement (target golf). Greens are large undulating and tricky to putt. If you are looking for change and want a challenge try Horn Rapids it will not disappoint.

Directions: the golf course is located on Highway 240 2 miles west of Richland Washington (the Vantage Highway). From I-182/Hwy12 in Richland, WA take exit #4 and proceed northbound to the golf course which is located 2.3 miles north. Look for signs indicating your turn to the golf course.

Course Yardage & Par:
T-6925 yards, par 72.
C-6348 yards, par 72.
M-5809 yards, par 72.
W-5118 yards, par 72.

Horseshoe Lake Golf Course (public, 18 hole course)

1250 S.W. Clubhouse Court; Port Orchard, WA 98367

Phone: (253) 857-3326. **Fax:** (253) 857-4352. **Internet:** www.HLgolf.com
Pro: Chris Morris, PGA. **Superintendent:** Jon Eby.
Rating/Slope: C 69.1/114; M 67.0/109; W 68.1/110. **Course record:** 64.
Green fees: W/D $29*/$16; W/E 34*/$20 (* includes cart on back 9);
Jr. and Sr. rates (M-F); twilight rates; M/C, VISA, AMEX, DIS.
Power cart: 9 hole fee $5 per person. **Pull cart:** $3. **Trail fee:** not allowed.
Reservation policy: yes, please call up to 7 days in advance for tee-times.
Or you can call up to one month in advance with credit card confirmation.
Winter condition: the golf course is open all year. Very dry conditions.
Terrain: front 9, flat; back 9 very hilly. **Tees:** grass. **Spikes:** no policy.
Services: club rentals, driving range, full service clubhouse, restaurant, lessons.
Comments: Excellent on course restaurant, and challenging golf course is
worth a special trip. You will have fantastic views of the countryside and the
Olympic Mountains from nearly every tee. Challenging course that can be tough.

Directions: from Hwy 16 take the Purdy
exit. Take Hwy 302 across the Purdy
Bridge to the top of the hill (approximately 2 miles). Turn right on 94th Ave.
The course is located 1.2 miles on left.

Course Yardage & Par:
C-6105 yards, par 71.
M-5604 yards, par 71.
W-5035 yards, par 71.

Hot Springs Golf Course (public, 18 hole course)

Saint Martin Road; P.O. Box 1169; Carson, WA 98610
Phone: (509) 427-5150. Fax: none. Internet: none.
Manager: John Broughten. Superintendent: Bob Henrdricksen.
Rating/Slope: C 72.1/125; M 70.4/122; W 68.9/116. **Course record:** 73.
Green fees: W/D $16/$9; W/E $19/$11; Sr. & winter rates available.
Power cart: $20/$10. **Pull cart:** $3.50/$2.50. **Trail fee:** no charge.
Reservation policy: yes, accepted for weekend tee-times, please call ahead.
Winter condition: the golf course is open all year long. Dry conditions.
Terrain: flat, some hills. **Tees:** all grass. **Spikes:** soft spikes preferred.
Services: snacks, beer, pro shop, driving range, putting & chipping greens.
Comments: Gentle rolling terrain and wind that roles through the tree lined
fairways characterize this golf course. Bunkered fairways along with water
come into play off the tee and approach shots. Greens are medium in size and
are well bunkered. Course plays much longer than the yardage would indicate.

Directions: the golf course is located 1 mile north of Hwy 14 on the east side of Carson. From Hwy 14 turn northbound toward Carson, Washington. Turn right on Hot Springs Avenue to the golf course. Look for signs along the way.

Course Yardage & Par:

C-6559 yards, par 73.
M-6150 yards, par 73.
W-5365 yards, par 73.

Husum Hills Golf Course (public, 9 hole course)
820 Highway 141, White Salmon, WA 98672
Phone: (509) 493-1211. **Fax:** (509) 493-1014. **Internet:** none.
Pro: Gary Tamietti, PGA. **Superintendent:** none.
Rating/Slope: 63.7/96; W 67.6/104. **Course record:** 31.
Green fees: $20/$12 all week long; credit cards are accepted.
Power cart: $20/$10. **Pull cart:** $4/$2. **Trail fee:** $5 for personal carts.
Reservation policy: yes, call up to 7 days in advance but are not necessary.
Winter condition: the golf course is open when playable. Fair conditions.
Terrain: flat to very hilly. **Tees:** grass. **Spikes:** soft spikes preferred.
Services: club rentals, restaurant, pro shop, wine, beer, putting/chipping green.
Comments: The course is well treed, with beautiful views of Mount Adams.
Grass bunkers abound which create some difficult lies. Good nine hole track
that can challenge any level of golfer. Course is adding new hazards as well as
rebuilding some tees to lengthen some holes. This should improve playability.

Directions: from I-5S take exit #7
to I-205S. Travel southbound to exit
#27 to Hwy14E. Proceed eastbound to
Hwy 141 then northbound on Hwy 141
for 8 miles to the golf course. Look for
signs marking your turn to the course.

Course Yardage & Par:
C-2631 yards, par 35.
M-2458 yards, par 35.
W-2390 yards, par 35.

Hylander Greens Golf Practice Center (public, 9 hole course)

1475 East Nelson Road; Moses Lake, WA 98837
Phone: (509) 766-1228. Fax: none. Internet: none.
Pro: Bill Porter, PGA. Superintendent: none.
Rating/Slope: the golf course is not rated. **Course record:** 25.
Green fees: W/D $10/$6; W/E $12/$7; Jr. & Sr. rates; no credit cards.
Power cart: $12/$7. **Pull cart:** $2/$1. **Trail fee:** no charge for personal carts.
Reservation policy: reservations are not needed, first come first served.
Winter condition: the golf course is closed December 1st to February 7th.
Terrain: flat, easy walking. **Tees:** all grass. **Spikes:** soft spikes only in summer.
Services: pro shop, club repair, club rentals, driving range, putting green.
Comments: a very well maintained 9 hole executive course. The areas best
driving range featuring an elevated tee with high quality range balls. Golf
professional Bill Porter is available to help you with all your golf needs. A new
clubhouse and continued course improvements are planned in 2001 to 2002.

Note: From E&W I-90 take exit 179.

* not to scale

to Ephrata

E Nelson RD

(17)

exit 179

Hylander Greens Golf P.C.

(90)

179 — East →

Directions: from I-90 E&W take the
Moses Lake/ Highway 17 exit #179. Go
northbound on Highway 17. Stay to your
right when the road splits. Turn right on
East Nelson Road and proceed to the
golf course. Look for signs to the course.

Course Yardage & Par:
M-1720 yards, par 29.
W-1720 yards, par 29.

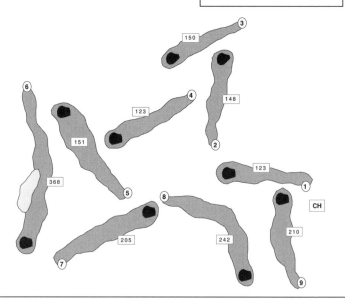

Indian Canyon Golf Course (public, 18 hole course)

West 4304 West Drive; Spokane, WA 99204
Phone: (509) 747-5353. Fax: (509) 747-0622. Internet: none.
Pro: Gary Lindeblad, PGA. Superintendent: Don Nelson.
Rating/Slope: C 70.7/126; M 69.3/123; W 73.9/132. **Course record:** 62.
Green fees: $16.50/$13.50 w/ discount card; $22.50/$16.50 w/o discount card.
The fees listed are week long fees; Jr. & Sr. rates are available; VISA, M/C.
Power cart: $23. **Pull cart:** $3. **Trail fee:** $9 for personal carts.
Reservation policy: yes, W/D 1 day in advance, W/E 1 week in advance.
Winter condition: the golf course is closed from November to March.
Terrain: very hilly. **Tees:** all grass. **Spikes:** soft spikes preferred.
Services: club rentals, lessons, restaurant, snack bar, beer, wine, pro shop,
driving range. **Comments:** consistently rated in the top 75 public courses by
Golf Digest. Greens are large and well bunkered. This golf course is extremely
well maintained and is worth a special trip if you are in the Spokane area.

Directions: from I-90 eastbound &
westbound take the Garden Springs exit.
#277 or #277A. Proceed north on Rustle
Street to the Sunset Hwy where you will
turn left. Proceed to Assembly Street and
turn right. Follow this to the golf course.
Look for signs marking your way.

Course Yardage & Par:
C-6296 yards, par 72.
M-5927 yards, par 72.
W-5318 yards, par 73.

Indian Summer Golf & Country Club (private, 18 hole course)
5900 Troon Lane SE; Olympia, WA 98501
Phone: (360) 459-3772. **Fax:** (360) 923-9037. **Internet:** none.
Pro: Dave Shelton, PGA. **Superintendent:** Bob Pearsall.
Rating/Slope: T 75.1/142; C 73.3/136; M 71.5/128; W 71.1/125. **Record:** 64.
Green fees: private club, members & guests of members only.
Power cart: $25. **Pull cart:** private club. **Trail fee:** private club, not allowed.
Reservation policy: have your golf pro call for reciprocity. Private club.
Winter condition: the golf course is open all year long. Dry conditions.
Terrain: flat, some hills. **Tees:** all grass. **Spikes:** soft spikes required.
Services: full service clubhouse, restaurant, snack bar, lounge, pro shop, lockers, driving range, putting & chipping greens. **Comments:** championship caliber course. The back 9 winds through Pacific Northwest old growth timber stands and bordering wetlands. The front 9 features wide open, rolling terrain and water on 7 holes. Home of the Pacific NW PGA offices. Great course.

Directions: from I-5S exit #108 College St. Proceed to College St. and turn right. Follow College St. for 3.4 miles to the Yelm Hwy. Turn right and follow for 1/2 mile to the golf course which will be on your left. From I-5N take exit #109. Take left on College St. and follow the same directions. Look for signs at your turn.

Course Yardage & Par:
T-7216 yards, par 72.
C-6786 yards, par 72.
M-6374 yards, par 72.
F-5766 yards, par 72.
W-5199 yards, par 72.

Inglewood Golf Club (private, 18 hole course)

6505 Inglewood Road NE; P. O. Box 70; Kenmore, WA 98028
Phone: (425) 488-7000. Fax: (425) 488-8975. Internet: inglewoodgolfclub.com
Pro: Bruce Christy, PGA. Superintendent: Tom McCarthy.
Course record: 63. **Competitive course record:** 64.
Rating/Slope: T 72.9/131; C 71.6/128; M 70.0/124; W 74.9/127.
Green fees: private club members & guests only; reciprocates; no credit cards.
Power cart: private club. **Pull cart:** private club. **Trail fee:** not allowed.
Reservation policy: private club members & guests only. Reciprocates call.
Winter condition: the golf course is open all year long.
Terrain: very hilly. **Tees:** all grass. **Spikes:** no metal spikes in summer.
Services: club rentals, lessons, snack bar, restaurant, lounge, beer, wine, liquor, shower, lockers, pro shop, driving range. **Comments:** past home of the Senior PGA event the "GTE Northwest Classic". Past host to the "Fred Couples Invitational". Hilly terrain gives a wide variety of fairway lies. Good course.

Directions: from I-5S take exit 177 to Hwy 104E (Forest Park Drive). Travel east 2.5 miles to Hwy 522 E (Bothell Way). Turn east for 1.3 miles to 68th NE-Juanita Dr. Turn south for .4 miles to NE 170th. Turn west to the golf course. From I-5N take exit 175 to NE 145th. Travel east for 1.5 miles to Bothell Way NE. Turn left and travel 3.1 miles to 68th-Juanita Dr. Turn right. Proceed .4 miles to NE 170th. Turn right to course.

Course Yardage & Par:
T-6731 yards, par 73; C-6460 yards, par 73. M-6150 yards, par 73; W-5176 yards, par 73.

Interbay Family Golf Center (public, 9 hole course)

2501 15th Avenue West; Seattle, WA 98199

Phone: (206) 285-2200. **Fax:** (206) 285-0239. **Internet:** www.familygolf.com.

Pro: Martin Leith, PGA. **Manager:** Bill Meyer. **Course record:** 25.

Rating/Slope: the golf course is not rated.

Green fees: W/D $11; W/E $13; Jr. & Sr. rates; VISA, M/C, AMEX, DINERS.

Power cart: $10. **Pull cart:** $2.50. **Trail fee:** $10.

Reservation policy: tee-times may be made 1 week in advance.

Winter condition: the golf course is open all year around. Dry conditions.

Terrain: some hills. **Tees:** grass. **Spikes:** soft spikes preferred.

Services: club rentals, lessons, restaurant, beer, wine, pro shop, driving range.

Comments: this Golden Bear designed golf course is a fantastic layout for the first time golfer or the experienced linksman. Extensive mounding and large greens make the golf course user friendly. Great change of pace golf course.

Directions: from I-5 N&S take exit #167 to Mercer Street. Follow arterial to Westlake (far right lane), turn right. Follow for 2.3 miles (it becomes Nickerson) to City Center exit. Proceed south on 15th Avenue to Gilman Drive. Turn right to course and range.

Course Yardage & Par:
M-1327 yards, par 28. **W-1204 yards, par 28.**

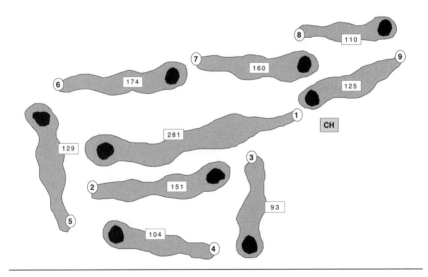

Ironwood Green Public Golf Course (public, 9 hole course)
8138 U.S. Highway 12; Glenoma, WA 98336
Phone: (360) 498-5425. Fax: none. Internet: none.
Owners: Jim & Alice Redmon. Superintendent: Jim Redmon Jr.
Rating/Slope: the golf course is not rated. **Course record:** 28.
Green fees: $7.50/$5.50; Sr. rates $6.50 all week long; no credit cards.
Power cart: $15/$8. **Pull cart:** $2. **Trail fee:** $7.50 for personal cart.
Reservation policy: not needed. Times on a first come first served basis.
Winter condition: the golf course is open all year long. Damp conditions.
Terrain: flat (easy walking). **Tees:** all grass. **Spikes:** metal spikes permitted.
Services: club rentals, pro shop, convenience store, RV park for overnighters.
Comments: Nestled in the foothills of the Cascade Mountains this tree lined executive course is an excellent test for your iron skills. A friendly family owned course. Flat and only 1500 yards it is very walker and senior friendly. Small bentgrass greens are a challenge for all who play. For those traveling in an RV there is an RV park along the 9th fairway.

Directions: from I-5 N&S take exit #68 onto Hwy 12. Proceed eastbound 47 miles to Glenoma. The golf course is located just off Hwy 12 on the right.

Course Yardage & Par:
M-1512 yards, par 30.
W-1500 yards, par 31.

Island Greens (public, 9 hole par 3 course)
3890 East French Road; Clinton, WA 98236
Phone: (360) 579-6042. Fax: (360) 579-2248.
Owners: Dave & Karen Anderson. **Internet:** www.whidbey.net/islandgreens.
Rating/Slope: the golf course is not rated. **Course record:** 25.
Green fees: W/D $6; W/E $7 (honor system @ times); no credit cards.
Power cart: not available. **Pull cart:** $1. **Trail fee:** no private carts.
Reservation policy: no policy, tee times are on a first come first serve basis.
Winter condition: the golf course is open all year long. Fair conditions.
Terrain: gently rolling terrain that is very walkable. **Tees:** grass & mats.
Services: club rentals, driving range. **Spikes:** soft spikes preferred.
Comments: this challenging par 3 course features rolling terrain, tree lined
fairways and well manicured greens. With three ponds, bunkered greens and a
good variety of hole lengths Island Greens can be a handful. Excellent course
that is especially worth a trip during the months of April thru June when the
Rhodys are in bloom. Great change of pace from the 6500 + yard back breaker.

Directions: take the Mukilteo-Clinton
ferry to Clinton. Follow Hwy 525 2
miles to Cultus Bay Road. Left on
Cultus Bay for 2 miles to French Road.
Right on French Road, golf course is
1/4 mile ahead on your left hand side.
Look for signs that are posted.

Course Yardage & Par:
C-1355 yards, par 27.
M-1135 yards, par 27.
W-859 yards, par 27.

Jackson Park Golf Club (public, 18 hole course, 9 hole par 3)

1000 NE 135th; Seattle, WA 98125   Internet: www.jacksonparkgolf.com
Phone: (206) 363-4747; Tee-Times: 301-0472. Fax: (206) 361-6636.
Pro: Kevin Earl, PGA. Superintendent: Don Hellstrom.
Rating/Slope: C 67.3/113; M 66.3/111; W 70.7/118. **Course record:** 61.
Green fees: $22 all week long; Jr. & Sr. rates (Mon. thru Fri.); M/C, VISA.
Power cart: $20/$13. **Pull cart:** $3.50. **Trail fee:** $10 for personal carts.
Reservation policy: up to 7 days ahead in person. Up to 7 days ahead by phone.
Winter condition: the golf course is open all year long. Damp conditions.
Terrain: very hilly. **Tees:** all grass. **Spikes:** soft spikes preferred.
Services: club rentals, lessons, snack bar, restaurant, beer, wine, pro shop.
Comments: the course is tree lined and features medium to small greens. Very busy during the peak golfing season so be sure call ahead. The course has a well stocked pro shop for all your golfing needs. Good value for your golfing dollar.

Directions: from I-5 N&S take exit #175 to NE 145th. Travel east for .5 miles to 15th Ave NE. Turn southbound on 15th Ave NE and proceed for .5 miles to NE 135th. Turn west on 135th and go up the hill to the entrance to the golf course which will be on your right. Look for signs marking your turn into Jackson Park.

Par 3 Yardage & Par:
970 yards, par 27.

Course Yardage & Par:
C-5946 yards, par 71.
M-5720 yards, par 71.
W-5495 yards, par 74.

Jade Greens Golf Course (public, 9 holes w/dual pin placements)

18330 SE Lake Holm Road; Auburn, WA 98092
Phone: (253) 931-8562. Fax: (253) 931-0549. Internet: none.
Pro: Joesph Bauman, PGA. General Manager: Jim Hawk Jr.
Rating/Slope: C 66.1/112; M 65.0/110; W 66.5/108. **Course record:** 61.
Green fees: W/D $21/$14; W/E $25/$16; Jr. & Sr. $16/$10 (M-F); M/C VISA.
Power cart: $20/$13. **Pull cart:** $2. **Trail fee:** $5/$2.50 for personal carts.
Reservation policy: yes, call up to 1 week in advance for your tee-times.
Winter condition: the golf course is open all year long. Dry conditions.
Terrain: flat, some hills. **Tees:** all grass. **Spikes:** soft spikes preferred.
Services: club rentals, lessons, deli, beer, wine, pro shop, lighted driving range.
Comments: course surrounds natural wetlands which adds to the natural beauty of this well taken care of track. Excellent drainage for winter play. Course has a 25 stall, covered & lighted driving range for those wanting to practice.

Directions: from I-5 take exit #142 (Hwy 18). Proceed eastbound on Hwy 18 to Auburn. Proceed just past the city limits on Hwy 18 where you will exit on the Auburn Black Diamond Road. Proceed for .5 miles to SE Lake Holm Road where you will turn right and proceed for 3.2 miles to the golf course.

Course Yardage & Par:
C-2656 yards, par 34; M-2531 yards, par 34; W-2232 yards, par 35.
Dual tees for 18 holes:
C-5348 yards, par 69; M-5099 yards, par 69; W-4501 yards, par 71.

Jefferson Park Golf Club (public, 18 hole course, 9 hole par 3)

4101 Beacon Ave. S; Seattle, WA 98108   Internet: www.jeffersonparkgolf.com
Phone: (206) 762-4513; T-Times: (206) 301-0472. Fax: (206) 762-2312.
Pro: Peter J. Guzzo, PGA. Superintendent: James Weir.
Rating/Slope: C 68.3/112; M 67.0/110; W 70.2/116. **Course record:** 62.
Green fees: $18.50 all week long; Jr. & Sr. rates (M-F) $13.50; M/C, VISA.
Power cart: $22/$13. **Pull cart:** $4. **Trail fee:** $10 for personal carts.
Reservation policy: up to 7 days ahead in person. Up to 6 days ahead by phone.
Winter condition: the golf course is open all year long. Damp conditions.
Terrain: relatively hilly. **Tees:** grass & mats. **Spikes:** soft spikes preferred.
Services: club rentals, lessons, snack bar, restaurant, beer, wine, lockers, pro
shop, lighted, covered and heated, driving range, putting green, executive golf
course. **Comments:** Jefferson has a flat front nine and a relatively hilly back
nine. Greens are large with a few greenside bunkers coming into play on your
approach shots. Many lovely views of the Seattle skyline can be seen from
several holes. Well stocked pro shop, and great lesson center. Good value.

Directions: from I-5 N&S take exit #163
to Columbia Way. Turn left at the light
and travel .3 miles to Beacon Avenue S.
Turn southbound for .2 miles to the golf
course on your left hand side. The pro
shop will be located on your right hand
side next to the driving range.

Course Yardage & Par:

C-6182 yards, par 70.
M-5857 yards, par 70.
W-5430 yards, par 73.

Par 3 Yardage & Par:
1225 yards, par 27.

Kahler Glen Golf Course (public, 18 hole course)

20700 Clubhouse Drive Leavenworth, WA 98826
Phone: (509) 763-4025. Fax: (503) 763-5030. Internet: www.kahlerglen.com.
Pro: Joe Turner, PGA. Office Manager: Randy Pelton.
Rating/Slope: M 65.7/115; W 67.1/114. **Course record:** 63.
Green fees: Monday thru Thursday $24/$16; Friday thru Sunday $36/$24.
Power cart: $26/$13. **Pull cart:** $5.50/$3.50. **Trail fee:** $10 for personal carts.
Reservation policy: yes, please call up to 2 weeks ahead for a tee time.
Winter condition: the golf course is closed during the winter months.
Terrain: flat, some hills. **Tees:** all grass. **Spikes:** soft spikes only.
Services: club rentals, lessons, full service resturant & lounge, pro shop, driving range, putting green. **Comments:** located near Lake Wenatchee State Park this course is surrounded by trees and sports narrow fairways. The greens are medium to large giving the golfer ample room to manoeuvre the ball. This definitely is a shot makers course. Great location for a unique and challenging golf getaway.

Directions: on Hwy 2 the course is located 15 miles west of Leavenworth. Turn northbound on to Hwy 207. Proceed 3.5 miles then follow signs to Kahler Glen Golf Course.

Course Yardage & Par:
C-6105 yards, par 70.
M-5682 yards, par 70.
W-4994 yards, par 70.

Kayak Point Golf Course (public, 18 hole course)

15711 Marine Drive; Stanwood, WA 98292   Internet: www.kayakgolf.com
Phone: (360) 652-9676; 1-800-562-3094. Fax: (360) 652-3812
Director of Golf: Rob Lindsey, PGA. Supt.: Randy Vander Vaate
Rating/Slope: C 72.9/138; M 70.2/127; W 71.1/125. **Course record:** 67.
Green fees: Monday-Thur. $29/$16; Friday-Sunday & Holidays $33/$18;
Jr. & Sr. & winter rates (Monday-Friday no holidays); M/C, VISA, AMEX.
Power cart: $27. **Pull cart:** $3.50. **Trail fee:** $13.50. (*add tax on all fees).
Reservation policy: please call ahead 7 days in advance. 1 month in advance
with credit card guarantee and $5 per per person advance reservation fee.
Winter condition: open, dry, golf course has excellent drainage for winter play.
Terrain: very hilly (consider a cart). **Tees:** grass. **Spikes:** metal permitted.
Services: club rentals, lessons, snack bar, restaurant, liquor, lounge, beer, wine,
pro shop, driving range, putting/chipping greens, Arnold Palmer Golf Academy.
Comments: one of the NW's most beautiful and difficult golf courses.
Tree-lined fairways demand accuracy off the tee. Greens are medium to large
and well bunkered. This course is worth a special trip any time of year.

Directions: from I-5 N&S take exit
199 (Marysville-Tulalip) to Hwy 528W.
Travel west on Hwy 528W for approximately 14 miles to the golf course
entrance which will be on your right.
Follow the road up the hill to the golf
course. **Note:** Look for a sign on the
Hwy marking your turn to the course.

Course Yardage & Par:
C-6719 yards, par 72.
M-6109 yards, par 72.
W-5332 yards, par 72.

Kenwanda Golf Course (public, 18 hole course)
14030 Kenwanda Drive; Snohomish, WA 98296
Phone: (360) 668-1166. Fax: call for number. Internet: none.
Manager: Curtis Creighton.
Rating/Slope: M 64.1/101; W 68.7/110. **Course record:** 63.
Green fees: $21/$15 all week long; VISA, M/C.
Power cart: $21/$15. **Pull cart:** $2.50. **Trail fee:** none.
Reservation policy: yes, call up to 1 week in advance.
Winter condition: the golf course is open all year round. Dry conditions.
Terrain: relatively hilly. **Tees:** all grass/mats in winter. **Spikes:** metal spikes
permitted. **Services:** club rentals, cafe, beer, beverages, small pro shop.
Comments: atop Fiddlers Bluff, Kenwanda boasts beautiful views of Mount
Rainier, Mount Baker, Snohomish Valley and the North Cascades. The course
has small greens, and wide sloping fairways lined by trees. Accuracy is a must.

Directions: from Hwy 9 turn right on
Broadway/131st Street. Follow approximately 1/2 mile to Connelly St. and turn
left. Go .2 miles to Kenwanda Dr. Turn
left. The clubhouse is at the top of the
hill and will be on your left hand side.
From I-405 take exit #23 to Hwy 522.
Follow Hwy 522 to Hwy 9 and follow
the above directions.

Course Yardage & Par:
M-5336 yards, par 69.
W-5336 yards, par 72.

Kitsap Golf & Country Club (private, 18 hole course)

3885 NW Golf Club Hill Road; Bremerton, WA 98312
Phone: (360) 373-5101. Fax: (360) 373-0685. Internet: kgcc@oz.net.
Pro: John Hildebrand, PGA. Supt.: Michael Hayes. 18 hole course.
Rating/Slope: C 70.1/120; M 69.6/118; W 72.0/122. **Course record:** 62.
Green fees: private club members and guests only; reciprocates.
Power cart: private club. **Pull cart:** private club. **Trail fee:** private club.
Reservation policy: yes, up to 2 days in advance. Members only.
Winter condition: the golf course is open all year long. Dry conditions.
Terrain: relatively hilly. **Tees:** all grass. **Spikes:** soft spikes preferred.
Services: coffee shop, dining room, ballroom, lounge, beverages, pro shop, driving range, lessons, putting & chipping green, club memberships available.
Comments: very demanding layout with tricky doglegs and well bunkered, fast greens. Fairways are tree lined and can be very narrow in spots. You must be accurate off the tee to score well. This private track is always in great condition.

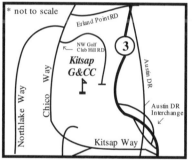

Directions: from Hwy 3 take the exit for Austin-Kitsap Lake. Turn right on Austin Road and proceed for 1.1 miles to Erland Point Road. Turn left and proceed for .5 miles to Chico Way. Turn Left and proceed for .3 miles to NW Golf Club Hill Road. Proceed to the golf course on NW Golf Club Hill Road. Look for a small sign marking your turn to the course.

Course Yardage & Par:

C-6329 yards, par 71.
M-6153 yards, par 71.
W-5590 yards, par 73.

Lake Chelan Golf Course (public, 18 hole course)
1501 Golf Course Drive; P.O. Box 1669; Chelan, WA 98816
Phone: (509) 682-8026 or 1-800-246-5361. Fax: (509) 682-2286.
Pro: Jim Oscarson, PGA. Superintendent: Don Hensley.
Rating/Slope: C 70.6/121; M 69.2/118; W 70.7/116. **Course record:** 65.
Green fees: $25/$15 all week long; VISA, M/C is accepted.
Power cart: $22/$12. **Pull cart:** $3/$2. **Trail fee:** $10 for personal carts.
Reservation policy: yes, call up to 1 week in advance for your tee-times.
Winter condition: the course is closed during the winter November to March.
Terrain: flat, some hills. **Tees:** grass. **Spikes:** soft spikes preferred.
Services: lessons, club rentals, snack bar, beer, wine, pro shop, driving range,
putting green. **Comments:** this is a beautiful course situated in a favorite
summer spot of weekend vacationers. This course is set atop a hill over looking
Lake Chelan and the surrounding landscape. Greens are small to medium in size
but can become very firm and fast in the summer months. Great course for the
summer golfer. The golf course has improved over the last few years.

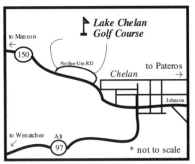

Directions: follow Hwy 150 through
Chelan toward Manson. About 1/4 mile
beyond the City Trailer Park take the
right fork of the No-See-Um Road to
the golf course. Look for signs to the
golf course on the Manson Highway
marking your turn.

Course Yardage & Par:
C-6440 yards, par 72.
M-6152 yards, par 72.
W-5501 yards, par 73.

Lake Cushman Golf Course (public, 9 hole course)

North 210 West Fairway Drive; Hoodsport, WA 98548
Phone: (360) 877-5505. Fax: (360) 877-6713. Internet: none.
Pro/Manager: Scott Wadewitz, PGA. Superintendent: N/A.
Rating/Slope: M 67.7/107; W 70.5/110. **Course record:** 62.
Green fees: W/D $16/$11; W/E & Holidays $19/$15; tightwad Tuesday $12/$6.
Power cart: $20/$12. **Pull cart:** $2. **Trail fee:** $5 for personal carts.
Reservation policy: yes, call ahead 14 days for tee-times (advised in summer).
Winter condition: damp conditions. The course is open weather permitting.
Terrain: flat, some hills. **Tees:** all grass. **Spikes:** soft spikes preferred.
Services: club rentals, snack bar, small pro shop, practice range, putting green,
club memberships. **Comments:** a very challenging 9 hole course set in the
beautiful Olympic Mountains. Fairways are tree-lined with few hazards coming
into play around the greens. Excellent on course range so plan to practice.

Directions: from I-5 N&S take exit 104
to Hwy 101. Follow to Hoodsport.
At the north end of Hoodsport turn left to
the Lake Cushman Resort. Follow for 2.8
miles to Fairway Village. Left, then right
to the golf course. Look for signs.

Course Yardage & Par:
C-2848 yards, par 35.
M-2957 yards, par 35.
W-2674 yards, par 35.
Dual tees for 18 holes:
C-5696 yards, par 70.
M-5914 yards, par 70.
W-5348 yards, par 70.

Lake Limerick Country Club (semi-private, 9 hole course)

E 790 Saint Andrews Drive; Shelton, WA 98584
Phone: (360) 426-6290. Fax: (360) 426-8922 Internet: none.
Pro: Terry O'Hara. Superintendent: Steve Cox.
Rating/Slope: M 67.2/114; W 70.9/120. **Course record:** 67.
Green fees: W/D $16/$11; W/E $20/$15; M/C, VISA, AMEX, DISC.
Power cart: $21/$13. **Pull cart:** $3/$2. **Trail fee:** $5 for personal carts.
Reservation policy: yes, call up to one week in advance for tee times.
Winter condition: the golf course is open all year long.
Terrain: flat, some hills. **Tees:** all grass. **Spikes:** soft spikes preferred.
Services: club rentals, restaurant, beer, wine, snack bar, pro shop, putting green.
Comments: narrow tree lined fairways and tricky greens makes this course a real test of golf. Greens are medium in size and fairly flat. Perfect golf course for a quick 9 holes on a weekend to the Olympic Peninsula. Do not let the lack of yardage fool you this course plays very tough in spots. Well kept golf course.

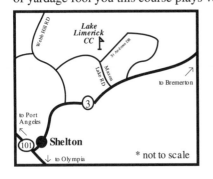

Directions: on Hwy 3 go 5 miles north of Shelton to Mason Lake Road. Turn left on Mason Lake Road and travel approximately 3 miles to the Lake Limerick entrance. Turn left on St. Andrews Drive and follow for 1 mile to the golf course. Look for signs marking your way to the golf course.

Course Yardage & Par:

M-2898 yards, par 36.
W-2658 yards, par 36.
<u>**Dual tees for 18 holes:**</u>
M-5779 yards, par 72.
W-5424 yards, par 72.

Lake Padden Golf Course (public, 18 hole course)

4882 Samish Way; Bellingham, WA 98226
Phone: (360) 738-7400. Fax: (360) 738-7303. Internet: www.greens.com
Pro: Kene Bensel, PGA. Superintendent: James Howes.
Rating/Slope: C 72.0/124; M 69.9/120; W 71.9/122. **Course record:** 63.
Green fees: $18/$14 Monday thru Friday; Sat. thru Sunday including hol. $24;
Jr./Sr. $14/$10 (M-F); twilight rates $18 (M-S) after 3pm; VISA, M/C, AMEX.
Power cart: $23/$13. **Pull cart:** $3. **Trail fee:** $5 for personal carts.
Reservation policy: yes, up to 1 week in advance. Advised during the summer.
Winter condition: the golf course is open all year long. Damp conditions.
Terrain: relatively hilly. **Tees:** all grass. **Spikes:** soft spikes only.
Services: club rentals, lessons, snack bar, beer, pro shop, putting & chipping
greens, covered & lighted driving range, home of Pacific Golf Schools.
Comments: Lake Padden's primary difficulty lies in the towering evergreens
surrounding every fairway. This course is well maintained and is a true pleasure
to play any time of year. Popular public course located in a recreational area.

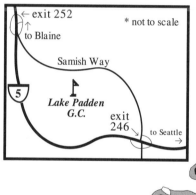

Directions: from I-5 southbound take exit
#252 to Samish Way. Travel east for 2.4
miles to the golf course which will be on
your right. If traveling on I-5 northbound
take exit #246 to Samish Way and proceed
2.5 miles to the golf course. The golf
course will be on your left hand side.

Course Yardage & Par:

C-6575 yards, par 72.
M-6133 yards, par 72.
W-5496 yards, par 72.

Lake Spanaway Golf Course (public, 18 hole course)
15602 Pacific Avenue; Tacoma, WA 98444
Phone: (253) 531-3660. Fax: (253) 531-7759. Internet: none.
Pro: Keith Johnson, PGA. Superintendent: Andy Soden.
Rating/Slope: C 73.0/125; M 70.2/118; W 73.4/123. **Course record:** 63.
Green fees: $21/$13.75 all week long; M/C, VISA.
Power cart: $20/$12. **Pull cart:** $3. **Trail fee:** $5 for personal carts.
Reservation policy: public can call up to 7 days in advance after 11:00 am.
Winter condition: the course is open all year. Dry, excellent drainage.
Terrain: flat, some hills. **Tees:** all grass. **Spikes:** soft spikes preferred.
Services: club rentals, lessons, snack bar, restaurant, beer, wine, pro shop,
putting green, covered driving range. **Comments:** the course is kept in excellent
condition all year long. The length, many bunkers, ponds, and trees will chal-
lenge you at every turn. Shot placement off the tee is very important. Good track.

Directions: from I-5 N&S take exit
#127 to Hwy 512 eastbound. Proceed
east on 512 to Hwy 7 S. Exit to Hwy 7
southbound. Proceed south on Hwy 7 for
2.8 miles to the golf course which will
be on your right hand side. Look for
signs marking your way to the course.

Course Yardage & Par:
C-6810 yards, par 72.
M-6405 yards, par 72.
W-5935 yards, par 74.

Lake Wilderness Golf Course (public, 18 hole course)
25400 Witte Road SE; Maple Valley, WA 98038
Phone: (425) 432-9405. Fax: (425) 432-2185. Internet: www.agc.com
Manager: Kelly Beymer. Pro: Bob Climer, PGA. Superintendent: N/A.
Rating/Slope: C 66.1/118; M 64.7/116; W 66.6/117. **Course record:** 64.
Green fees: W/D $20/$13; W/E $25; Jr/Sr, twi-lite rates; VISA, M/C, AMEX.
Power cart: $20/$12. **Pull cart:** $4. **Trail fee:** $7.50 for personal carts.
Reservation policy: yes, call up to 1 week in advance for your tee-times.
Winter condition: the golf course is open all year long. Dry conditions.
Terrain: relatively hilly. **Tees:** all grass. **Spikes:** soft spikes preferred.
Services: club rentals, lessons, snack bar, lounge, restaurant, beer, wine, liquor, club memberships, pro shop. **Comments:** new layout is not long but yet is very demanding. Out of bounds comes into play on every hole. Challenging course.

Directions: from I-5 N&S exit to I-405 to Renton. Take exit #4 for Hwy 169. Take Hwy 169 going south. Upon entering Maple Valley (about 15 minutes), take a right at the 4th stoplight onto Witte Road SE. Go approximately 1 mile. You will pass the 18th fairway on your left. You will take the 2nd left to the golf course. From I-90 exit to I-405 southbound. Proceed south and exit to Hwy 169 and follow the above directions.

Course Yardage & Par:
C-5494 yards, par 70.
M-5146 yards, par 70.
W-4767 yards, par 70.

Lake Woods Golf Course (public, 9 hole course)

240 State Park Road; P.O. Box 427; Bridgeport, WA 98813
Phone: (509) 686-5721. Fax: none. Internet: none.
Manager: Dick Field. Superintendent: Cliff Pins.
Rating/Slope: M 66.7/115; W 67.8/115. Course record: 63.
Green fees: W/D $16/$11; W/E $18/$12; Jr. & Sr. rates; VISA, M/C.
Power cart: $18/$11. Pull cart: $2.60. Trail fee: $2.75.
Reservation policy: advance tee-time reservations are not required.
Winter condition: course is closed October to April, depending on weather.
Terrain: flat, some hills. **Tees:** all grass. **Spikes:** metal spikes permitted.
Services: club rentals, restaurant, beer, pro shop, putting green, driving range.
Comments: the course runs partially along the Columbia River although it does
not come into play. Small, sloping well bunkered greens make approach shots
very difficult. Campground near the course for those wanting to spend the night.

Directions: the golf course is located off
Hwy 17 by Bridgeport State Park, south
of Bridgeport. Watch for the sign on the
highway directing you to the golf course.
You will turn on State Park Road to the
golf course. From Hwy 97 turn east on
Hwy 17 for 8.1 miles to the Bridgeport
State Park Road. Proceed to the course.

Course Yardage & Par:

M-2845 yards, par 35.
W-2543 yards, par 35.
Dual tees for 18 holes:
M-5646 yards, par 70.
W-5091 yards, par 70.

LakeLand Village Golf & Country Club (semi-private, 27 hole course)
E 200 Old Ranch Road; P. O. Box 670; Allyn, WA 98524
Phone: (360) 275-6100. Fax: (360) 275-0266. Internet: www.lakelandvillagegolf.com
Pro: Randy Jensen, PGA. Superintendent: Steve Anderson.
Rating/Slope I/II: C 68.5/117; M 67.7/114; W 69.6/119. **Course record:** 62.
Green fees: W/D $22.25; W/E $28.25; Sr. rates Monday & Thur. only $17/$12.
Power cart: $24. **Pull cart:** $3. **Trail fee:** personal carts are not allowed.
Reservation policy: yes, please call 7 days in advance for tee times.
Winter condition: the golf course is open all year long. Damp conditions.
Terrain: flat, some hills. **Tees:** all grass. **Spikes:** soft spikes preferred.
Services: club rentals, lessons, snack bar, restaurant, beer, wine, liquor,
pro shop, club memberships, two driving ranges (full woods), putting green.
Comments: well maintained, this beautiful layout sports 14 water hazards to
challenge any golfer. Good golf course that is much improved over the years.

Directions: from the Bremerton ferry
veer left to 1st St. for 1 block to Pacific.
Turn right. Travel 1 block to Burwell
(Hwy 304 W). Turn left and follow signs
to Shelton to Hwy 3 S. Turn south on
Hwy 3 S to Allyn. Turn right on Lakeland Drive and proceed to the golf course.
The golf course is located just off of Hwy
3 toward Shelton or Bremerton.

Course Yardage & Par:
Generation I
C-2584 yards, par 35.
M-2551 yards, par 35.
W-2336 yards, par 36.
Generation II
C-3140 yards, par 36.
M-2952 yards, par 36.
W-2589 yards, par 36.
Generation III
C-3331 yards, par 36.
M-3134 yards, par 36.
W-2745 yards, par 36.

Lakeview Golf & Country Club (private, 18 hole course)

19457 Golf Club NW; Soap Lake, WA 98851
Phone: (509) 246-0336. Fax: none. Internet: none.
Pro: Don Tracy, PGA. Superintendent: Dave Paulson.
Rating/Slope: C 70.9/114; M 69.5/111; W 72.4/117. **Course record:** 62.
Green fees: private club; members only; reciprocates; no credit cards.
Power cart: private club. **Pull cart:** private club. **Trail fee:** private club.
Reservation policy: private club members only. No public play is allowed.
Winter condition: the golf course is open all year long. Dry conditions.
Terrain: very flat. **Tees:** all grass. **Spikes:** soft spikes preferred.
Services: club rentals, lessons, restaurant, snack bar, lounge, beer, wine, liquor,
pro shop, showers, lockers, putting green and chipping green, driving range.
Comments: the course is unique in as much as there are no adjoining fairways.
Greens are medium to large in size well bunkered and fast. Tree's dot the
landscape and can be a major factor off the tee. Excellent private facility.

Directions: from Hwy 17, take the 19th
NW exit south of Soap Lake. Proceed 2
blocks and turn right to the course. From
I-90 Take the Ephrata exit and follow
Hwy 583 to Ephrata. Proceed to Road 19
NW and turn westbound to the course.

Course Yardage & Par:
C-6638 yards, par 71.
M-6340 yards, par 71.
W-5754 yards, par 71.

Lakeview Golf Challenge (public, 9 hole par 3 course)

2425 NW 69th Street; Vancouver, WA 98665
Phone: (360) 693-9116. Fax: (360) 699-6197. Internet: none.
Manager: Charley Greene. Superintendent: Charley Greene.
Rating/Slope: the golf course is not rated. **Course record:** 53 for 18 holes.
Green fees: $13/$7 all week long; Sr. rates $9/$5; M/C, VISA.
Power cart: not available. **Pull cart:** $1. **Trail fee:** not allowed.
Reservation policy: reservations are not required. First come first served.
Winter condition: the golf course is open all year long. Damp conditions.
Terrain: very flat. **Tees:** grass & mats. **Spikes:** soft spikes only.
Services: club rentals, small pro shop, beverages, putting green.
Comments: difficult golf course that will challenge you at every turn. The course sports sloping well bunkered greens. Water comes into play on several holes and is a major factor. If you are looking for change of pace, try Lakeview.

Directions: I-5 N&S take exit for 78th St. Travel west to the end of the road. Turn left (on Lakeshore DR) and travel .7 miles. Turn right (sharp) on south side of the overpass to Whitney Road which becomes 69th St. Proceed on 69th Street to the golf course. Look for signs marking your turn to the facility.

Course Yardage & Par:
M-852 yards, par 27.
W-852 yards, par 27.
<u>Dual tees for 18 holes:</u>
M-1855 yards, par 54.
W-1855 yards, par 54.

Lams Golf Links (public, 9 hole course)

585 West Ducken Road; Whidbey Island, WA 98277
Phone: (360) 675-3412. Fax: none. Internet: none.
Manager: Bill Lam. Superintendent: Bill Lam.
Rating/Slope: the golf course is not rated. **Course record:** 26.
Green fees: W/D $9/$6; W/E $12/$9; Sr. rates; no credit cards.
Power cart: none available. **Pull cart:** $3. **Trail fee:** not allowed.
Reservation policy: reservations are not needed, first come first served.
Winter condition: the golf course is closed from December through March.
Terrain: flat (easy to walk). **Tees:** grass. **Spikes:** metal spikes permitted.
Services: very limited services, vending machines, putting green.
Comments: executive length golf course located on scenic Whidbey Island just
south of the Deception Pass Bridge. Golf course has an honor box for green fees
if the clubhouse is not open. Very easy to just walk on for a quick 9 holes.

Directions: the course is located 1 mile
south of Deception Pass off Hwy 20.
Turn left on Ducken Road to the golf
course. **Note:** Look for a sign on Hwy
20 marking the turn to the golf course.

Course Yardage & Par:
M-1347 yards, par 28. **W-1347 yards, par 28.**

Latah Short Course (public, 9 hole par 3 course)

5840 Meadowlane Road; Spokane, WA 99204
Phone: (509) 443-9751. Fax: same as phone number. Internet: none.
Manager: Terry Kelly. Superintendent: Chris Becker.
Rating/Slope: the golf course is not rated. **Course record:** 21.
Green fees: Adults: $10; Seniors: $6; Juniors $5; Each additional 9 $3.
Power cart: none. **Pull cart:** $2. **Trail fee:** no personal carts.
Reservation policy: call and reserve tee times 1 week in advance.
Winter condition: the golf course is closed from December to February.
Terrain: flat. **Tees:** grass. **Spikes:** metal spikes permitted.
Services: club rentals, snack bar, beer, wine, lessons, night golf, free clinics.
Comments: a well maintained Par 3 with a lake and a stream running through the course layout. The course sits among four old barns and gives the track some character. Great course for the first time or beginner golfer.

Directions: From I-90 E&W (#279) exit to Hwy 195 and proceed southbound. Turn eastbound on Meadow Lane Road. Follow this to the golf course. Look for signs that are posted along the way.

Course Yardage & Par:
M-730 yards, par 27.
W-730 yards, par 27.

Leavenworth Golf Club (semi-private, 18 hole course)

9101 Icicle Road; P.O. Box 247; Leavenworth, WA 98826
Phone: (509) 548-7267. Fax: (509) 548-4668. Internet: www.leavenworthgolf.com
Pro: Jim Van Tuyl, PGA. Superintendent: Michael Snyder.
Rating/Slope: M 67.0/110; W 69.6/112. **Course record:** 61.
Green fees: W/D $22/$15; W/E $25/$16; M/C, VISA, DIS, AMEX.
Power cart: $22. **Pull cart:** $2.50. **Trail fee:** $5 for personal carts.
Reservation policy: call Monday to book the week (Monday to Monday).
Winter condition: the golf course is closed from mid November to March.
Terrain: flat, some slight hills. **Tees:** grass. **Spikes:** soft spikes only.
Services: club rentals, snack bar, beer, wine, lessons, pro shop, putting green.
Comments: a beautiful setting in the heart of the Cascade Mountains. Many trees, sand traps, and the Wenatchee River come into play on a number of holes. Fairways are tree-lined and can be narrow in spots. The town of Leavenworth and the Bavarian village alone are worth the trip. Some restricted tee times, Sunday AM men members only; Wednesday AM women members only.

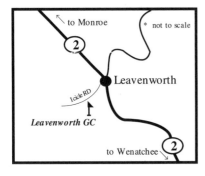

Directions: golf course located 1 mile west of Leavenworth. From Hwy 2 go south on Icicle Road for 0.6 miles to the golf course which will be on your left hand side. **Note:** Look for a sign on the Hwy marking your turn to the course.

Course Yardage & Par:
M-5711 yards, par 71.
W-5343 yards, par 71.

Legion Memorial Golf Course (public, 18 hole course)
144 W Marine View Drive; Everett, WA 98201
Phone: (425) 259-4653. Fax: (425) 257-6877. Internet: www.legionmemorialgolf.com
Pro: Mike Coury, PGA. Superintendent: Edward Phelps.
Rating/Slope: C 71.2/116; M 70.0/114; W 69.7/100. **Course record:** 65.
Green fees: W/D Everett resident $22/$15; non resident $33/$23; W/E Everett
resident $26/$18; non resident $37/$26; early bird (M-Th); twilight; Jr/Sr rates.
Power cart: $22/$14. **Pull cart:** $3. **Trail fee:** $5 for personal carts.
Reservation policy: W/D 1 week in advance. Call Monday 9am for W/E times.
Winter condition: the golf course is open all year long. Very dry conditions.
Terrain: flat, some hills. **Tees:** grass. **Spikes:** metal spikes permitted.
Services: newly remodeled clubhouse featuring the Greenside Grill and bever-
age cart service, pro shop, club rentals, lessons, lockers, showers, putting green.
Comments: The golf course was renovated with all 18 holes open in September
1998. The "new" course is expected to become one of the driest winter courses
in western Washington. Water hazards and sand bunkers add beauty, challenge
and playability to the course. Managed by Golf Resources Northwest.

Directions: from I-5 N take exit 195.
Turn left on Marine View Drive and
follow for 2.1 miles to the golf course.
From I-5 S take exit 194. Go west for .1
mi to Walnut. Go north for 1.2 miles to
Marine View Drive and turn west for
1.3 miles to golf course. Look for signs.

Course Yardage & Par:
T-6900 yards, par 72.
C-6627 yards, par 72.
M-6111 yards, par 72.
W-4805 yards, par 72.

Lewis River Golf Course (public, 18 hole course)
3209 Lewis River Road; Woodland, WA 98674
Phone: (360) 225-8254. Fax: (360) 225-5869. Internet: oregongolf.com.
Pro: Dick Smith, PGA. Superintendent: Terry Vanderstoop.
Rating/Slope: C 70.1/123; M 68.1/118; W 69.7/119. **Course record:** 62.
Green fees: Monday thru Thursday $26/$16; Friday $32/$18; Saturday thru Sunday & holidays $35/$20; Jr/Sr rates $20 (Monday-Thursday); M/C, VISA.
Power cart: $26/$13. **Pull cart:** $2. **Trail fee:** $8 for personal carts.
Reservation policy: yes, please call up to 1 week in advance.
 Winter condition: the golf course is open all year long. Very dry conditions.
Terrain: flat, some hills. **Tees:** all grass. **Spikes:** metal spikes permitted.
Services: club rentals, lessons, snack bar, lounge, restaurant, beer, wine, liquor, driving range, pro shop, club memberships, putting and chipping greens.
Comments: Lewis River sports the longest golf hole in Washington, a 649 yard par 5. Great winter & summer course. Course can play very tough with water and sand coming into play on several holes. Excellent course that is worth a special trip. Play golf and take in Mount Saint Helens in the same day.

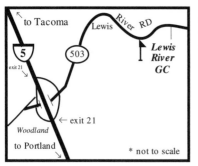

Directions: the golf course is located east of Woodland. From I-5 N&S take exit #21. Travel east for 4.7 miles to the golf course which will be located on your right hand side of the road. This golf course has great freeway access. Look for signs.

Course Yardage & Par:
C-6352 yards, par 72.
M-5903 yards, par 72.
W-5260 yards, par 73.

Liberty Lake Golf Course (public, 18 hole course)

24403 E Sprague Avenue; Liberty Lake, WA 99019
Phone: (509) 255-6233. **Fax:** (509) 255-5105. **Internet:** none.
Pro: Kit DeAndre. **Superintendent:** Mike Kingsley.
Rating/Slope: C 69.8/121; M 68.7/118; W 72.6/125. **Course record:** 61.
Green fees: resident $16/$12; non $22/$15.50; Jr/Sr rates (Mon.-Fri.).
Power cart: $25/$12.50. **Pull cart:** $3. **Trail fee:** $6.
Reservation policy: yes, call Tuesday to make your upcoming tee-times.
Winter condition: dry. The golf course is closed during inclement weather.
Terrain: flat, some hills. **Tees:** all grass. **Spikes:** soft spikes preferred.
Services: club rentals, lessons, snack bar, beer, wine, pro shop, driving range, putting green. **Comments:** the golf course is easy to walk with many well-trapped greens. Liberty Lake can play much tougher than the layout indicates. Shot placement from the tee is a must. This is one of the finest public golf courses in the state of Washington. Worth a trip if in the Spokane area.

Directions: the golf course is located east of Spokane. From I-90 eastbound and westbound take exit #296 and go south to Sprague Avenue. Turn left on Sprague Avenue and continue to the golf course. Look for signs marking your turn to the golf complex.

Course Yardage & Par:
C-6373 yards, par 70.
M-6121 yards, par 70.
W-5801 yards, par 74.

Linden Golf & Country Club (private, 9 hole course)

2519 Main Avenue East; Puyallup, WA 98371
Phone: (253) 845-2056. Fax: none. Internet: none.
Pro: David Leon Jr, PGA. Superintendent: Dean Hanson.
Rating/Slope: M 69.7/120; W 74.1/123. **Course record:** 62.
Green fees: private club members & guests only; no credit cards.
Power cart: private club. **Pull cart:** private club. **Trail fee:** private club.
Reservation policy: private club members only. No public play is allowed.
Winter condition: the golf course is open all year long. Dry conditions.
Terrain: flat, some hills. **Tees:** grass. **Spikes:** soft spikes preferred.
Services: lessons, pro shop, lockers, showers, club memberships, putting green.
Comments: private 9 hole course with separate tee boxes for 18 hole play.
Rolling terrain small greens and bunkers enhance this interesting course design.
The course is well kept with water coming into play on two holes.

Directions: from I-5 N&S take exit # 135 to Hwy 167 N. Turn north and travel 5.3 miles to Meridian Street N. Turn south for .4 miles to Main Avenue E. Proceed east for 1.5 miles to the golf course on your left hand side.

Course Yardage & Par:
M-3120 yards, par 36.
W-3110 yards, par 37.
<u>**Dual tees for 18 holes:**</u>
M-6112 yards, par 72.
W-6017 yards, par 73.

Lipoma Firs Golf Course (public, 27 hole course)

18615 110th Avenue East; Puyallup, WA 98374
Phone: (253) 841-4396; 1-800-649-4396. Fax: (253) 847-0641.
Pro: Dean Bass, PGA. Supt.: Rod Ragsdale. Internet: www.lipomafirs.com
Rating/Slope: C 72.5/124; M 70.2/120; M 69.5/118; W 71.0/117. **Record:** 64.
Green fees: W/D $20/$13; W/E $25/$16; Jr. & Sr., twilight rates; M/C, VISA.
Power cart: $20/$12. **Pull cart:** $3. **Trail fee:** $6 for personal carts.
Reservation policy: yes, call up to 1 week in advance for your tee times.
Winter condition: the golf course is open all year long. Dry conditions.
Terrain: flat, some hills, **Tees:** all grass. **Spikes:** soft spikes preferred.
Services: club rentals, lessons, snack bar, beer, wine, beverages, pro shop,
driving range, 2 practice greens, practice bunkers, club memberships.
Comments: the course is always in good condition, excellent drainage provides
good winter play. Fairways are tree lined and narrow in certain areas. You must
be able to position your ball in the right place off the tee in order to score well.

Directions: from I-5 N&S take the exit
for Hwy 512E. Travel 8 miles to Hwy
161S. Proceed 6 miles to 187th. The
course will located on your left hand side.

Course Yardage & Par:	
Green Course	**Gold Course**
C-3302 yards, par 36.	C-3420 yards, par 36.
M-3123 yards, par 36.	M-3094 yards, par 36.
W-2716 yards, par 36.	W-2760 yards, par 36.

Course Yardage & Par (Blue Course)
C-3385 yards, par 36. M-3051 yards, par 36.
W-2757 yards, par 36.

Lobo Country Club (public, 9 hole par 3 course)
12015 84th Street SE; Snohomish, WA 98290
Phone: (360) 568-1638. Fax: none. Internet: none.
Owners: Gordon & Fedora Loth.
Rating/Slope: the golf course is not rated. **Course record:** 25.
Green fees: $15/$10 all week long; Jr./Sr. rates $14/$8 (M-F); no credit cards.
Power Cart: $12/$8. **Pull Cart:** $2. **Trail fee:** not available.
Reservation policy: advance tee times are not required.
Winter condition: the golf course is closed November through February.
Terrain: flat, some hills. **Tees:** all grass. **Spikes:** metal spikes permitted.
Services: club rentals, clubhouse, vending machines, chipping & putting greens.
Comments: friendly family owned course, surrounded by a beautiful country setting. If you are looking for a place to take the first time golfer, try Lobo CC.

Directions: from Hwy 2 exit at the Snohomish 88th Street SE exit eastbound. Proceed on 88th Street to 123rd Avenue SE turn north to the course. Look for signs marking your turn to the golf course.

Course Yardage & Par:
M-1014 yards, par 27.
W-1005 yards, par 27.

Longview Country Club (private, 18 hole course)
41 Country Club Drive; Longview, WA 98632
Phone: (360) 425-3132. Fax: (360) 414-9339. Internet: none.
Pro: Jeff Bartleson, PGA. Superintendent: Ben Davis.
Rating/Slope: M 69.2/122; W 70.6/118. **Course record:** 64.
Green fees: private club, members only; reciprocates; VISA, M/C.
Power cart: private club. **Pull cart:** private club. **Trail fee:** not allowed.
Reservation policy: private club, members only. No public play allowed.
Winter Condition: the golf course is open all year long. Damp conditions.
Terrain: relatively hilly. **Tees:** all grass. **Spikes:** soft spikes preferred.
Services: club rentals, lessons, snack bar, restaurant, beer, wine, liquor, pro
shop, lockers, showers, club memberships, practice range, putting green.
Comments: course has newly redesigned three holes that are now in excellent
condition. Challenging, well maintained greens are this course's trademark.

Directions: from I-5 take exit # 39
and follow to the Ocean Beach Hwy,
continuing to Pacific Hwy. Travel north
on Pacific Hwy to Country Club Road.
Turn right on Country Club Road to the
golf course.

Course Yardage & Par:
M-6220 yards, par 70.
W-5565 yards, par 73.

Loomis Trail Golf Club (resort/private, 18 hole course)

4342 Loomis Trail Road; Blaine, WA 98230
Phone: (360) 332-8138, 800 231-4425. **Fax:** (360) 332-2232. **Internet: none.**
Pro: Keith Henderson, PGA. **Superintendent:** Vance Much.
Rating/Slope: T 75.1/145; C 72.4/136; M 70.0/132; W 71.9/125. **Record:** 64.
Green fees: $95/$55. For membership information call (360) 332-1725.
Power cart: included in fee. **Pull cart:** N/A. **Trail fee:** not allowed.
Reservation policy: 90 days-Inn at Semiahmoo guest. 30 days-non-resort guest.
Even numbered days only. Credit card guarantee is required. M/C, VISA.
Winter condition: the golf course is open all year long. Dry conditions.
Terrain: flat, some hills. **Tees:** all grass. **Spikes:** soft spikes only.
Services: pro shop, restaurant, lodging for members & guests, memberships.
Comments: Open since 1993, the course was rated 3rd best new private course
by *"Golf Digest"*. This 18 hole layout was also ranked #3 best course in Washington State. This challenging layout sports numerous bunkers, ponds and tree
lined fairways. Combined with Semiahmoo it is worth a special trip anytime.

Directions: from I-5 N&S take exit #270
(Birch Bay - Lynden Rd.). Travel W for .2
miles to Peace Portal. Turn N for 1.5
miles to Loomis Trail Road. Turn W for
1.2 miles to the golf course.

Course Yardage & Par:
T-7137 yards, par 72.
C-6611 yards, par 72.
M-6167 yards, par 72.
W-5475 yards, par 72.

Lopez Island Golf Course (public, 9 hole course)

Airport Road; Box 124; Lopez Island, WA 98261
Phone: (360) 468-2679. Fax: none. Internet: none.
Pro Shop Manager: L. Holmes. Superintendent: none.
Rating/Slope: C 65.2/110; M 62.8/105; W 67.0/114. **Course record:** 68.
Green fees: $20/$14 all week long; Jr rates; no credit cards.
Power cart: power carts are not available. **Pull cart:** $1. **Trail fee:** no charge.
Reservation policy: advance tee times are not required.
Winter Condition: the golf course is open all year long. Damp conditions.
Terrain: relatively hilly, walkable. **Tees:** grass. **Spikes:** soft spikes preferred.
Services: club rentals, pro shop. **Comments:** situated in the scenic San Juan
Islands this course is easy to walk with few hazards. Good course in a very
beautiful part of Washington. If in the islands make sure to bring your clubs.

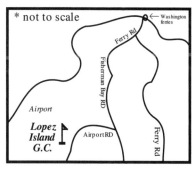

Directions: from I-5 N&S take exit
#230 to Hwy 20W to Anacortes and the
San Juan ferry terminal. Board the ferry
for Lopez Island. From the Lopez ferry
landing proceed south on Ferry Road on
to Fisherman Bay Road. Turn right on
Airport Road. Proceed for .5 miles and
turn left to the golf course which will be
on your right hand side. Look for signs
that will be posted indicating your turn.

Course Yardage & Par:
M-2711 yards, par 35.
W-2427 yards, par 35.

Lower Valley Golf Club (public, 18 hole course)

31 Ray Road; Sunnyside, WA 98944
Phone: (509) 837-5340. Fax: (509) 837-5340. Internet: none.
Pro: Craig Thomas, PGA. Superintendent: Kelly Bowen.
Rating/Slope: C 70.2/112; M 68.4/108; W 70.6/111. **Course record:** 63.
Green fees: W/D $19/$14; W/E & Holidays $22/$15; M/C, VISA.
Power cart: $22/$11. **Pull cart:** $3. **Trail fee:** $5 for personal carts.
Reservation policy: you may call ahead 1 week in advance for tee times.
Winter condition: dry conditions. Course is open all year, weather permitting.
Terrain: flat (easy walking). **Tees:** all grass. **Spikes:** soft spikes only.
Services: club rentals, Henry-Griffits club fitting, lessons, pro shop,
practice range, vending machines, beverages, putting & chipping green.
Comments: this course is an excellent facility which added a new nine in spring
of 1995. This track is a challenging golf course that is easy to walk and demand-
ing. Water comes into play on 10 holes and the greens are of varing sizes.

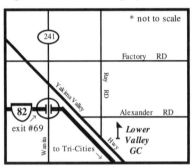

Directions: from I-82 eastbound take
exit # 69 (Sunnyside). Travel north on
Wanita to the Yakima Valley Hwy. Turn
eastbound. Proceed 1.5 miles to Ray Rd.
and the golf course. Look for signs.

Course Yardage & Par:
C-6664 yards, par 72.
W-6271 yards, par 72.
W-5618 yards, par 72.

Lynnwood Municipal Golf Course (public, 18 hole course)
20200 68th Avenue West; Box 5008; Lynnwood, WA 98046
Phone: (425) 672-4653. Fax: (425) 712-8554. Internet: none.
Pro: Dan Smith, PGA. Superintendent: Gary Stormo.
Rating/Slope: M 62.0/100; W 62.5/95. **Course record:** M 59; W 65.
Green fees: Monday-Thursday $23/$15; Friday-Sunday & holidays $25/$15;
Jr. & Sr. rates Monday thru Friday, Sr.'s $20 and Jr.'s $20.
Power cart: $22/$11. **Pull cart:** $3. **Trail fee:** not allowed.
Reservation policy: please call up to 7 days in advance for Monday thru
Friday tee-times. Call up to 5 days in advance for Saturday & Sunday times.
Winter condition: the golf course is open all year long. Dry conditions.
Terrain: flat, some hills. **Tees:** all grass. **Spikes:** soft spikes preferred.
Services: club rentals, lessons, restaurant, pro shop, driving range, lessons,
putting green. **Comments:** Excellent, short length golf course that is very
demanding off the tee. Tree lined fairways, bunkers and ponds make this track a
challenge. If you are looking for a change of pace from the standard 6000+ yard
golf course, try Lynnwood Municipal it will not disappoint. Good golf course.

Directions: from I-5 N&S take exit
179 and travel west on 220th St. SW.
Proceed to Hwy 99 and turn right
(north). Follow to 208th St. SW and turn
left. Then take the immediate right on
68th Ave. W. The entrance to the golf
course is on 68th and 204th. The golf
course is located adjacent to the
Edmonds Community College campus.
Look for signs indicating your turns.

Course Yardage & Par:
M-4741 yards, par 65. W-4094 yards, par 65.

M A 8 Golf (public, 9 hole course)
453 Wapato Lake Road; Manson, WA 98831
Phone: (509) 687-6338. **Fax:** none. **Internet:** none.
Manager: Garrey Hayes. **Pro:** none.
Rating/Slope: the golf course is not rated. **Course record:** 27.
Green fees: $22/$12 all week long; Jr. rates $18/$10.
Power cart: none available. **Pull cart:** $4. **Trail fee:** not allowed.
Reservation policy: yes, please call ahead for tee-times. No time limit.
Winter condition: the course is closed in the winter November to March.
Terrain: flat, some hills. **Tees:** all grass. **Spikes:** soft spikes preferred.
Services: club rentals, snack bar, driving range, putting & chipping green.
Comments: the course is fairly flat and easy to walk. Although not overly long the course can play tough if the wind blows. This track has large greens with few traps that hold shots well. Those vacationing in the Chelan area might want to take a chance and play a course off the beaten path.

Note: the golf course is located right off Hwy 150.

Directions: the golf course is located near the Manson Hwy. From Lake Chelan on Hwy 150 proceed westbound for 6 miles. Turn right on Wapato Lake Road and proceed to clubhouse. The golf course is located right next to the Hwy.

Course Yardage & Par:
M-1881 yards, par 30. **W-1881 yards, par 30.**

Madrona Links Golf Course (public, 18 hole course)
3604 22nd Avenue NW; Gig Harbor, WA 98335
Phone: (253) 851-5193. Fax: (253) 851-3844. Internet: none.
Pro: Philip Massara, PGA. Superintendent: Chad Niedermeier.
Rating/Slope: C 65.5/110; M 63.7/107; W 65.6/110. **Course record:** 59.
Green fees: Monday-Thursday $22/$16; Friday-Sun. & Hol. $25/$19; Jr. rates
$14/$9; Sr. rates $17/$12 (M-F); early bird & twilight specials, M/C, VISA.
Power cart: $22/$13. **Pull cart:** $3.50. **Trail fee:** $8 for personal carts.
Reservation policy: yes, call up to 1 week in advance for tee times.
Winter condition: the golf course is open all year long. Dry conditions.
Terrain: flat, some hills. **Tees:** grass. **Spikes:** metal spikes permitted.
Services: club rentals, lessons, snack bar, lounge, restaurant, beer, wine, liquor,
beverages, pro shop, club memberships, driving range, putting green.
Comments: friendly, well kept, tree-lined course. Great golf course that is worth
a special trip. If you are looking for a quality course that is excellent for tourna-
ments and company outings try Madrona. This course will not disappoint.

Directions: from Hwy 16 take the exit
for Olympic Dr. Follow Olympic Dr. to
Pt. Fosdick Dr. NW and turn left. Travel
.9 miles to 36th Avenue NW. Turn left
(it is not well marked). The golf course
is located .4 miles ahead on your left.

Course Yardage & Par:
C-5602 yards, par 71.
M-5193 yards, par 71.
W-4737 yards, par 73.

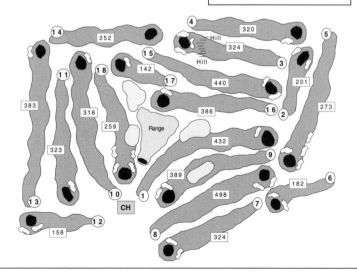

Manito Golf & Country Club (private, 18 hole course)
5303 South Hatch Road; Spokane, WA 99203
Phone: (509) 448-5829. **Fax:** (509) 448-9607. **Internet:** none.
Pro: Steve Prugh, PGA. **Superintendent:** Tim Ansett.
Rating/Slope: C 70.0/123; M 69.2/120; W 72.3/125; W 69.2/118. **Record:** 60.
Green fees: private club members & guests only; reciprocates.
Power cart: private club. **Pull cart:** private club. **Trail fee:** not allowed.
Reservation policy: private club members & guests only. No outside play.
Winter condition: the golf course is closed during winter months.
Terrain: flat . **Tees:** all grass. **Spikes:** no metal spikes are permitted.
Services: club rentals, lessons, restaurant, snack bar, lounge, beer, wine, liquor, showers, pro shop, driving range, putting and chipping greens, memberships.
Comments: premium put on accuracy due to many sand traps, well bunkered greens and tight tree-lined fairways. Holes 9 and 18 are on an island and are very demanding. Excellent private facility that is very hard to score on.

Directions: from I-90 E&W take the exit for Hwy 195S southbound #279. Travel for approximately 4.5 miles to the Hatch Road exit. Proceed eastbound uphill for 2 miles to the stop sign (stay left at the fork). Turn left at the stop sign and proceed to the golf course 1/2 mile ahead on the right hand side of the road.

Course Yardage & Par:
C-6378 yards, par 70. M-6153 yards, par 71. W-5678 yards, par 72. W-5401 yards, par 72.

Maple Grove Golf (public, 9 hole course)

175 State Route 12; P. O. Box 205; Randle, WA 98377
Phone: (360) 497-2741. Fax: (360) 497-2744. Internet: none.
Owner: Kim Resort. Superintendent: none.
Rating/Slope: M 53.7/72; W 55.2/76. **Course record: 26.**
Green fees: $12/$7.50; all day $16; Jr. & Sr. rates (weekdays); M/C, VISA.
Power cart: available. **Pull cart:** $2. **Trail fee:** no charge.
Reservation policy: for tournaments only. Everyone else first come first served.
Winter condition: the golf course is open all year long. Dry conditions.
Terrain: flat, some hills. **Tees:** all grass. **Spikes:** soft spikes only.
Services: club rentals, snack bar, beer, wine, pro shop, driving range, RV
parking and hook-ups. **Comments:** course situated in Maple Grove Park. Short
course that has medium sized greens with few hazards. The course is wide open
with few hazards coming into play. Good track for the senior or first time golfer.

Directions: from I-5 N&S cut-off
eastbound on Highway 12 exit #68
toward Randle, Washington. Turn right
on (Hwy 131 South). Proceed to the golf
course which will be located on your left
hand side. Look for signs marking your
way to the golf course.

Course Yardage & Par:
C-1521 yards, par 31.
M-1521 yards, par 31.
W-1521 yards, par 31.

Maplewood Golf Course (public, 18 hole course)
4050 SE Maple Valley Highway; Renton, WA 98058
Phone: (425) 430-6800. Fax: (425) 430-6801. Internet: none.
Pro: Mike Toll, PGA. Superintendent: Steve Meyers.
Rating/Slope: C 68.8/115; M 67.4/113; W 69.1/115. **Course record:** 62.
Green fees: W/D $22/$17; W/E $25/$17; Jr. & Sr. rates; M/C, VISA.
Power cart: $22/$14. **Pull cart:** $4/$2.50. **Trail fee:** $8 for personal carts.
Reservation policy: yes, call up to 1 week in advance for weekday times, call
Monday for the following weekend. (Be sure to call ahead during the summer).
Winter condition: the golf course is open all year long. Drains fairly well.
Terrain: flat, some hills. **Tees:** grass & mats. **Spikes:** soft spikes preferred.
Services: club rentals, lessons, restaurant, lounge, beer, wine, liquor, pro shop,
club memberships, 30 stall driving range (covered & heated), banquet rooms.
Comments: measuring over 6,000 yards in length, the course's wide variety of
holes provide a good test for all level of golfers. The front side has water on
seven of the nine holes and the back side will challenge even the straightest
drivers with tight tree lined fairways. The course can get very busy in summer.

Directions: from I-405 N&S take exit
#4 to Hwy 169 southbound. Travel
south for 1.7 miles to the golf course on
your left hand side.

Course Yardage & Par:

C-6005 yards, par 72.
M-5640 yards, par 72.
W-5133 yards, par 73.

McCormick Woods (public, 18 hole course)

5155 McCormick Woods Drive SW; Port Orchard, WA 98367
Phone numbers: (360) 895-0130 or 1-800-323-0130.
Fax: (360) 876-2254. Internet: www.mccormickwoodsgolf.com
Pro: Scott Ashworth, PGA. Superintendent: Howard Sisson. Record: 64.
Rating/Slope: T 74.6/136; C 72.6/131; M 70.5/125; W 73.6/131; E 66.6/115.
Green fees: Mon.-Thurs. $42/$30; Friday-Sunday & Holidays $57/$35; Early
Bird/Twilight rates available. Call for times and prices; VISA, M/C, DIS, AMX.
Power cart: $13/$8 per person. **Pull cart:** $5/$3. **Trail fee:** not allowed.
Reservation policy: recommended, call up to 7 days in advance for tee times.
Winter condition: the course is open all year long. Dry, excellent drainage.
Terrain: flat, some hills. **Tees:** all grass. **Spikes:** metal spikes permitted.
Services: club rentals, lessons, snack bar, beer, wine, restuarant, lounge, pro
shop, driving range. **Comments:** ranked in the top 50 public golf courses by
Golf Digest Magazine. Golfweek voted McCormick Woods the #1 course in
Washington State. Championship caliber track. Well bunkered by grass and
sand bunkers. Great golf course that is worth a special trip. You will often see
deer walking down your fairway so if you are in the area don't miss this course.

Directions: from I-5 N&S take the exit
for Hwy 16 westbound. Follow Hwy
16 to the Old Clifton/Tremont exit.
Turn left and proceed 1.8 miles to the
entrance on your left side. **Note:** look
for signs on Hwy 16 to the course.

Course Yardage & Par:
T-7040 yards, par 72.
C-6658 yards, par 72.
M-6165 yards, par 72.
W-5758 yards, par 72.
Exc-5299 yards, par 72.

Meadow Park Golf Course (public, 18 hole, 9 hole par 3 course)

7108 Lakewood Drive West; Lakewood, WA 98499
Phone: (253) 473-3033. **Fax:** (253) 471-9266. **Internet:** none.
Pro: Gerry Mehlert, PGA. **Superintendent:** Chris Goodman.
Rating/Slope: C 68.9/116; M 67.3/11; W 70.2/115. **Course record:** 64.
Green fees: W/D $22/$15; W/E $25/$16; Jr./Sr. rates (M-Friday); VISA, M/C.
Green fees for Williams 9: $12/$8 all week long; Jr. & Sr. rates (M-Friday).
Power cart: $22/$13. **Pull cart:** $3. **Trail fee:** $6 for personal carts.
Reservation policy: yes, call up to 1 week in advance for your tee times.
Winter condition: the golf course is open all year long. Dry conditions.
Terrain: flat, some hills. **Tees:** all grass. **Spikes:** soft spikes preferred.
Services: club rentals, lessons, snack bar, lounge, restaurant, pro shop, beverages, club memberships, covered driving range, putting & chipping greens.
Comments: the golf course has been completely revamped with a stunning new layout. Greens are large with bunkers coming into play on several holes. Fairways are fairly wide giving the golfer room off the tee. Good winter course.

Directions: from I-5 N&S take exit #129 to S 74th St. Travel westbound for 2.1 miles to Lakewood Drive W. Turn north. The golf course is located .1 miles ahead on your left hand side. Look for signs.

Course Yardage & Par:
C-6093 yards, par 71.
M-5763 yards, par 71.
W-5225 yards, par 71.

Par 3 Course Yardage & Par:
M-1475 yards, par 29.
W-1475 yards, par 29.

Meadow Springs Country Club (private, 18 hole course)

700 Country Club Place; Richland, WA 99352
Phone: (509) 627-2321. Fax: (509) 627-7427. Internet: mscountryclub.org
Pro: Greg Moore, PGA. Supt.: Mark Dalton. GM: Otto Hartman.
Rating/Slope: C 73.3/132; M 71.3/127; M 68.9/123; W 73.3/128. **Record:** 63.
Green fees: private club; members & guests only; reciprocates; M/C, VISA.
Power cart: private club. **Pull cart:** private club. **Trail fee:** private club.
Reservation policy: private club; members & guests only. No outside play.
Winter condition: the golf course open all year long weather permitting, dry.
Terrain: relatively hilly. **Tees:** all grass. **Spikes:** metal spikes not permitted.
Services: lessons, restaurant, lounge, beer, wine, liquor, lockers, driving range,
pro shop, putting green. **Comments:** a very challenging course featuring well-
placed traps, elevated greens and a fair amount of water. Meadow Springs is
the host course for the Buy.com Tri-Cities Open. Excellent well balanced layout.

Directions: from I-182 take the exit for
Keene Road #3. Continue to Gage Blvd.
You will run right in to Gage Blvd. Turn
left on Bellerive Drive to Country Club
Place and proceed to the golf course.
From I-82 take exit #109 to Leslie Road.
Proceed to Broadmore Street and turn
right. Proceed to Bellerive Drive and
turn left to Country Club Place. Turn left
and proceed to the clubhouse. Look for
signs to the clubhouse.

Course Yardage & Par:

C-6957 yards, par 72.
M-6537 yards, par 72.
M-5940 yards, par 72.
W-5471 yards, par 72.

Meadowmeer Golf & Country Club (semi-private, 9 holes)

8530 Renny Lane NE; Bainbridge Island, WA 98110
Phone: (206) 842-2218. Fax: (206) 842-8119. Internet: www.orgsites.com/wa/meadowmeergc
Pro: Tom Mueller, PGA. Supterintendent: Gary Duffner.
Rating/Slope: M 67.2/122; W 70.2/120. **Course record:** 64.
Green fees: Monday thru Thursday $19/$14.50; Friday thru Sunday &
Holidays $23/$17; Jr & Sr rates (Monday-Thursday only); M/C, VISA, DIS.
Power cart: $21.50/$13. **Pull cart:** $3/$2. **Trail fee:** $7 for personal carts.
Reservation policy: up to 1 week in advance, public play is restricted at times.
Winter condition: the golf course is open all year long. Dry conditions.
Terrain: flat, some hills. **Tees:** grass. **Spikes:** soft spikes optional.
Services: club rentals, lessons, snack bar, beer, pro shop, club memberships.
Comments: the course is just 35 minutes from Seattle on the Winslow-Seattle
ferry. Good winter golf course. Easy to walk on even during the summer, so
if you are looking to play golf on your visit to the Olympic Peninsula try
Meadowmeer. The layout can play much longer than the scorecard states.

Directions: from the Seattle-Winslow
ferry terminal in Winslow take Hwy 305
northbound to Koura Road. Turn left on
Koura Road. 1/4 mile up you will see
signs for the golf course on your right
hand side. Follow the signs to the golf
course. **Note:** Look for signs marking
your way to the golf course from state
highway 305.

Course Yardage & Par:
M-2824 yards, par 35.
W-2765 yards, par 38.
Dual tees for 18 holes:
M-5589 yards, par 71.
W-5170 yards, par 74.

LinksTime.com
a division of Book4golf.com

MeadowWood Golf Course (public, 18 hole course)
E 24501 Valley Way; Liberty Lake, WA 99019
Phone: (509) 255-9539. Fax: (509) 255-5044. Internet: none.
Pro: Bob Scott, PGA. Superintendent: Mike Kingsley.
Rating/Slope: C 72.1/126; M 70.7/122; W 73.5/137. **Course record:** 64.
Green fees: non-resident: $22/$16; resident: $16/$12.
Power cart: $24/$12. **Pull cart:** $3. **Trail fee:** $6 for personal carts.
Reservation policy: yes, call in advance on Tuesday for the rest of the week.
Winter condition: the golf course is closed from November to March.
Terrain: rolling terrain. **Tees:** all grass. **Spikes:** metal spikes permitted.
Services: club rentals, lessons, restaurant, snack bar, beer, wine, pro shop,
driving range, putting green, club memberships. **Comments:** designed by
Robert Muir Graves this course is one of the nicest public play courses in
eastern Washington. A links-type course, MeadowWood features mounds,
water, and sand bunkers. A **Four-Star** golf course that is worth a special trip.

Directions: from I-90 E&W take exit
296. Go through the stoplight 1 mile
to Molter Road. Turn right on Molter
Road. Proceed for 1 mile and turn left
on Valley Way. Proceed to the golf
course. Look for signs marking your
way to the complex.

Course Yardage & Par:

C-6874 yards, par 72.
M-6429 yards, par 72.
W-5880 yards, par 72.

Members Club at Aldarra, The (private, 18 hole course)
28902 SE Duthie Hill Road; Fall City, WA 98024
Phone: (425) 222-7828. Fax: (425) 222-3650. Internet: none.
Pro: Bill Tindall, PGA. Superintendent: Paul Colleran.
Rating/Slope: the golf course is to new to be rated. **Record:** N/A.
Green fees: private club. Member and guests only. No reciprocates.
Reservation policy: private club. Members only & guests of members only.
Winter condition: the golf course is open all year long. Dry conditions.
Terrain: relatively hilly. **Tees:** all grass. **Spikes:** soft spikes required.
Services: lessons, lounge, restaurant, beer, wine, liquor, pro shop, lockers,
showers, driving range. **Comments:** this Tom Fazio designed golf course will
most likely be known as the best maintained course in the state of Washington.
The final course layout will be a challenging par 71 with championship play
length at 7000 yards and regular play from 5500 yards. Located on 225 acres
of pristine rolling hills with evergreen and deciduous trees, the course will be
playable on a year round basis. This is sure to be an outstanding private club.

Directions: from I-5 N&S take exit
168B to Hwy 520 eastbound. Travel
east to Hwy 202 E (Redmond-Fall City
Road). Turn right and travel 10.2 miles
to Duthie Hill Road where you will turn
right. The course is located on your left.

Course Yardage & Par:
T-7000 yards, par 71. C-6700 yards, par 71. **M-6500 yards, par 71. F-5500 yards, par 71.**

Meridian Greens G. C. & D. R. (public 9 hole par 3 course)

9705 136th Street East; Puyallup, WA 98373
Phone: (253) 845-7504. **Fax:** none. **Internet:** none.
Pro: Rusty Fancher, PGA. **Superintendent:** Frank Poole.
Rating/Slope: course ratings not available. **Course record:** 25.
Green fees: W/D $12/$7; W/E $14/$9; VISA, M/C.
Power cart: not allowed. **Pull cart:** $2. **Trail fee:** not allowed.
Reservation policy: calls up to 1 week in advance, have priority.
Winter condition: the golf course is open all year long.
Terrain: flat (easy walking). **Tees:** all grass. **Spikes:** metal spikes permitted.
Services: lessons, club rentals, pro shop, covered and lighted driving range.
Comments: flat course which is easy to walk. Mount Rainier comes into view on several of the holes. Great course for every level of golfer. The golf course also has a practice putting green and a lighted, covered driving range.

Directions: from I-5 N&S take exit #127 to Hwy 512 eastbound. Travel east to the 9th St. SW exit, turn right at the first light and proceed 2 miles south on 9th St. SW. **Note:** (9th St. SW changes to 94th Ave. E) to 136th St. E where you will turn left to the course. You may also travel a little farther east on Hwy 512 to the South Hill/ Eatonville exit. Turn right on Meridian E (Hwy 161). Follow to 136th and turn right to the course right after the post office.

Course Yardage & Par:
M-1350 yards, par 29.
W-1230 yards, par 29.

Meridian Valley Golf & Country Club (private, 18 hole course)
24830 136th Avenue SE; Kent, WA 98042
Phone: (253) 631-3133. **Fax:** (253) 631-9014. **Internet:** www.meridianvalleycc.com
Pro: Greg Manley, PGA. **Superintendent:** Craig Benson.
Rating/Slope: C 72.4/134; M 70.3/130; W 73.1/129. **Record:** M 64, W 62.
Green fees: private club members & guests of members only; reciprocates.
Power cart: private club. **Pull cart:** private club. **Trail fee:** not allowed.
Reservation policy: private club members only. No outside play allowed.
Winter condition: the golf course is open all year long. Damp conditions.
Terrain: relatively hilly. **Tees:** grass. **Spikes:** no metal spikes permitted.
Services: lessons, lounge, restaurant, beer, wine, liquor, pro shop, driving range,
lockers, showers, club memberships. **Comments:** former home of the LPGA
Safeco Classic. Demanding layout with well-trapped greens, tree-lined fairways
and water. This private golf course is challenging from nearly every tee.

Directions: from I-5 N&S take exit
149 to Hwy 516 eastbound. Travel
eastbound for 7.7 miles (through Kent)
to 132nd Avenue SE. Turn north and
proceed 1.4 miles to SE 247th. Turn
east for .1 mile to 136th Avenue SE.
Turn south to the golf course.

Course Yardage & Par:
C-6652 yards, par 72.
M-6233 yards, par 72.
M-5940 yards, par 72.
W-5724 yards, par 72.

Meriwood Golf Course (public, 18 hole course)

4550 Meriwood Drive; Lacey, WA 98516 Internet: www.cybergolf.com/meriwood
For Tee-times: 1-800-55-TEE IT. (360) 412-0495. Fax: (360) 491-9091.
Dir. of Golf: Ron Coleman. Pro: Warren Orr, PGA. Supt.: Scott Brooke.
Rating/Slope: T 75.1/135; C 72.6/129; M 70.2/123; W 73.0/127. **Record:** 64.
Green fees: Monday thru Thursday $45 includes cart; Friday thru Sunday
& Hol. $53 includes cart; winter, Jr./Sr., twilight rates; M/C, VISA, AMEX.
Power cart: included in green fee. **Pull cart:** have none. **Trail fee:** not allowed.
Reservation policy: please call up to 7 days in advance for tee times.
Winter condition: the golf course is open all year long. Good conditions.
Terrain: flat, some rolling hills. **Tees:** grass. **Spikes:** spikeless April thru Sept.
Services: club rentals, lessons, lounge, coffee shop, beer, pro shop, driving
range, putting green, all grass putting course. **Comments:** this golf course has
been well received by all. This track features rolling terrain, tree lined fairways
and well bunkered greens. Excellent course that will challenge you at every turn.
Worth a special trip at any time. Professionally managed by Golf Resources NW.

Directions: from the north take exit #111 from I-5. Turn right at the light. Go approximately 125 yards and turn right on Hogum Bay Rd. Go .3 miles to Meridian Campus Entrance at Willamette Dr., go 2.2 miles to the golf course. From the south take exit #111 from I-5. Turn left at the light and go over the freeway. Proceed through stop light and follow the above directions.

Course Yardage & Par:
C-7170 yards, par 72.
M-6579/6159 yards, par 72.
W-5707/5600 yards, par 72.

Mill Creek Country Club (private, 18 hole course)

15550 Country Club Drive; Mill Creek, WA 98012
Phone: (425) 743-5664. **Fax:** (425) 338-7025. **Internet:** none.
Pro: Tom Sursley, PGA. **Superintendent:** Paul Hoffman.
Rating/Slope: C 70.8/128; M 69.8/124; W 73.0/126; W 71.7/123. **Record:** 62.
Green fees: members only; some reciprocation; no credit cards.
Power cart: private club. **Pull cart:** private club. **Trail fee:** not allowed.
Reservation policy: private club members only. No outside play allowed.
Winter condition: the golf course is open all year long. Damp conditions.
Terrain: relatively hilly. **Tees:** all grass. **Spikes:** no metal spikes in summer.
Services: club rentals, lessons, lounge, restaurant, beer, wine, liquor, pro shop, driving range, lockers, showers, club memberships. **Comments:** rolling terrain, tree-lined fairways and many hazards put emphasis on shot placement. Greens are fairly large with undulations throughout. Excellent well kept private facility.

Directions: from I-5 N&S take exit #183 to Martha Lake Road (164th St. SW). Travel eastbound for 2 miles to Mill Creek Road. Turn left and travel .3 miles to Village Green Drive. Turn left and proceed .3 miles to Country Club Drive. Turn left to the golf course.

Course Yardage & Par:
C-6331 yards, par 72.
M-6022 yards, par 72.
W-5560 yards, par 72.

Mint Valley Golf Course (public, 18 hole course)

4002 Pennsylvania Street; Longview, WA 98632
Phone: (360) 577-3395, 1-800-928-8929. Fax: none. Internet: none.
Pro: Mahlon Moe, PGA. Superintendent: Scott Knapp.
Rating/Slope: C 69.4/114; M 67.2/109; W 69.0/109. **Course record:** 63.
Green fees: Weekdays $19/$14; Weekends $24/$19; Sr. rates $14/$11 (Monday thru Sunday); winter rates/twilight rates are available 7 days a week. Jr. rates $11.50/$9.50 or Jr.'s can play for $2 after 1pm with a paid adult on the W/E.
Power cart: $24/$13. **Pull cart:** $3. **Trail fee:** $10 for personal carts.
Reservation policy: yes, call up to 1 week in advance for tee times.
Winter condition: the golf course open all year long. Excellent conditions.
Terrain: flat, very easy to walk. **Tees:** grass. **Spikes:** soft spikes required.
Services: club rentals, lessons, snack bar, beer, pro shop, driving range.
Comments: not overly long, strategically placed bunkers and lakes challenge any golfers shot making. Greens are in excellent condition and putt well. The course does play longer than the yardage would indicate. Most golfers agree "Mint Valley has matured into a challenging yet fun golf course". Worth a trip.

<u>Directions:</u> from I-5 N&S take exit # 39 or any other Longview/Kelso exit and proceed west to Highway 4 (Ocean Beach). Turn right on 38th, then turn left on Pennsylvania and proceed to the golf course. Look for signs marking your turns to the golf course the way is well marked.

Course Yardage & Par:
C-6304 yards, par 71. M-5800 yards, par 71. W-5214 yards, par 71.

Monroe Golf Course (public, 9 hole course)
22110 Old Owen Road; Monroe, WA 98272
Phone: (360) 794-8498. Fax: (360) 794-3657. Internet: www.monroegc.com
Pro/Manager: Ray Bloom, PGA. Superintendent: Ray Bloom.
Rating/Slope: M 61.8/92; W 66.4/100. **Course record:** 27.
Green fees: W/D $15/$10; W/E $18/$12. Sr. rates $16/$8.
Power cart: $20/$10. **Pull cart:** $4/$2.50. **Trail fee:** $6 per 9 holes.
Reservation policy: yes, please call in advance for tee-times. No time limit.
Winter condition: the golf course is open all year long. Dry conditions.
Terrain: flat, some slight hills. **Tees:** grass. **Spikes:** metal spikes permitted.
Services: club rentals, snack bar, pro shop, lockers, club memberships, picnic
area, putting green. **Comments:** golf course can play tight due to many trees
lining most fairways. Friendly staff and good food in the club house can make
up for any bad day on the course. Great family golf course.

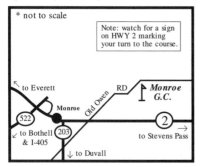

Directions: from I-405 N&S take
the exit for 522 eastbound to Hwy 2
eastbound. Travel east to Old Owen
Road, (the third light in the town of
Monroe) to the golf course. The golf
course will be on your right. **Note:** Look
for a sign on the Hwy 2 marking your
turn to the golf course.

Course Yardage & Par:
M-2451 yards, par 33; W-2451 yards, par 33.

Moses Lake Golf & Country Club (private, 18 hole course)

P.O. Drawer G; West Highway 90; Moses Lake, WA 98837
Phone: (509) 765-5049. Fax: (509) 765-5371. Internet: none.
Pro: Mike Eslick, PGA. Superintendent: Carl Thompson.
Rating/Slope: C 69.5/111; M 68.5/109; W 68.2/109. **Course record:** 63.
Green fees: private club members & guests only; reciprocates; M/C, VISA.
Power cart: private club. **Pull cart:** private club. **Trail fee:** private club.
Reservation policy: private club members & guests only. No outside play.
Winter condition: the golf course is closed from December to January.
Terrain: flat, some hills. **Tees:** all grass. **Spikes:** no metal spikes permitted.
Services: lessons, restaurant, lounge, beer, wine, pro shop, driving range.
Comments: beautiful lush green fairways and excellent putting surfaces
make this a very enjoyable course. Greens are small with hazards fronting them.
Fairways are generous and forgiving off the tee. The course is very easy to walk.

Directions: from I-90 eastbound and
westbound take the first Moses Lake exit
#174. Travel north to the golf course.

Course Yardage & Par:
C-6436 yards, par 71.
M-6187 yards, par 71.
W-5131 yards, par 71.

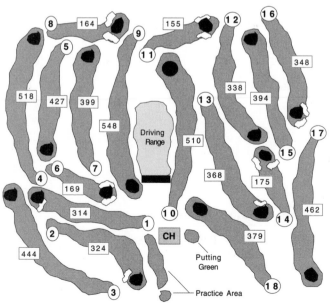

Moses Pointe Golf Resort (semi-private, 18 hole course)

4524 Westshore Drive; Moses Lake, WA 98837

Phone: (509) 764-2275. **Fax:** (509) 764-0831. **Internet:** www.mosespointe.com

Manager: Jim Tallman. **Pro:** Kelly DeShaw, PGA.

Rating/Slope: T 75.6/134; C 73.2/129; M 70.6/127; W 73.8/132. **Record:** 66.

Green fees: W/D $32/$22; W/E $42/$32; VISA, M/C, AMEX.

Power cart: $24/$14. **Pull cart:** $4/$3. **Trail fee:** $8 for personal carts.

Reservation policy: yes, call up to 7 days in advance for tee times.

Winter condition: the golf course open all year long. Very dry conditions.

Terrain: flat, some hills. **Tees:** all grass. **Spikes:** soft spikes only.

Services: club rentals, lessons, full service restaurant, snack bar, beer, wine, liquor, pro shop, lockers, driving range, putting green, chipping green.

Comments: this new course opened in July of 1999 and is one of the brightest spots on the eastern Washington golf scene. The course sports generous landing areas off the tee. Greens are firm and fast. With views of Moses Lake the Cascade Mountain's and plenty of sunshine this track is sure to please.

Directions: from I-90 eastbound and westbound take the first Moses Lake exit #174 (Mae Valley). Travel northbound for approximately 3 miles up Westshore Drive to the golf course. Look for signs that are posted at you entrance to the resort complex.

Course Yardage & Par:

T-7428 yards, par 72.
C-6889 yards, par 72.
M-6342 yards, par 72.
W-5807 yards, par 72.

LinksTime.com
a division of Book4golf.com

Mount Adams Country Club (semi-private, 18 hole course)
1250 Rocky Ford Road; Toppenish, WA 98948
Phone: (509) 865-4440. Fax: (509) 865-8975. Internet: none.
Pro: Scott Galbraith, PGA. Superintendent: Rick Cullen.
Rating/Slope: C 70.6/121; M 74.1/126; W 73.9/124. **Course record:** 65.
Green fees: $21/$14; Jr. rates, weekdays only; VISA, M/C.
Power cart: $21/$11. **Pull cart:** $2.50/$1.25. **Trail fee:** $3.
Reservation policy: yes, you may call ahead for a tee time. Call prior Thursday
for your weekend reservations. Some other times are restricted by member play.
Winter condition: the golf course is open all year long. Dry conditions.
Terrain: flat (easy walking). **Tees:** all grass. **Spikes:** soft spikes preferred.
Services: lessons, restaurant, lounge, beer, wine, pro shop, driving range.
Comments: the course features semi-wide fairways and small quick bent grass
greens that are the best greens you might putt anywhere. This Eastern Washington course has beautiful views of Mount Adams and the surrounding countryside
from many spots on the golf course. Very enjoyable golf course to play.

Directions: from I-82 eastbound take
the exit for Highway 97 southbound to
Toppenish. Continue 2 miles south of
Toppenish to the golf course. The golf
course will be located on your left hand
side. Look for signs.

Course Yardage & Par:
C-6524 yards, par 72.
M-6292 yards, par 72.
W-5831 yards, par 73.

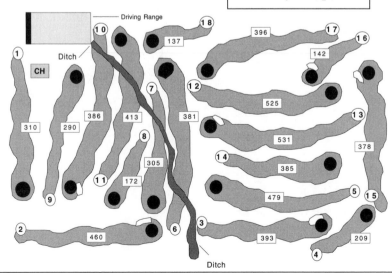

Mount Cashmere Golf Course (public, 9 hole course)

6404 Kimber; Cashmere, WA 98815

Phone: (509) 782-1207. **Fax:** (509) 782-1024. **Internet:** none.

Owners: Scammahorn Family. **Superintendent:** Paul Hansen.

Rating/Slope: the golf course is not yet rated.

Green fees: $20/$12 all week long; no credit cards.

Power cart: $15/$10. **Pull cart:** $3. **Trail fee:** $3 for personal carts.

Reservation policy: you may call ahead up to 6 days in advance.

Winter condition: the golf course is closed from November to February. During the winter months the golf course opens for cross country skiing.

Terrain: relatively hilly. **Tees:** all grass. **Spikes:** metal spikes permitted.

Services: club rentals, lessons, snack bar, pro shop, driving range.

Comments: the fairways at Mt. Cashmere are bordered by apple and cherry trees. The course is set among beautiful hills and orchards. Be sure to call ahead for your tee-times as the course can be busy during the summer months. RV parking is available at the Chelan Co. Fairground for those spending the night.

Directions: the course is located through Cashmere. Follow Old Highway West (approximately 1 mile). Look for "Fairgrounds" signs. The course is located .25 miles west of the Fairgrounds at the end of Kimber Road.

Course Yardage & Par:
M-2600 yards, par 35.
W-2400 yards, par 35.

Mount Si Golf Course (public, 18 hole course)

9010 Boalch Avenue SE; P.O. Box 2020; Snoqualmie, WA 98065
Phone: (425) 391-4926 or (425) 888-1541. Fax (425) 888-7079.
Pros: John Sanford, PGA, Matt Campbell, PGA, Ron Lee, PGA.
Superintendent: Mike Moore.   Internet: mtsigolf.com
Rating/Slope: C 68.5/114; M 67.3/111; W 69.5/109. **Course record:** 62.
Green fees: W/D $29/$17; W/E $35/$20; Jr /Sr $24/$16 (M-Th) & winter rates.
Power cart: $24/$14. **Pull cart** $4/$3. **Trail fee:** $5 for personal carts.
Reservation policy: yes, please call ahead for your Tee-time. No restrictions.
Winter condition: the golf course is open all year long. Dry conditions.
Terrain: flat, some hills. **Tees:** grass. **Spikes:** metal spikes permitted.
Services: club rentals, lessons, junior golf program, snack bar, restaurant, beer,
wine, liquor, lockers, pro shop, driving range, putting & chipping green.
Comments: Scenic setting near the base of Mt. Si. Course offers a full service
restaurant with fantastic views. Greens are well kept, large and putt well. If you
are looking for a good course with a friendly staff Mount Si is sure to please.

Directions: From I-90 eastbound take
exit #27. At the stop sign turn left and go
1 mile to a left turn lane for "Snoqualmie
Falls". Turn left, following the
"Snoqualmie Falls" sign until you reach a
traffic light. Continue straight through the
light, past Mount Si High School to Park
Street. Turn right onto Park Street. The
course will be 1 mile ahead on your left.

Course Yardage & Par:
C-6261 yards, par 72.
M-6008 yards, par 72.
W-5475 yards, par 72.

New World Golf Center (public, 9 hole par 3 course)

5022 Guide Meridian; Bellingham, WA 98226
Phone: (360) 398-1362. Fax: none. Internet: none.
Golf Instructor: in season only. Superintendent: none.
Rating/Slope: the golf course is not rated. **Course record:** 22.
Green fees: $8/$6 all week long; Sr. rates; no credit cards.
Power cart: none. **Pull cart:** none. **Trail fee:** personal carts are not allowed.
Reservation policy: advance reservations not required, first come first served.
Winter condition: the golf course is closed from November to March.
Terrain: flat, some slight hills. **Tees:** all grass. **Spikes:** metal spikes permitted.
Services: club rentals, limited pro shop, pop, covered driving range.
Comments: fair par 3 golf course with medium to small sized greens. A creek
runs through 2 and 9 and does present some challenges. The complex also has
a covered driving range for those wanting to practice their iron play on.

Directions: From I-5 N&S take exit #256
to Meridian Street. Proceed north on
Hwy 539N for 3 miles to the golf course
on your right hand side of the highway.
Look for a sign indicating your turn.

Course Yardage & Par:
M-947 yards, par 27.
W-947 yards, par 27.

Newaukum Valley Golf Course (public, 27 hole course)

153 Newaukum Golf Drive; Chehalis, WA 98532
Phone: (360) 748-0461. Fax: (360) 748-9544. Internet: book4golf.com
Manager: Alan Browning. Superintendent: Scott Date.
Rating/Slope: West/South C 69.9/113; M 68.0/108; W 70.6/112. **Record:** 62.
Green fees: W/D $17/$12; W/E $23/$15; Sr. & Jr. rates; M/C, VISA.
Power cart: $20/$10. **Pull cart:** $3/$2. **Trail fee:** $6 for personal carts.
Reservation policy: call in advance for tee times from March to September.
Winter condition: the golf course is open all year long. Dry conditions.
Terrain: flat, some hills. **Tees:** all grass. **Spikes:** soft spikes preferred.
Services: club rentals, restaurant, beer, wine, pro shop, putting green.
Comments: A full irrigation system keeps the course in great shape all year round. Good public golf course that expanded to 27 holes in March of 1996. Greens are large and have very good putting surfaces. This new layout is much more user friendly and enjoyable. Good public track at very affordable prices.

Directions: from I-5 N&S take exit # 76 to 13th St. Go east on 13th to Market St. Turn right on Market which becomes Jackson Highway. Follow for 4 miles to the golf course. Look for signs.

Course Yardage & Par:
West Course: C-3268 yards, M-3087 yards, W-2847 yards, par 36.
South Course: C-3223 yards, W-2981 yards, W-2672 yards, par 36.
East Course: C-2945 yards, M-2813 yards, W-2440 yards, par 36.

Rating/Slope:
South/East: C 68.5/109; M 66.8/105; W 68.3/108.
East/West: C 68.4/109; M 67.0/105; W 68.9/110.

Nile Golf & Country Club (semi-private, 18 hole course)
6601 204th SW; Mountlake Terrace, WA 98043
Phone: (425) 776-5154. Fax: (425) 672-1833. Internet: none.
Pro: Randy Puetz, PGA. Superintendent: Davis Korsmoe.
Rating/Slope: M 64.0/104; W 65.4/105. **Course record:** 64.
Green fees: Shriners $15/$10; guests $28/$17; M/C, VISA.
Power cart: $22/$12. **Pull cart:** $3. **Trail fee:** $5 for personal carts.
Reservation policy: members may call up to 1 week in advance for tee times.
The public may call ahead 3 days and reserve times on a "space available basis".
Winter condition: the golf course is open all year long. Good drainage.
Terrain: flat, some hills. **Tees:** all grass. **Spikes:** soft spikes preferred.
Services: lessons, well stocked pro shop, club repair, putting green.
Comments: short, but a test of skill for all players. This beautifully tree-lined
well bunkered course is a joy to play. The new layout has no two holes that are
the same. Be sure to play the Nile while the public is allowed to play.

Directions: from I-5 N&S take exit # 177
to 244th SW-205th St-Hwy 104W. Travel
westbound for .3 miles to the golf course
entrance, which will be on your right.
Note: Look for the Nile Temple entrance
and this will take you into the grounds of
the golf course and clubhouse

Course Yardage & Par:
M-4786/5001 yards, par 66/67.
W-4382/4578 yards, par 66/67.

Nisqually Valley Golf Course (public, 18 hole course)
15425 Mosman Street SW; Yelm, WA 98597
Phone: (360) 458-3332, 800-352-2645. Fax: none. Internet: none.
Pro: Eric Olsen, PGA. Superintendent: Al Simpson
Rating/Slope: C 68.0/113; M 67.1/111; W 71.4/115. **Course record:** 62.
Green fees: W/D $17/$10; W/E $20; Jr & Sr rates $10/$5 (M-F).
Power cart: $15/$8. **Pull cart:** $2. **Trail fee:** none.
Reservation policy: yes, up to 2 weeks in advance, for weekends times only.
Winter condition: the golf course is open all year long. Fair conditions.
Terrain: flat, some hills. **Tees:** all grass. **Spikes:** soft spikes preferred.
Services: club rentals, lessons, lounge, restaurant, beer, wine, liquor, pro shop.
Comments: very dry and easy to walk golf course that has very few hazards.
Very scenic course with beautiful views of Mount Rainier and the surrounding
countryside. Good public golf course that has excellent greens all year round.

Directions: from I-5 N&S take exit
111 onto Hwy 510 and travel southeast
toward the town of Yelm. When in Yelm
turn right on Edwards Street (at
McDonalds). Proceed on Edwards Street
for .6 miles to Mosman Street where you
will turn to the golf course. Look for
signs indicating your turn to the course.

Course Yardage & Par:
C-6007 yards, par 72.
M-5815 yards, par 72.
W-5751 yards, par 72.

North Bellingham Public Golf Course (public, 18 hole course)

205 West Smith Road; Bellingham, WA 98226 **Internet:** www.nbellinghamgc.com
Phone: (360) 398-8300; 888-322-6242. **Fax:** (360) 398-2523.
Pro: Nathan Vickers, PGA. **Superintendent:** Duane Zander.
Rating/Slope: C 72.2/125; M 69.1/119; W 68.9/112. **Course record:** 65.
Green fees: W/D $35/$20 (+tax); W/E $38/$22 (+tax); M/C, VISA.
Power cart: $12/$8 (per person). **Pull cart:** $3. **Trail fee:** not allowed.
Reservation policy: please call up to 1 week in advance for tee times.
Winter condition: the course is open all year long, weather permitting. Dry.
Terrain: flat, some rolling hills. **Tees:** grass. **Spikes:** soft spikes only.
Services: club rentals, lessons, lounge, restaurant, beer, wine, liquor, pro shop,
driving range, putting green. **Comments:** newer public golf course. The course
is of championship caliber and length. From the back tees the course plays 6800
yards and is demanding. Ponds, grass and sand bunkers dot the entire course.

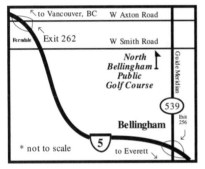

Directions: from I-5 N take exit #256
(Guide Meridian, Hwy 539). Proceed
north on Hwy 539 until you reach W
Smith Road. Turn left on W Smith Road
and proceed to course entrance on your
left hand side. From I-5 S take exit #262
W Axton Rd. Proceed east on W Axton
Rd. to Guide Meridian Hwy 539. Turn
right on Hwy 539. Proceed to W Smith
Rd. where you will turn right to the golf
course located on your left hand side.

Course Yardage & Par:

C-6816 yards, par 72.
M-6179 yards, par 72.
W-5160 yards, par 72.

LinksTime.com
a division of Book4golf.com

North Shore Golf Course (public, 18 hole course)

4101 North Shore Boulevard NE; Tacoma, WA 98422
Phone: (253) 927-1375, 800-447-1375. Fax: (253) 838-5898.
Pro: David Wetli, PGA. Superintendent: Michael Tight.
Rating/Slope: C 70.3/129; M 69.1/126; W 71.4/123. **Course record:** 65.
Green fees: Monday-Tuesday $20/$12.33*; Wednesday-Thursday $25/$15*;
Friday-Sunday $30/$15; twi-lite rates $18* (*add tax fees); VISA, M/C, AMEX.
Power cart: $24/$12*. **Pull cart:** $3*. **Trail fee:** $24/$12* (*add tax to all fees).
Reservation policy: yes, call up to 1 week in advance for your tee-times.
Winter condition: the golf course is open all year long. Dry conditions.
Terrain: relatively hilly. **Tees:** all grass. **Spikes:** soft spikes preferred.
Services: club rentals, lessons, snack bar, lounge, restaurant, beer, wine, liquor,
well stocked pro shop, lighted and covered driving range, banquet, tournament
facilities available. **Comments:** sand bunkers, water hazards and undulating
terrain make this course a true challenge. Greens are medium to large in size.
This golf course is worth a special trip anytime. The Northshore pro shop was
voted for the ninth straight year as one of the countries top pro shops by Golf
Shop Operations magazine. Excellent golf course that is well run and fun to play.

Directions: from I-5 N&S take exit
142B. Travel westbound for 5 miles.
Turn left on Nassau Avenue. Travel for
1/2 mile to Oakmont. Turn left. Take the
next left onto Northshore Blvd. The golf
course will be 1/10 mile ahead on your
right hand side. Look for signs the roads
to the golf course are well marked.

Course Yardage &Par:
C-6305 yards, par 71.
M-6039 yards, par 71.
W-5442 yards, par 73.

Oakbrook Golf & Country Club (private, 18 hole course)

8102 Zircon Drive SW; Tacoma, WA 98498
Phone: (253) 584-8770. **Fax:** (253) 581-3397. **Internet:** www.oakbrookgncc.com
Pro: to be determined. **Superintendent:** Jay Griswold.
Rating/Slope: B 72.5/130; W 70.5/125; R 73.8/128; Y 70.6/120. **Record:** 60.
Green fees: private club, members & guests only; reciprocates.
Power cart: private club. **Pull cart:** private club. **Trail fee:** not allowed.
Reservation policy: private club members & guests only. No outside play.
Winter condition: the golf course is open all year long. Dry conditions.
Terrain: flat, some hills. **Tees:** grass. **Spikes:** no metal spikes permitted.
Services: club rentals, lessons, lounge, beer, wine, liquor, lockers, showers,
pro shop, driving range. **Comments:** narrow tree-lined fairways and many
sand bunkers routinely challenge any golfer's game. Greens tend to get firm in
the summer months and can be hard to hold. Excellent private golf course.

Directions: from I-5 N&S take exit #129 to S 74th. Go west for 2.3 miles, then S 74th will become Custer Road. Continue to 88th St. Turn right on 88th. 88th becomes Steilacoom. At your second light turn right on Phillips. Stay on Phillips until you come to the end of the arterial (sign). Turn left on Turquoise. At the first stop sign turn right on Zircon. Stay on Zircon and this should lead to the clubhouse.

Course Yardage &Par:

Blue-6658 yards, par 71.
White-6268 yards, par 71.
Yellow-5774 yards, par 72.
Red-5220 yards, par 72.

Oaksridge Golf Course (public, 18 hole course)

1052 Monte-Elma Road; Elma, WA 98541
Phone: (360) 482-3511. Fax: (360) 482-5060. Internet: none.
Pro: Rich Walker, PGA. Superintendent: Rick Denholm.
Rating/Slope: M 65.3/100; W 68.9/108. **Course record: 61.**
Green fees: $17/$10 all week long; Jr. & Sr. rates $12/$6 (M-F); VISA, MC.
Power cart: $16/$9. **Pull cart:** $2. **Trail fee:** $5 for personal carts.
Reservation policy: yes, taken for weekends and holidays only.
Winter condition: the golf course is open all year long, weather permitting.
Terrain: flat. **Tees:** all grass. **Spikes:** metal spikes permitted.
Services: club rentals, lessons, pro shop, driving range, club memberships.
Comments: course is easy to walk and has few hazards. Fairways are tree-lined and fairly wide. For the senior golfer this course is very friendly. During the week it offers discounted rates on green fees to all seniors and juniors.

Directions: from I-5 N&S take exit # 104 to Hwy 101 and continue to Hwy 8 westbound. Proceed to Highway 12 westbound. Follow past the town of Elma and turn right on Schouweiler Road. (Watch for your turn because it can come up very quickly). At Monte-Elma Road turn west to the golf course which will be located on your left. **Note:** you will be able to see the course from Highway 12.

Course Yardage & Par:
M-5643 yards, par 70.
W-5423 yards, par 72.

Oasis Park Par 3 (public, 9 hole par 3 course)

2541 Basin Street SW; Ephrata, WA 98823
Phone: (509) 754-5102. **Fax: same as phone number. Internet: none.**
Owners: Mike & Patti Donovan.
Rating/Slope: the golf course is not rated. **Course record:** 23.
Green fees: $5; all day pass $9; Jr & Sr rates are available.
Power cart: not available. **Pull cart:** $1.50. **Trail fee:** not allowed.
Reservation policy: reservations are not needed or required.
Winter condition: the golf course is closed from November to mid-March.
Terrain: flat, some hills. **Tees:** grass. **Spikes:** metal spikes permitted.
Services: club rentals, vending machines, limited pro shop.
Comments: Treed, well groomed & challenging par 3 course. Holes are fairly short in length. RV parking is available for those wanting to stay at the park.

<u>Directions:</u> the course is located 1 mile south of Ephrata on the west side of Hwy 28. Look for signs to the golf course.

Course Yardage & Par:
M-930 yards, par 27.
W-930 yards, par 27.

Ocean Shores Golf Course (public, 18 hole course)

Box 369; 500 Canal Drive; Ocean Shores, WA 98569
Phone: (360) 289-3357. Fax: (360) 289-0149. Internet: none.
Pros: Ronnie Espedal, PGA, Curt Zander, PGA.
Rating/Slope: C 70.2/115; M 68.8/113; W 69.6./115. **Course record:** 66.
Green fees: $27/$16 everday; Sr. rates $20/$10 (M-F); winter rates; M/C, VISA.
Power cart: $22/$14. **Pull cart:** $3. **Trail fee:** $7.50/$5 for personal carts.
Reservation policy: call in advance for tee times. No time limit on reservations.
Winter condition: the golf course is open all year long. Dry conditions.
Terrain: flat (easy walking). **Tees:** all grass. **Spikes:** metal spikes permitted.
Services: club rentals, lessons, snack bar, beer, wine, liquor, pro shop, club
memberships, putting & chipping greens. **Comments:** back nine very wooded,
front nine winds by the ocean, a very distinctive setting. The golf course can play
very tough at times especially if the wind picks up. Excellent facility that is very
popular with the summer crowd that vacations at the ocean. Ocean Shores is a
fantastic winter course because it drains well and stays very dry.

Directions: from I-5 N&S take exit
#104 to Hwy 101. Follow Hwy 101 to
Aberdeen/Ocean Beaches. Proceed to
Hwy 109. Exit to Hwy 115 southbound
and follow the signs to the golf course.
The course is located on the Washington
coast. **Note:** Keep following the signs to
Ocean Beaches and this will get you to
Aberdeen then Ocean Shores.

Course Yardage & Par:

M-6252 yards, par 71.
W-5173 yards, par 72.

Odessa Golf Club (public, 9 hole course)
off of Highway 28; Box 621; Odessa, WA 99159
Phone: (509) 982-0093. Fax: none. Internet: none.
Manager: Gary Valenta. Superintendent: Gary Valenta.
Rating/Slope: M 68.8/113; W 72.3/112. **Course record:** 67.
Green fees: Weekdays $15/$10; Weekends & Holidays $17.50/$11;
All day rates: Weekdays $18, W/E's & Holidays $20 all day; M/C, VISA, DIS.
Power cart: $5 per person per 9 holes. **Pull cart:** $2. **Trail fee:** $5.
Reservation policy: yes, you may call ahead for a tee time, no restrictions.
Winter condition: the golf course is closed from Novemeber to February.
Terrain: relatively hilly. **Tees:** all grass. **Spikes:** metal spikes permitted.
Services: club rentals, snack bar, beer, pro shop, putting green, discounted
RV hook-ups for golfers. **Comments:** a tough medium length golf course
with elevated greens and wide fairways. This track has excellent greens during
the peak golfing season. Adjacent to the golf course is RV parking with full
hook-ups. Odessa is a great bargain for those wanting to stay and play!!!

Directions: from I-90 take the exit #206
for Hwy 21 northbound to Odessa. Travel
north to Odessa and once in Odessa exit
to Hwy 28 westbound to the golf course.
The golf course is located west of the city
limits on Hwy 28. Look for signs.

Course Yardage & Par:
M-3070 yards, par 36.
W-2894 yards, par 37.
<u>**Dual tees for 18 holes:**</u>
M-6248 yards, par 72.
W-5885 yards, par 74.

Okanogan Valley Golf Club (semi-private, 9 hole course)

Golf Course Drive; Box 1692; Omak, WA 98841
Phone: (509) 826-6937. Fax: (509) 826-4043. Internet: none.
Pro: Bill Sproule, PGA. Superintendent: none.
Rating/Slope: M 69.2/117; W 72.7/125. **Course record:** 65.
Green fees: W/D 15/$10; W/E $20/$15; no credit cards.
Power cart: $20/$11. **Pull cart:** $1.50. **Trail fee:** no charge.
Reservation policy: yes, call 4 days in advance for a tee times.
Winter condition: the course is closed from mid-October to mid-March.
Terrain: flat, some hills. **Tees:** grass. **Spikes:** soft spikes preferred.
Services: club rentals, lessons, snack bar, beer, pro shop, putting/chipping green.
Comments: closed to the public Wednesday, men only, Thursday am women only. Rated by the *National Golf Foundation* as one of the top 9 hole courses in the state. Well layed out track with water and sand coming into play throughout. Greens are on the small size with tricky undulations. Great eastern Wa. course.

Directions: the golf course is located between Omak and Okanogan. From southbound Hwy 97 take the Hwy 215 exit and enter Omak. Note the signs and turns to the course southwest of town.

Course Yardage & Par:
M-3040 yards, par 35.
W-2955 yards, par 38.
<u>**Dual tees for 18 holes:**</u>
M-6152 yards, par 70.
W-5880 yards, par 76.

Olympia Country & Golf Club (private, 18 hole course)
3636 Country Club Drive NW; Olympia, WA 98502
Phone: (360) 866-9777. Fax: (360) 866-2058. Internet: none.
Pro: Scott Smith, PGA. Superintendent: Matt Schuldt.
Rating/Slope: C 69.6/116; M 68.6/114; W 70.7/123. **Course record:** 63.
Green fees: private club members & guests only; reciprocates.
Power cart: private club. **Pull cart:** private club. **Trail fee:** private club.
Reservation policy: members only club no public play is allowed.
Winter condition: the golf course is open all year long. Damp conditions.
Terrain: very hilly. **Tees:** all grass. **Spikes:** soft spikes preferred.
Services: lessons, lounge, restaurant, beer, wine, liquor, beverages, pro shop,
showers, club memberships, driving range, chipping and putting greens.
Comments: the front nine is short and tricky demanding shot placement from
the tee. The back nine is long and more difficult. Small greens are well bunkered
and can be hard to hold and fast in peak season. Excellent private facility.

Directions: from I-5 N&S take exit
#104 to Hwy 101 to the Port Angeles-
Aberdeen. Follow to the Black Lake-
West Olympia exit. Turn right off the
exit to Cooper Point Road. Turn left
and travel 4 miles to the golf course.

Course Yardage & Par:
C-6048 yards, par 71.
M-5801 yards, par 71.
W-5265 yards, par 74.
W-5313 yards, par 75.

Orcas Island Golf Course (public, 9 hole course)
2171 Orcas Road; East Sound, WA 98245
Phone: (360) 376-4400. Fax: (360) 376-8204. Internet: http//www.orcasisle.com/golf/
Manager: Chantelle Blake. Superintendent: to be determined.
Rating/Slope: C 70.6/117; M 67.1/114; W 71.1/114. **Course record:** 65.
Green fees: $30/$22 all week long; no special rates; M/C, VISA.
Power cart: $20/$15. **Pull cart:** $3. **Trail fee:** $5 for personal carts.
Reservation policy: yes, call in advance, no restrictions on tee times.
Winter condition: the golf course is open all year long. Dry, drains well.
Terrain: relatively hilly. **Tees:** all grass. **Spikes:** soft spikes only.
Services: club rentals $8, snack bar, pro shop, club memberships, putting green.
Comments: the golf course is set in the scenic San Juan Islands, a very popular area for vacationers in the summer months. The track features hilly terrain, water and bunkers. One of the best kept secrets in the entire northwest region.

Directions: take the Anacortes ferry to Orcas Island. From the terminal in Orcas follow Horseshoe Hwy toward Eastsound. The golf course is approximately 10 minutes from the ferry landing. Turn right at Sunderland Road for the entrance to the golf course.

Course Yardage & Par:
M-3060 yards, par 36.
W-3000 yards, par 37.
Dual tees for 18 holes:
M-5803 yards, par 71.
W-5464 yards, par 73.

Orchard Hills Golf & Country Club (private, 18 hole course)

605 39th Street; Washougal, WA 98671
Phone: (360) 835-5444. Fax: (360) 835-0104. Internet: none.
Pro: Rick Edwards, PGA. Superintendent: Mike Combs.
Rating/Slope: C 68.7/117; M 67.8/116; W 70.6/121. **Course record:** 62.
Green fees: private club members & guests only; reciprocates; M/C, VISA.
Power cart: private club. **Pull cart:** private club. **Trail fee:** private club.
Reservation policy: private club members & guests only. No outside play.
Winter condition: the golf course is open all year long. Dry conditions.
Terrain: relatively hilly. **Tees:** grass. **Spikes:** soft spikes required.
Services: lessons, snack bar, lounge, restaurant, beer, wine, liquor, pro shop, lockers, showers, club memberships, driving range, putting & chipping greens.
Comments: the front nine is flat, easy to walk and sports narrow tree lined fairways. The back nine is more wide open but plays much longer than the yardage indicates. Greens are well bunkered with some being fronted by water.

Directions: from I-5 southbound take exit # 7 to I-205 southbound. Travel south to exit # 27, Hwy 14E. Travel eastbound to the Washougal exit. Follow the signs to "E" St. and proceed 1.5 miles to 39th. Turn left on 39th to the golf course.

Course Yardage & Par:
C-5896 yards, par 70.
M-5722yards, par 70.
W-5405 yards, par 73.

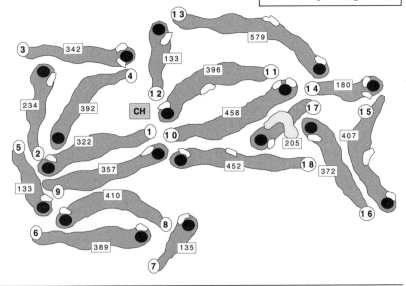

Oroville Golf Club (public, 9 hole course)

3468-A Nighthawk Road; Oroville, WA 98844
Phone: (509) 476-2390. Fax: (509) 476-2408. Internet: none.
Manager: Dolly Sneve. Superintendent: Cindy Boyer.
Rating/Slope: M 69.1/125; W 74.0/126. Course record: 62.
Green fees: W/D $16/$12; W/E $20/$15; no special rates; VISA, M/C.
Power cart: $10 per 9 holes. **Pull cart:** $2. **Trail fee:** $7 for personal carts.
Reservation policy: yes, you may call ahead for a tee time. No restrictions.
Winter condition: the golf course is closed from November to February.
Terrain: relatively hilly. **Tees:** grass. **Spikes:** soft spikes preferred.
Services: club rentals, snack bar, beer, pro shop, putting & chipping greens.
Comments: the course is well-conditioned with dual tees for those wanting a different look for their second nine. Fairways are tree-lined but fairly open and there are a few sand traps which enter play on approach shots. Good 9 hole track. Be sure to call well in advance for your tee times as this course gets very busy.

Directions: from Highway 2 westbound cut-off at Highway 97 northbound via Hwy 17 northbound. Travel north to Oroville and Nighthawk Road. Turn left and proceed 2 miles to the golf course. Look for signs marking your way to the golf course.

Course Yardage & Par:
M-2897 yards, par 36.   W-2897 yards, par 37.   <u>Dual tees for 18 holes:</u>   M-5938 yards, par 72.   W-5938 yards, par 74.

Othello Golf Club (public, 9 hole course)

West Bench Road; P.O. Box 185; Othello, WA 99344
Phone: (509) 488-2376. Fax: (509) 488-1457. Internet: none.
Pro & Owner: Doug Buck, PGA. Superintendent: Kevin Stickel.
Rating/Slope: M 68.6/115; W 74.2/123. **Course record:** 61.
Green fees: W/D $17/$10; W/E $19/$12; M/C, VISA.
Power cart: $20/$10. **Pull cart:** $2. **Trail fee:** $5 for personal carts.
Reservation policy: you may call 2 days in advance for a tee time.
Winter condition: dry, course closed sometimes in December and January.
Terrain: flat, easy walking. **Tees:** grass. **Spikes:** no metal spikes permitted.
Services: club rentals, lessons, restaurant, lounge, beer, wine, liquor, pro shop,
lockers, showers, driving range. **Comments:** the course features many mature
trees lining the fairways. Bunkers front many of the greens that are medium to
large in size. Designed by the Trent Jones Corporation this golf course is kept
immaculate. For those traveling in an RV the course provides plenty of spaces.

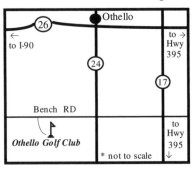

Directions: from Hwy 17 take the exit
for Bench Road. Travel west to the golf
course. The golf course will be located
on your left. The course is located 2
miles SW of Othello. Look for signs.

Course Yardage & Par:
M-3066 yards, par 35. **W-3066 yards, par 36.**

Overlake Golf & Country Club (private, 18 hole course)
8000 NE 16th; Bellevue, WA 98004
Phone: (425) 454-5031. **Fax:** (425) 451-3598. **Internet: none.**
Pro: Ron Hoetmer, PGA. Superintendent: Jeff Gullikson
Rating/Slope: C 71.2/127; M 69.6/123; M 67.8/117; W 65.8/113. **Record:** 61.
Green fees: private club members & their guests; reciprocates; M/C, VISA.
Power cart: private club. **Pull cart:** complimentary. **Trail fee:** not allowed.
Reservation policy: private club members only. No outside play allowed.
Winter condition: the golf course is open all year long. Damp conditions.
Terrain: flat, some hills. **Tees:** all grass. **Spikes:** soft spikes preferred.
Services: club rentals, lessons, snack bar, lounge, restaurant, beer, wine, liquor,
pro shop, club memberships, driving range, putting and chipping greens.
Comments: the course is relatively flat, well bunkered and fairly wide open.
Greens are fast and always in excellent condition. This track can play very tough
during the summer months. Past host to the Fred Couples Invitational.

Directions: from I-5 N&S take exit
#168B to Hwy 520E. Travel east to the
84th Avenue NE exit. Take the exit and
go south for 1 mile to NE 12th. On 12th
travel west for .5 miles to Evergreen
Point Road. Turn north and travel to NE
16th. On 16th proceed east to the golf
course. Look for a small sign at the turn.

Course Yardage & Par:
C-6556 yards, par 71.
M-6150 yards, par 71.
M-5709 yards, par 71.
W-5709 yards, par 73.

Overlook Golf Course (public, 9 hole course)

1753 State Highway 9; Mount Vernon, WA 98273
Phone: (360) 422-6444. Fax: none. Internet: none.
Manager/Owner/Superintendent: Neil Hansen.
Rating/Slope: C 61.2/101; M 60.4/97; W 60.6/96. **Course record:** 59.
Green fees: W/D $17/$10; W/E $20/$12; Sr rates (weekdays); no credit cards.
Power cart: $19/$10. **Pull cart:** $2. **Trail fee:** no charge for personal carts.
Reservation policy: yes, you may call 14 days in advance for tee times.
Winter condition: the golf course is open all year long. Fair conditions.
Terrain: flat, some hills. **Tees:** grass. **Spikes:** metal spikes permitted.
Services: club rentals, snack bar, lounge, beer, pro shop, putting green.
Comments: very friendly, family-owned facility that is fun for all. The golf
course is fairly open with lovely views of Big Lake and the surrounding moun-
tains. The course features elevated tees, small greens and fairly wide open
fairways. This course is not a back-breaker so enjoy the peaceful area.

Directions: from I-5 N&S take exit
#227 to Hwy 538 eastbound in Mount
Vernon. Travel east to Hwy 9. Turn
southbound and continue to Big Lake
and the golf course. The golf course is
located 7 miles from I-5. Look for signs
marking your turn to the parking lot.

Course Yardage & Par:
C-2213 yards, par 33.
M-2026 yards, par 33.
W-1809 yards, par 33.

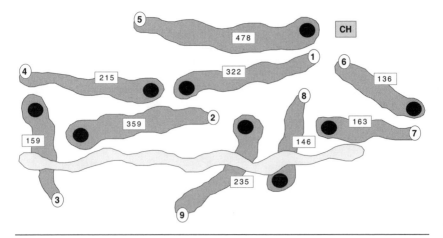

Painted Hills Golf Club (public, 9 hole course)

South 4403 Dishman-Mica; Spokane, WA 99206
Phone: (509) 928-4653. Fax: (509) 927-8825. Internet:www.spokanegolf.com
Teaching Pro: Patti Marquis. Superintedent: Ron Ridl.
Rating/Slope: M 70.2/113; W 69.0/110. **Course record:** 63.
Green fees: W/D $16/$12; W/E $18/$12; Jr. & Sr. rates Monday thru Thursday.
Power cart: $6 per 9 holes. **Pull cart:** $3. **Trail fee:** $4 for personal carts.
Reservation policy: yes, call ahead for a tee time. No restrictions.
Winter condition: the golf course is open all year long. Dry conditions.
Terrain: flat (easy walking). **Tees:** all grass. **Spikes:** no metal spikes permitted.
Services: lessons, club rentals, restaurant, pro shop, putting green, range.
Comments: beautiful fairways, sand traps and water come into play. A well-conditioned golf course. Quality rental clubs for traveling executives. Great golf course that plays tough. This course is worth a trip if you are in the area.

Directions: from I-90 E&W take the Argonne/Dishman exit #287 and travel 5 miles south to the golf course. Argonne Road will become Dishman-Mica Hwy just south of Sprague Road.

Course Yardage & Par:
M-3288 yards, par 36.
W-2621 yards, par 36.
Dual tees for 18 holes:
M-6532 yards, par 72.
W-5417 yards, par 73.

Pasco Golfland (public, 9 hole par 3 course)
2901 Road 40; Pasco, WA 99301
Phone: (509) 544-9291. Fax: (509) 544-0355. Internet: none.
Pro: Jeff Hendler, PGA. Superintendent: Bill McIntyre.
Rating/Slope: the course is not rated. **Course record:** 47.
Green fees: $9 all week long; VISA, M/C.
Power cart: not available. **Pull cart:**$2. **Trail fee:** no charge.
Reservation policy: please call ahead for a tee time during the summer.
Winter condition: the course will be closed during inclement weather.
Terrain: flat. **Tees:** grass and mats. **Spikes:** soft spikes preferred.
Services: club rentals, lessons, club repair, pro shop, driving range.
Comments: the par 3 course is open and waiting for you to come bring the family! Dual tees are available for a full 18 hole round of golf. Be sure to heed the warnings of the out of bounds and do not retrieve your balls from the driving range area. Good practice center that will help improve your entire game.

Directions: from I-182 take the 20th Avenue exit. Proceed north to Argent. Left on Argent to Road 40. The range and course is located on your right hand side. Look for signs.

Course Yardage & Par:
M-1103 yards, par 27.
W-1103 yards, par 27.

Pend Oreille Golf & Country Club (public, 9 hole course)
off of Hwy 31; Box 97; Metaline Falls, WA 99153
Phone: no phone. Fax: none. Internet: none.
Pro: none. Manager: none.
Rating/Slope: the golf course is not rated. **Course record:** 27.
Green fees: $1; $1.50 weekends; students play for free; no credit cards.
Power cart: none. **Pull cart:** none. **Trail fee:** none.
Reservation policy: none needed. First come first served.
Winter condition: the golf course is closed from October to April.
Terrain: flat, some hills. **Tees:** grass. **Spikes:** metal spikes permitted.
Services: none. Bring your snacks, lunch, etc.
Comments: the course is on the honor system. Greens fees are placed in a honor box. The course features sand greens, rake before and after putting. The golf course has changed from 6 to 9 holes in the last few years. This course is on the rough side to say the least.

Directions: the golf course is located 4 miles north of Metaline Falls off of Hwy 31. Note the golf course/gun club sign for the turn off. Take the road second from the right to the golf course.

Course Yardage & Par:
M-2183 yards, par 31.
W-2183 yards, par 40.

Peninsula Golf Club (private, 18 hole course)
824 South Lindberg Road; Port Angeles, WA 98362
Phone: (360) 457-6501. **Fax:** (360) 457-6501. **Internet:** cmrepass@olympus.net
Pro: Chris Repass, PGA. **Superintendent:** Merle Pearce.
Rating/Slope: C 70.3/122; M 69.1/119; W 70.3/120. **Record:** 62.
Green fees: private club members and guests only; reciprocates. M/C, VISA.
Power cart: private club. **Pull cart:** private club. **Trail fee:** private club.
Reservation policy: yes, up to 1 week in advance for members. Private club
Winter condition: the golf course is open all year long.
Terrain: very hilly. **Tees:** all grass. **Spikes:** metal spikes allowed.
Services: club rentals, lessons, snack bar, lounge, restaurant, beer, wine, liquor,
pro shop, driving range. **Comments:** beautiful view of the mountains and the
Strait of Juan de Fuca. This private course which used to be open to the public
is near downtown Port Angeles and sports many unique features. Some of the
holes are cut into a hillside offering a wide variety of lies in the fairway.

Directions: from Hwy 101. When you
are first entering Port Angeles turn on
Golf Course Road (south toward the
mountains) and proceed .6 miles
to Lindberg Road. Turn left on Lindberg
Road and proceed to the golf course.

Course Yardage & Par:
C-6308 yards, par 72.
M-6235 yards, par 72.
M-5929 yards, par 72.
W-5480 yards, par 72.

Peninsula Golf Course (public, 9 hole hole course)

9604 Pacific Highway; P.O. Box 675; Ocean Park, WA 98640
Phone: (360) 642-2828. Fax: none. Internet: none.
Manager: Brad Suchy. Superintendent: Brad Suchy.
Rating/Slope: M 59.9/90; W 64.2/100. Course record: 27.
Green fees: $17/$11 all week long; VISA, M/C, DISCOVER, AMEX.
Power cart: $17/$11. **Pull cart:** $2. **Trail fee:** $3 for personal carts.
Reservation policy: please call in advance for tee times. No time limit.
Winter condition: the golf course is open all year long, damp conditions.
Terrain: flat (easy walking). **Tees:** grass. **Spikes:** soft spikes preferred.
Services: club rentals, snack bar, small pro shop, putting green.
Comments: located in picturesque Long Beach on the Washington coast, this
course is very flat and easy to walk. Fairways are narrow in scope but greens
have generous landing areas. A great location for a relaxing round of golf.

Directions: from I-5 N&S take exit #104
to Hwy 101 W. Follow 101 westbound
to Long Beach. As you approach the
peninsula turn right on Highway 103
northbound through Seaview. Proceed for
3 miles. The golf course is located just
beyond the northern city limits.

Course Yardage & Par:
M-2057 yards, par 33.
W-2057 yards, par 33.
Dual tees for 18 holes:
M-4213 yards, par 65.
W-4213 yards, par 65.

Pine Acres Par 3 Golf Course (public, 9 hole par 3 course)

11912 North Division; Spokane, WA 99218
Phone: (509) 466-9984. **Fax:** (509) 466-1143. **Internet:** none.
Owner/Pro: Jim Tucker, Sr., PGA. **Superintendent:** Jim Tucker, Jr.
Rating/Slope: the golf course is not rated. **Course record:** 22.
Green fees: $10/$7 all week long; Jr. & Sr. rates (Mon. thru Fri.) $8.50/$5.50.
Power cart: not available. **Pull cart:** $1. **Trail fee:** not allowed.
Reservation policy: advance reservations for tee times are not required.
Winter condition: damp, the golf course is open weather permitting.
Terrain: flat, slight some hills. **Tees:** mats. **Spikes:** metal spikes permitted.
Services: club rentals, lessons, pro shop, snack bar, driving range, putting green.
Comments: Good par 3 golf course that plays fairly short. Holes range from 62 to 115 yards in length. The facility has a great driving range which has been said to be the "best in the Spokane area".

Directions: the golf course is located 7 miles north of Spokane city center off of Hwy 395N. From I-90 east & west exit on Hwy 395 northbound. Proceed on Hwy 395N to the golf course which will be located on your right hand side.

Course Yardage & Par:
M-760 yards, par 27.
W-760 yards, par 27.

Pine Crest Golf Course (public, 9 hole par 3 course)

2415 NW 143rd Street; Vancouver, WA 98685
Phone: (360) 573-2051. **Fax:** none. **Internet:** none.
Pro: none. **Managers:** Mark & Kathy Hart.
Rating/Slope: the golf course is not rated. **Course record:** 25.
Green fees: W/D $6.50; W/E $7; Sr. rates (M-F) $5.50.
Power cart: not available. **Pull cart:** $1.75. **Trail fee:** not allowed.
Reservation policy: advance reservations for tee times are not required.
Winter condition: damp, the golf course is open all year, weather permitting.
Terrain: rolling hills (walkable). **Tees:** mats. **Spikes:** metal spikes permitted.
Services: club rentals, snack bar, beer, practice green, small pro shop.
Comments: great par 3 course that will challenge you at every turn. Several holes are bordered by a steep canyon that will catch any misguided tee shots. Greens are medium in size and can generally be found in good condition. Great course for the family golf outing.

Directions: From I-5 take the 134th Street exit. Proceed westbound for about 2 miles to NW 143rd Street. Turn left on NW 143rd Street and proceed to the golf course. Look for signs marking your way to the course.

Course Yardage & Par:
M-1206 yards, par 27.
W-1206 yards, par 27.

Plateau Club, The (private, 18 hole course)

25625 Plateau Drive; Sammamish, WA 98074
Phone: (425) 836-4653. **Fax:** (425) 836-4421. **Internet:** www.theplateauclub.com
Pro: Dominic Marconi, PGA. **Superintendent:** Rick Hancock.
Rating/Slope: T 76.3/152; C 71.9/141; M 70.4/130; W 70.6/123. **Record:** 65.
Green fees: private club, members and guest only; limited reciprocation.
Power cart: private club. **Pull cart:** private club. **Trail fee:** private club.
Reservation policy: members may call ahead for a tee time.
Winter condition: the course is considered dry and open all year long.
Terrain: some hills. **Tees:** all grass. **Spikes:** no metal spikes permitted.
Services: club rentals, lessons, lounge, restaurant, snack bar, beer, wine, liquor, showers, lockers, pro shop, driving range, putting, chipping greens, pool, tennis.
Comments: newer private golf club owned by Oki Development Inc. The course features well manicured fairways, large undulating greens with numerous ponds and bunkers fronting them. Hazards abound on nearly every hole throughout the course. Shot placement is a must in order to score well at The Plateau Club.

Directions: from I-90 E take exit #15. Turn left onto the Renton-Issaquah Rd. (it will become SE 56th Street). Proceed to E. Lake Samammish Pkwy SE, turn left. Travel on E. Lake Samammish Pkwy SE and turn right on to SE 43rd Way which will become 228th Ave. S.E. Proceed to S.E. 8th St. Turn right. Follow to course.

Course Yardage & Par:
T-7167 yards, par 72.
C-6469 yards, par 72.
M-6047 yards, par 72.
W-5523 yards, par 72.

Pomeroy Golf Course (public, 9 hole course)
1610 Arlington Street; Box 400; Pomeroy, WA 99347
Phone: (509) 843-1197. **Fax:** none. **Internet:** none.
Pro: none. **Manager:** Alice Gwinn.
Rating/Slope: M 60.2/92; W 62.5/100. **Course record:** 29.
Green fees: $12/$10 all week long; $20 all day; Jr. & Sr. rates; no credit cards.
Power cart: $20/$10. **Pull cart:** $3. **Trail fee:** $3 for personal carts.
Reservation policy: none, some restrictions do apply during league play.
Winter condition: the golf course is closed from November through March.
Terrain: relatively hilly. **Tees:** grass & mats. **Spikes:** soft spikes preferred.
Services: club rentals, driving net, putting green, small pro shop.
Comments: this course sports a number of rather hilly holes which increases its difficulty. Greens are very small in size and can be hard to hold. The course is very short in length but the course still can be hard to score on. This rustic course can get somewhat busy during the mid to late summer months

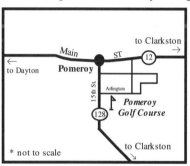

Directions: from Hwy 12 exit on Hwy 128 (15th Street). Proceed to Arlington Street and turn left. Proceed to the golf course. Look for signs marking your way to the golf course.

Course Yardage & Par:
M-2042 yards, par 31.
W-2042 yards, par 32.

Port Ludlow Golf Course (public, resort 27 holes)

751 Highland Drive; Port Ludlow, WA 98365 Internet: www.visitportludlow.com
Phone: (360) 437-0272; 1-800-455-0272 WA. **Fax:** (360) 437-0637.
Dir. of Golf: Mike Buss, PGA. **Pro:** Bill Shea, PGA. **Supt.:** Jerry Mathews.
Rating/Slope: Tide/Timber C 73.3/135; M 70.7/129; W 72.6/127.
Green fees: peak season $59/$30; off season, winter rates; AMEX, VISA, M/C.
Power cart: $14/$7.50 per person. **Pull cart:** $3/$1.50. **Trail fee:** not allowed.
Reservation policy: resort guests-upon room confirmation; public 5 days ahead.
Winter condition: the golf course is open all year long. Dry conditions.
Terrain: relatively hilly. **Tees:** all grass. **Spikes:** soft spikes preferred.
Services: club rentals, lessons, snack bar, beer, wine, pro shop, driving range.
Comments: Robert Muir Graves designed golf course. New "Trail" 9 has been totally redone and is tough. Facility regarded as one of the nation's best. The golf course meanders through fir trees and offers spectacular views of the nearby inlet. Greens are large with undulations and can get firm and quick. Worth a trip.

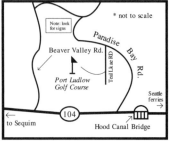

Directions: from Hwy 104 exit to Port Ludlow (immediately west of the Hood Canal Bridge). You will be on Paradise Bay Rd. Follow and turn left on Teal Rd. Stay on Teal Rd. Follow to Highland Dr. turn right. Follow to the clubhouse.

Additional Course Ratings:
Trail/Tide:
C 73.1/133.
M 70.6/132.
W 71.0/124.
Trail/Timber:
C 73.4/138.
M 71.1/132.
W 70.8/125.

Course Yardage & Par:
Tide 9: 3357 yards, par 36.
Timber 9: 3430 yards, par 36.
Trail 9: 3418 yards, par 36.

LinksTime.com
a division of Book4golf.com

Port Townsend Golf Course (public, 9 hole course)
1948 Blaine; Port Townsend, WA 98368
Phone: (360) 385-4547. Fax: (360) 385-3945. Internet: none.
Pro: Mike Early, PGA. Superintendent: Mike Early.
Rating/Slope: M 65.8/114; W 70.4/121. **Course record:** 61.
Green fees: $20/$13; Jr. rates $6 for 9 holes (M-F); Sr. rates (M-F); VISA, M/C.
Power cart: $20/$12. **Pull cart:** $4/$2. **Trail fee:** none (may change).
Reservation policy: yes, call up to 1 week in advance for tee times.
Winter condition: the course is open all year. The course drains very well.
Terrain: relatively hilly. **Tees:** all grass. **Spikes:** soft spikes preferred.
Services: club rentals, lessons, restaurant, beer, pro shop, club memberships,
driving range (grass tees), putting green. **Comments:** the course sets atop a hill
overlooking the town of Port Townsend and surrounding inlet. Rolling terrain,
sand traps, small greens and water will challenge your shot making ability.
Good public course that gets alot of play during the peak golfing season.

Directions: from Hwy 101 northbound
exit to Hwy 20 eastbound toward Port
Townsend. At Port Townsend turn left
on Kearney Road. Go up the hill to Blaine
Road. Turn right on Blaine road to the
golf course which will be on your left.
Look for signs marking your way.

Course Yardage & Par:
M-2763 yards, par 35.
W-2821 yards, par 35.
<u>Dual tees for 18 holes:</u>
M-5604 yards, par 70.
W-5604 yards, par 71.

Potholes Golf Course (public, 9 hole course)
6897 O'Sullivan Dam Road; Othello, WA 99344
Phone: (509) 346-9491. **Fax:** (509) 346-8700. **Internet: none.**
Manager: Randy DuFord. **Superintendent: none.**
Rating/Slope: C 60.2/090; M 59.5/088; W 62.4/093.
Green fees: $13/$9 (Monday-Thursday); $16/$11 (Friday-Sunday & Holidays).
Power cart: $17/$11. **Pull cart:** $2. **Trail fee:** $4 for personal carts.
Reservation policy: yes, call up to 1 week in advance for tee times.
Winter condition: the course is open all year long weather permitting. Dry.
Terrain: flat, easy walking. **Tees:** all grass. **Spikes:** soft spikes preferred.
Services: club rentals, lessons, restaurant (Italian menu), beer, wine, pro shop,
driving range, RV spots, putting & chipping greens, club memberships.
Comments: narrow golf course that plays much longer than the yardage would
indicate. RV hookups with full services and cable TV. The restaurants claim to
fame is "We make the best garlic bread in North America". Good test of golf
that can be demanding on your shot making ability. Fair public golf course.

Directions: from Hwy 26 through Royal
City to State Rd. 262. Turn left. Proceed
14 miles south to the course. From I-90
exit 179 turn left on Hwy 17 to "M" St.
(2 1/2 miles) turn right. Proceed 7-8
miles to O'Sullivan Dam Road turn right
(west) to the golf course. Look for signs.

Course Yardage & Par:
M-2269 yards, par 33.
W-2167 yards, par 33.
Dual tees for 18 holes:
M-4638 yards, par 66.
W-4334 yards, par 66.

Quail Ridge Golf Course (public, 18 hole course)
3600 Swallow's Nest Drive; Clarkston, WA 99403
Phone: (509) 758-8501. Fax: (509) 758-4644. Internet: none.
Pro: unavailable. Superintendent: none.
Rating/Slope: C 68.1/114; M 68.1/113; W 66.2/107. **Course record:** 63.
Green fees: $17/$13 all week long; $19/$13 W/E in the summer; M/C, VISA.
Power cart: $22/$13. **Pull cart:** $5. **Trail fee:** $5 (annual fee available).
Reservation policy: please call 1 week in advance for your tee-times.
Winter condition: the golf course is open weather permitting. Dry conditions.
Terrain: flat, some hills. **Tees:** all grass. **Spikes:** soft spikes only.
Services: coffee shop, beer, beverages, pro shop, driving range, putting green.
Comments: formerly called Swallow's Nest the golf course been expanded to 18 holes recently and is worth a trip. The new nine has spectacular views of the surrounding countryside and rolling terrain. Good public track.

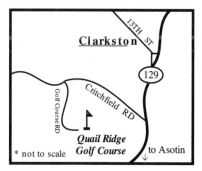

Directions: the golf course is located south of Clarkston WA. From Hwy 129 Turn westbound on Critchfield Road (across from the Snake River). Proceed on Critchfield Rd. for a 1/4 mile to Golf Course Rd. Turn left. Proceed to the golf course off of Swallow's Nest Loop.

Course Yardage & Par:
C-5861 yards, par 71.
M-5603 yards, par 71.
M-4720 yards, par 71.
W-4637 yards, par 71.

Quincy Valley Golf (public, 18 hole course)
1705 5th NW; Quincy, WA 98848
Phone: (509) 787-3244. Fax: (509) 787-6602. Internet: none.
Managers: Rob & Chuck Anabel. Pro: Bill Porter.
Rating/Slope: C 67.3/101; M 67.0/100; W 74.0/117. **Course record:** 32.
Green fees: W/D $15/$12; W/E $20/$15; Jr. & Sr. rates; M/C, VISA.
Power cart: $18/$10. **Pull cart:** $3/$2. **Trail fee:** $5 for personal carts.
Reservation policy: required for summer weekends. Call 4-5 days in advance.
Winter condition: the golf course is open all year long, when playable.
Terrain: flat, some hills. **Tees:** all grass. **Spikes:** soft spikes preferred.
Services: club rentals, snack bar, pro shop, driving net. **Comments:** the golf
course is well-conditioned with beautiful fairways and excellent greens.
RV sites are available for those overnighters who want to stay and play golf.
Very friendly golf course. The new 9 holes were opened in early 1997.

Directions: from Hwy 281 take 5 NW (White Trail Road) to the golf course. From I-90 E&W exit at Hwy 281 and proceed toward Quincy. The golf course will be off of the Hwy on your left hand side. Look for sign marking your turn.

Course Yardage & Par:

C-5979 yards, par 70.
M-5680 yards, par 70.
W-5305 yards, par 70.

Rainier Golf & Country Club (private, 18 hole course)

133 Des Moines Memorial Drive S.; Seattle, WA 98168
Phone: (206) 242-2800. Fax: (206) 242-4600. Internet: none.
Pro: Tony Wilkins, PGA. Superintendent: Ronald Proctor.
Rating/Slope: C 71.1/132; M 70.3/130; W 73.3/130. **Course record:** 63.
Green fees: private club, members and guests only; reciprocates.
Power cart: private club. **Pull cart:** private club. **Trail fee:** not allowed.
Reservation policy: private club, yes, up to 1 week in advance. No public play.
Winter condition: the golf course is open all year long. New drainage system.
Terrain: very hilly. **Tees:** all grass. **Spikes:** soft spikes June thru October.
Services: lessons, snack bar, beer, wine, pro shop, lockers, showers, driving range, putting & chipping green. **Comments:** beautiful views of Mount Rainier are seen from this course which sports tree-lined fairways, tricky greens, and many sand traps to contend with. Excellent private course that plays tough.

Directions: from I-5 N&S take exit # 158B to the South Boeing Access Road. Go west for .4 miles to Pacific Hwy S. Turn south on Pacific Hwy S. and follow for .5 miles to S 116th. Turn west on 116th up winding hill to 2nd light at Des Moines Memorial Drive, turn right going north to 112th turn left & proceed to the golf course.

Course Yardage & Par:
C-6352 yards, par 72.
M-6190 yards, par 72.
W-5756 yards, par 74.

Raspberry Ridge Golf Community (public, 9 hole course)

6827 Hannegan Road; Everson, WA 98247
Phone: (360) 354-3029. Fax: (360) 354-1225. Internet: none.
Owner: Bill Robins. Superintendent: John Olson.
Rating/Slope: C 65.1/106; M 63.9/104; W 67.3/110. **Course record:** 63.
Green fees: $18/$12 daily; Jr & Sr rates, $16/$11; M/C, VISA, AMEX.
Power cart: $18/$12. **Pull cart:** $2. **Trail fee:** no charge for personal carts.
Reservation policy: yes, please call up to 7 days in advance for tee times.
Winter condition: the golf course is open all year long, dry (drains very well).
Terrain: flat, some hills. **Tees:** all grass. **Spikes:** no spike restrictions.
Services: club rentals, snack bar, lounge, restaurant, beer, wine, pro shop, club
memberships, putting green. **Comments:** beautifully maintained golf course
with spectacular views of Mount Baker and the surrounding countryside.
Although relatively short, this course will challenge you at every turn. Water
and well bunkered greens are every where. Accuracy off the tee is a must for
scoring. Great out of the way course. Worth a special trip if you are in the area.

Directions: from I-5 N&S take exit
256A to Hwy 539 northbound and
continue 7.7 miles to Hwy 544
eastbound. Turn south on Hannegan
Road and proceed to the golf course.
Look for a sign marking your turn to
the golf course community.

Course Yardage & Par:
C-2825 yards, par 34.
M-2585 yards, par 34
W-2335 yards, par 34.

Ritzville Municipal Golf Course (public, 9 hole course)

104 East 10th Street; Ritzville, WA 99169

Phone: (509) 659-9868. Fax: (509) 659-1836. Internet: rabrgc@agritel.net

Pro: Ron Barker, PGA. Superintendent: Ron Barker.

Rating/Slope: M 67.1/112; W 71.8/123. **Course record:** 62.

Green fees: $16/$11; Jr & Sr rates (weekdays only); no credit cards.

Power cart: $20/$10. **Pull cart:** $2. **Trail fee:** no charge for personal carts.

Reservation policy: advance tee times are not needed or required.

Winter condition: the course is closed from mid November to mid February.

Terrain: flat, some hills. **Tees:** grass. **Spikes:** soft spikes preferred.

Services: club rentals, lessons, restaurant, beer, pro shop, putting green.

Comments: a good walking course. Ritzville is fairly flat and in good condition. The track sports two sets of tees for a different look for 18 holes. Convenient RV park close by. Some greens are fronted by bunkers and sloping terrain. The golf course can play very tough if the wind picks up. Greens are in great shape.

Directions: from I-90 take the Ritzville exit #221 and travel north 2 blocks to the golf course. The course has great freeway access. Look for signs marking your turn to the golf course.

Course Yardage & Par:
M-2812 yards, par 35.
W-2812 yards, par 36.
Dual tees for 18 holes:
M-5597 yards, par 70.
W-5597 yards, par 72.

Riverbend Golf Complex (public, 18 hole, 9 hole par 3)

Physical address: 2019 West Meeker; Kent, WA 98032   Internet: none.
Mailing Address: 2204 4th Avenue South; Kent, WA 98032
Phone: (253) 854-3673 or (253) 859-4000. Fax: (253) 859-3541
Pro: Brett Wilkinson, PGA. Superintendent: Pete Petersen.
Rating/Slope: C 70.6/118; M 68.6/112; W 70.8/119. **Course record:** 64.
Green fees: W/D $26/$17; W/E $30/$18; Jr & Sr rates (M-Th.); M/C, VISA.
Green fees for the par 3 course: W/D $8 1st 9 holes; W/E $10 for 9 holes.
Power cart: $22/$11. **Pull cart:** $3/$2. **Trail fee:** personal carts not allowed.
Reservation policy: please call 1 week in advance for your tee times.
Winter condition: the golf course is open all year long. Drains fairly well.
Terrain: flat (easy walking). **Tees:** all grass. **Spikes:** soft spikes preferred.
Services: club rentals, lessons, snack bar, beer, chipping & putting green,
driving range, pro shop. **Comments:** championship caliber track. The course
is flat, well-bunkered and water comes in to play on 7 holes. The golf course is
excellent and worth a special trip. Be sure to call well ahead for your tee time.

Directions: from I-5 N&S take exit
149 to Hwy 516 eastbound. Travel
east for 1.3 miles to West Meeker.
Turn east on Meeker to the golf course,
located on your left, the range and par 3
course will be on your right hand side.

Course Yardage & Par:
C-6633 yards, par 72.
M-6208 yards, par 72.
W-5538 yards, par 72.

Par 3 Course Yardage & Par:
M/W-1260 yards, par 27.

Riverside Golf Club (public, 18 hole course)

1451 NW Airport Road; Chehalis, WA 98532
Phone: (360) 748-8182, 800-242-9486. Fax: (360) 748-4699. Internet: none.
Pro: Steve McNelly, PGA. Superintendent: Darin Thompson.
Rating/Slope: C 69.3/118; M 67.6/112; W 71.2/116. **Record:** 61, 18 holes.
Green fees: M-Th $18/$14; Fri. $21/$17; W/E's & Holidays. $25; M/C, VISA.
Senior rates (Monday thru Friday); winter rates; winter specials.
Power cart: $22/$16 reserve the cart. **Pull cart:** $4. **Trail fee:** $10.
Reservation policy: yes, please call up to 1 week in advance for tee times.
Winter condition: the golf course is open all year long. Good conditions.
Terrain: flat, some slight hills. **Tees:** grass. **Spikes:** soft spikes preferred.
Services: lessons, snack bar, restaurant, beer, wine, pro shop, driving range,
putting and chipping greens, club memberships. **Comments:** this course winds
along the Chehalis River and is noted for its fast, undulating greens that are in
great shape all year long. Fairways are tree-lined with medium sized landing
areas. Great golf course to stop and play anytime of year. Easy freeway access.

Directions: from I-5 N&S take exit # 79.
Head west. Turn left on Louisiana St.
Go to stop sign. Turn right on Airport Rd.
The golf course is 0.7 miles ahead on the
left. **Note:** Look for signs marking your
way to the golf course.

Course Yardage & Par:
C-6155 yards, par 71.
M-5771 yards, par 71.
W-5456 yards, par 72.

Riverside Golf Course (public, 9 hole course)
5799 Riverside Drive; Ferndale, WA 98248
Phone: (360) 384-4116. **Fax:** none. **Internet:** none.
Owner: Jeanne Olson Estie. **Superintendent:** none.
Rating/Slope: C 67.6/104; M 66.9/103; W 70.4/112. **Course record:** 66.
Green fees: W/D $12/$8; W/E & holidays $13/$9; Jr & Sr rates; M/C, VISA.
Power cart: $20/$10. **Pull cart:** $4/$2. **Trail fee:** no charge.
Reservation policy: advance reservations are not taken or required.
Winter condition: the golf course is open all year long. Damp conditions.
Terrain: flat, easy walking. **Tees:** all grass. **Spikes:** soft spikes preferred.
Services: club rentals, snack bar, restaurant, pro shop, putting green, club
memberships. **Comments:** the course is well-kept, particularly the greens.
Fairways are wide with generous landing areas. Greens are of medium size and
have few hazards fronting them. A very friendly staff makes this facility a
pleasure to visit and a treat to play. The golf course is generally flat and easy to
walk. Easy freeway access for those traveling on I-5.

Directions: from I-5 N&S take exit
262. Travel west for 1/10 of a mile
to the golf course. Look for signs that
are posted indicating your turn for the
golf course.

Course Yardage & Par:
M-3000 yards, par 36.
W-2860 yards, par 37.

Riviera Golf & Country Club (private, 9 hole course)

11019 Country Club Drive; Anderson Island, WA 98303
Phone: (253) 884-9634. Fax: (253) 884-9767. Internet: none.
Manager: Gary Henson. Superintendent: Ron Hall.
Rating/Slope: M 55.3/99; W 56.3/95. Course record: 26.
Greens fee: private club, members & guests only; no credit cards.
Power cart: none. **Pull cart:** members & guests only. **Trail fee:** $5.
Reservation policy: yes, members may call for weekend tee times.
Winter condition: the golf course is open all year long. Wet conditions.
Terrain: relatively hilly. **Tees:** grass. **Spikes:** soft spikes preferred.
Services: restaurant, beer, wine, pro shop, putting green, club memberships.
Comments: friendly private course set in a beautiful island community of
Washington State. This executive length golf course is a challenge at every turn.
Greens are small and the fronts are well bunkered. Fairways are very narrow.

Directions: northbound from Olympia
take the Dupont/Steilacoom exit from I-5.
Go straight until you reach the ferry dock.
Am ferry leaves at 6am,7:40am, 9am and
12pm. From I-5 southbound take exit 129.
Go westbound to South Tacoma Way.
Right to Steilacoom Boulevard then left to
the ferry dock. Look for signs marking
your way to the golf course.

Course Yardage & Par:
M-1610 yards, par 29.
W-1579 yards, par 32.

Rock Island Golf Club (public, 9 hole course)

314 Saunders Road; Rock Island, WA 98850
Phone: (509) 884-2806. Fax: none. Internet: none.
Manager: Pam Orr. Superintendent: none.
Rating/Slope: M 70.1/112; W 73.4/120. **Course record:** 68 for 18 holes.
Green fees: W/D $18/$11; W/E $18/$11; Jr/Sr rates (Tues & Th); M/C, VISA.
Power cart: $19/$11. **Pull cart:** $2. **Trail fee:** no charge for personal carts.
Reservation policy: yes, you may call ahead for a tee time. No restrictions.
Winter condition: the course is open all year long, weather permitting.
Terrain: very flat. **Tees:** all grass. **Spikes:** soft spikes preferred.
Services: club rentals, lessons, restaurant, lounge, beer, wine, pro shop, driving range, putting & chipping greens. **Comments:** this course sports large greens with some bunkers coming into play on approach shots. The course plays long from the back tees leaving many long irons for your second shots. Water comes into play on a number of holes. You can usually walk on during the summer.

Directions: from Hwy 28 take the Rock Island exit. At the end of the street, turn left. Follow to Delaware and turn right. At the stop sign, turn right on Saunders Road and follow to the golf course. Look for signs marking your way to the golf course.

Course Yardage & Par:
M-3396 yards, par 36.
W-2884 yards, par 36.
Dual tees for 18 holes:
M-6467 yards, par 72.
W-5995 yards, par 72.

Rolling Hills Golf Course (public, 18 hole course)
2485 NE McWilliams Road; Bremerton, WA 98311
Phone: (360) 479-1212. Fax: (360) 479-2450. Internet: none.
Director of Golf: Tedd Hudanich, PGA. Pro: Roger O'Hara.
Rating/Slope: M 68.0/115; W 71.1/117. **Course record:** 63.
Green fees: weekdays $23/$15; weekends $25/$16; Jr. & Sr. $16 (M-F);
military rates $16 (Monday-Friday); M/C, VISA, AMEX, DISCOVER.
Power cart: $22/$14. **Pull cart:** $2. **Trail fee:** $5 for personal carts.
Reservation policy: yes, you may call 7 days in advance for tee-times.
Winter condition: the golf course is open all year long, damp conditions.
Terrain: relatively hilly. **Tees:** grass. **Spikes:** soft spikes optional.
Services: club rentals, lessons, snack bar, beer, wine, beverages, pro shop,
excellent driving range, club memberships, putting green, practice bunker.
Comments: the course offers a beautiful view of the Olympic Mountains and
Mt. Rainier. Excellent public course with well bunkered greens and medium
wide fairways. The course has a well stocked pro shop for all your golfing needs.

Directions: from the Bremerton ferry
terminal take Washington. Turn north
for .8 miles to Warren. Turn right on
Warren and proceed 3.6 miles to
McWilliams Rd. Turn right to the golf
course. Look for signs to the course.
From Hwy 3 exit at Wagga Way that
turns in to Hwy 303. Follow Hwy 303
until you reach McWilliams Rd. where
you will turn left. Course on the right.

Course Yardage & Par:
M-5910 yards, par 70.
W-5465 yards, par 70.

Royal City Golf Course (public, 9 hole course)

13702 Dodson Road South; Royal City, WA 99357
Phone: (509) 346-2052. **Fax:** none. **Internet:** none.
Manager: Kay Rasor. **Superintendent:** Ron Herodes.
Rating/Slope: M 68.4/110; W 71.3/112. **Course record:** 65.
Green fees: Mondays $7; Tuesdays $8; Wednesdays thru Friday $13/$10;
weekends & Holidays $15/$11; no special rates; no credit cards accepted.
Power cart: $18/$10. **Pull cart:** $4/$2.50. **Trail fee:** $5/$3 for personal carts.
Reservation policy: please call 1 day in advance for tee-times.
Winter condition: course is open weather permitting. Pay in the honor box.
Terrain: flat, some hills. **Tees:** grass. **Spikes:** soft spikes only.
Services: snack bar, pro shop, driving range, putting green, RV parking.
Comments: newer course that varies in terrain. A canal runs through two holes
and can present problems with your tee or approach shots. Fairways are wide
and firm. RV park is next to the course with water, sewer & electric hookups.

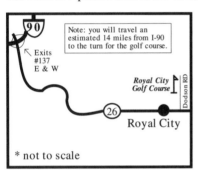

Note: you will travel an estimated 14 miles from I-90 to the turn for the golf course.

Exits #137 E & W

Royal City Golf Course

Dodson RD

26 Royal City

* not to scale

Directions: from I-90 E&W take the exit
#137 for Hwy 26 to Royal City. Travel
eastbound for approximately 14.2 miles
to Dodson Road. Turn left. The clubhouse and golf course will be on your left
hand side. Signs are posted indicating
your turn on Dodson Road to the course.

Course Yardage & Par:

M-3106 yards, par 36.
W-2850 yards, par 36.

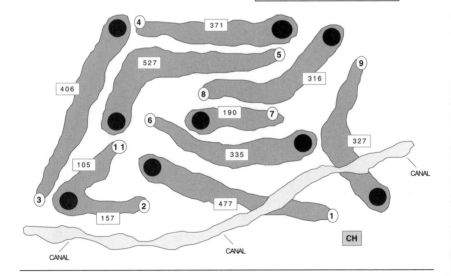

Royal Oaks Country Club (private, 18 hole course)

8917 NE Fourth Plain Road; Vancouver, WA 98662
Phone: (360) 256-1350. Fax: (360) 256-1252. Internet: none.
Pro: Steve Bowen, PGA. Superintendent: Alan Neilsen.
Rating/Slope: T 73.1/133; C 71.2/125; M 69.5/122; W 72.6/127. **Record:** 64.
Green fees: private club members & guests only; reciprocates; M/C, VISA.
Power cart: private club. **Pull cart:** private club. **Trail fee:** private club.
Reservation policy: no time limit for members, public is not allowed.
Winter condition: the golf course is open all year long. Dry conditions.
Terrain: flat, some hills. **Tees:** grass. **Spikes:** soft spikes April thru October.
Services: lessons, restaurant, lounge, beer, wine, liquor, pro shop, lockers, showers, club memberships, driving range, putting & chipping greens.
Comments: regarded as one of the state's best, Royal Oaks fairway's are tight and tree-lined. Greens are well bunkered and hard to hold. A very difficult layout that is demanding from the tee and on the greens. Good private course.

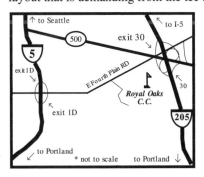

Directions: from I-5 N&S take exit # 1D (Fourth Plain Blvd E). Travel east just beyond the 4 mile post to the golf course which will be on your right hand side. Look for a small sign at your turn.

Course Yardage & Par:
T-6900 yards, par 72.
C-6516 yards, par 72.
M-6138 yards, par 72.
F-5695 yards, par 72.
W-5208 yards, par 72.

Sage Hills Golf Club (public, 18 hole course)

10400 Sage Hills Road SE; Warden, WA 98857
Phone: (509) 349-2603. Fax: (509) 349-0420. Internet: none.
Pro: Daniel Nighswonger. Superintendent: Martin Gallardo.
Rating/Slope: C 71.4/122; M 70.1/117; W 69.0/114. **Course record:** 64.
Green fees: W/D $18/$10; W/E $22/$12; Jr & Sr rates (M-F); M/C, VISA.
Power cart: $23/$12. **Pull cart:** $4/$2. **Trail fee:** $6/$3 for personal carts.
Reservation policy: yes, you may call 7 days in advance for tee-times.
Winter condition: the golf course is usually closed December to January.
Terrain: flat, some hills. **Tees:** grass. **Spikes:** soft spikes only.
Services: club rentals, lessons, restaurant, lounge, beer, wine, pro shop,
showers, putting and chipping greens, RV park with 42 hookups.
Comments: Good public course that can play very difficult if the wind picks up.
Greens are medium in size with some being fronted by bunkers. Water comes
into play on 5 holes and is a major factor off the tee and on your approach shots.
A full service RV park is adjacent to the parking lot for those spending the night.

Directions: the golf course is located 2
miles south of the Warden cut-off on the
west side of Hwy 17. From I-90 exit #179
to Hwy 17 and proceed southbound to the
golf course. Make sure that you look for
signs to the golf course from the Hwy.

Course Yardage & Par:

C-6591 yards, par 71.
M-6355 yards, par 71.
W-5128 yards, par 74.

Sahalee Country Club (private, 27 hole course)

21200 Sahalee Country Club Drive; Redmond, WA 98053
Phone: (425) 453-0484. Fax: (425) 868-2877. Internet: none.
Golf Professional: Jim Pike, PGA. Superintendent: Rich Taylor.
Rating/Slope: T 74.0/137; C 73.2/132; M 71.6/129; W 73.4/132. **Record:** 65.
Green fees: private club members & guests only; reciprocates (very limited).
Power cart: private club. **Pull cart:** private club. **Trail fee:** private club.
Reservation policy: private club members & guests only. No public play.
Winter condition: the golf course is open all year long. Dry conditions.
Terrain: relatively hilly. **Tees:** all grass. **Spikes:** soft spikes May-October.
Services: club rentals, lessons, lounge, restaurant, beer, wine, liquor, pro shop,
lockers, showers, club memberships, driving range, dress code, putting green.
Comments: course record was set by Nick Price and Greg Kraft during the
PGA Championship. Ranked in *Golf Digest's* top 100 courses in the nation
Sahalee is both demanding and spectacular. Fantastic private golf course.

Directions: from I-5 N&S take exit
#168B to Hwy 520 eastbound. Go east
to Hwy 202E (Redmond-Fall City
Road). Travel east for 2 miles to 208th
Avenue NE-Sahalee Way NE. Turn
south for 1 mile to NE 36th. Veer left to
Sahalee Dr. W to NE 28th. Turn east to
the golf course.

Course Yardage & Par:
North: T-3467 yards, C-3377yards, M-3172 yards, W-2867 yards, par 36.
South: T-3488 yards, C-3377 yards, M-3159 yards, W-2845 yards, par 36.
East: T-3464 yards, C-3392 yards, M-3163 yards, W-2880 yards, par 36.

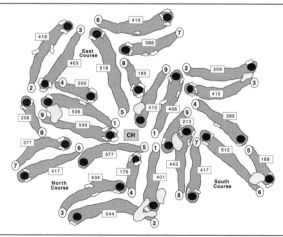

Saint John Golf & Country Club (semi-private, 9 hole course)
off Hwy 23; P.O. Box 232; Saint John, WA 99171
Phone: (509) 648-3259. Fax: none. Internet: none.
Pro: none. Manager: N/A. Superintendent: Curt White.
Rating/Slope: C 67.0/111; M 66.0/106; W 68.4/109. **Course record:** 32.
Green fees: $15 (all day); non-members welcome; no credit cards.
Power cart: none available. **Pull cart:** $2. **Trail fee:** $3 all day rate.
Reservation policy: advance tee times are not needed or required.
Winter condition: the golf course is closed from November thru February.
Terrain: very flat, easy walking. **Tees:** grass. **Spikes:** soft spikes preferred.
Services: lessons, (occasionally), limited services. **Comments:** the course is
impeccably maintained with beautiful lush green fairways. A few sand traps and
one creek come into play. Easy walking golf course that is great for the senior.
The clubhouse is often closed so green fees are sometimes on the honor system.

Directions: the golf course is located on
the northwest side of St. John off Hwy
23. Look for signs off of Hwy 23 in St.
John marking your way to the golf course.
The course is located right off Hwy 23.
Signs are posted at your turn.

Course Yardage & Par:
C-2876 yards, par 35.
M-2770 yards, par 35.
W-2564 yards, par 35.

San Juan Golf & Country Club (public, 9 hole course)
806 Golf Course Road; P.O. Box 246; Friday Harbor, WA 98250
Phone: (360) 378-2254. Fax: (360) 378-3107. Internet: none.
Pro: Steve Nightingale, PGA. Superintendent: Alan Dufur.
Rating/Slope: M 68.6/110; W 71.0/115. **Course record:** 66.
Green fees: $40/$23 all week long (summer); twilight rates $17; M/C, VISA.
Power cart: $24/$14. **Pull cart:** $5/$3. **Trail fee:** $15 (for pass unlimited use).
Reservation policy: yes, call 1 day ahead for tee-times June through September.
Winter condition: the golf course is open all year long. Dry conditions.
Terrain: flat, some hills. **Tees:** all grass. **Spikes:** soft spikes only.
Services: club rentals, lessons, restaurant/lounge, lockers/showers, pro shop,
driving range, putting green, chipping green, RV parking, banquet facilities.
Comments: set in the scenic San Juan Islands, the course is easy to walk but
can be very tough to score on. Tee shots play to medium size landing areas.
Two sets of tees are available for those wanting to play a full 18 hole round.
Rated in the top 20, nine hole courses in Washington, Oregon and Idaho.

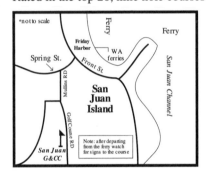

Directions: board the Anacortes ferry to
Friday harbor. Leaving the the ferry
dock take Spring Street for 5 blocks to
Mullins Rd. Turn left on Mullins Road.
for 1.8 miles to Golf Course Road. Turn
left and proceed to the golf course.

Course Yardage & Par:
M-3347 yards, par 35.
W-2697yards, par 36.
Dual tees for 18 holes:
M-6694 yards, par 71.
W-5483 yards, par 72.

Sand Point Country Club (private, 18 hole course)

8333 55th NE; Seattle, WA 98115
Phone: (206) 523-4994. Fax: (206) 525-9867. Internet: none.
Pro: Ron Stull, PGA. Superintendent: Craig Sampson.
Rating/Slope: C 69.9/129; M 68.2/125; W 72.0/127; F 70.5/123. **Record:** 61.
Green fees: private club members and guests only; M/C, VISA.
Power cart: private club members and guests only. **Trail fee:** not allowed.
Reservation policy: private club members and guests only. No outside play.
Winter condition: the golf course is open all year long. Fair conditions.
Terrain: very hilly. **Tees:** all grass. **Spikes:** soft spikes only May to October.
Services: club rentals, lessons, snack bar, lounge, restaurant, beer, wine, liquor,
pro shop, club memberships, putting & chipping greens, driving range, tennis.
Comments: the course offers a sweeping view of Lake Washington. Numerous
sand traps, rolling terrain, and many trees provide a great test of golf.

Directions: from I-5 S take exit # 172 to
NE 80th. Turn east to Banner Way NE.
Turn south on Banner which will become
NE 75th. Proceed 2.3 miles to the golf
course. From I-5 N take exit # 171 to NE
73rd. Travel east for .1 mile to 12th NE.
On 12th go north for .1 mile to NE 75th.
Turn east for 1.8 miles to the golf course.

Course Yardage & Par:
C-6040 yards, par 71.
M-5690 yards, par 71.
W-5488 yards, par 71.
W-5127 yards, par 72.

Sandy Point Golf Course (private, 9 hole course)
4460 Decadure Drive; Box 1418; Ferndale, WA 98248
Phone: (360) 384-3921. **Fax:** none. **Internet:** none.
Manager: none. **Superintendent:** home owners.
Rating/Slope: the golf course is not rated. **Course record:** 24.
Greens fee: private club, members & guests only; no credit cards.
Power cart: none. **Pull cart:** members & guests only. **Trail fee:** private.
Reservation policy: tee-times are on first come first served basis.
Winter condition: the golf course is open all year long. Wet conditions.
Terrain: flat gentle rolling terrain. **Tees:** grass. **Spikes:** soft spikes preferred.
Services: limited services. Club members and guests are only permitted.
Comments: postage stamp greens are this private courses trademark. These greens can be very hard to hold during the summer months when they are firm.

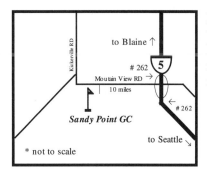

Directions: from I-5 N&S take exit #262 to Mountain View Road. Follow Mountain View Road westbound for 10 miles. The golf course and development is located on your left hand side.

Course Yardage & Par:
M-1000 yards, par 27.
W-1000 yards, par 27.

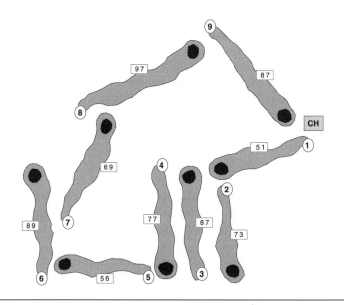

Sauk Mountain View Golf Course (public, 9 hole course)
839 Fruitdale Road; Sedro Woolley, WA 98284
Phone: (360) 856-0315. Fax: (360) 856-1177. Internet: none.
Pro: Wellington Lee, PGA. Superintendent: Bo Giltner.
Rating/Slope: C 68.7/115; M 68.0/114; W 68.2/114. **Course record:** 31.
Green fees: W/D \$14/\$10; W/E & Hol. \$16/\$13; Sr. rates M-F; M/C, VISA.
Power cart: \$22/\$13. **Pull cart:** \$3/\$2. **Trail fee:** \$1 per 9 holes.
Reservation policy: no, play happens on a first come first served basis.
Winter condition: the course is open all year, weather permitting. Damp.
Terrain: relatively hilly. **Tees:** grass, mats. **Spikes:** soft spikes preferred.
Services: club rentals, lessons, snack bar, beer, pro shop, chipping area, putting green, club memberships. **Comments:** ditches, ponds and creeks come into play throughout the course. Fairways have generous landing areas giving the golfer room off the tee. Peek a boo views of the Cascades from many tees and fairways.

Directions: from I-5 N&S take exit #232 to Cook Road. Travel east for 4.4 miles to Hwy 20 E. Turn east for .7 miles to Fruitdale Road. Proceed on Fruitdale Road to the golf course. Look for signs locating the turn to the course.

Course Yardage & Par:
C-3050 yards, par 36.
M-2914 yards, par 36.
W-2500 yards, par 36.

Scott Lake Golf Course (public, 9 hole course)
11746 Scott Creek Drive SW; Olympia, WA 98512
Phone: (360) 352-4838. Fax: none. Internet: none.
Owners: Joel and Karen Boede. Superintendent: Darrin Boede.
Rating/Slope: M 62.9/94; W 64.4/97. **Course record:** 62.
Green fees: W/D \$12/\$8; W/E \$16/\$9; Jr & Sr rates (W/D's); no credit cards.
Power cart: \$16/\$9. **Pull cart:** \$2. **Trail fee:** \$5/\$3 for personal carts.
Reservation policy: yes, call up to 10 days the during summer and weekends.
Winter condition: the golf course is open all year long. Damp conditions.
Terrain: flat (easy walking). **Tees:** all grass. **Spikes:** metal spikes permitted.
Services: club rentals, coffee shop, beer, wine, pro shop, putting green, club
memberships. **Comments:** this friendly, family run 9 hole golf course sports
dual tees for a full 18 hole round. Greens are medium in size and sport few
undulations. Fairways are tree-lined and well kept. Two lakes come into play
throughout half of the nine hole track. Good golf course for family outing.

Directions: from I-5 N&S take exit #99.
Travel east on 93rd Avenue SW to Case
Avenue SW. Turn south. Proceed to
Scott Creek Dr. SW and follow to the
golf course. Look for signs to the course.

Course Yardage & Par:
M-2600 yards, par 35.
W-2189 yards, par 36.
Dual tees for 18 holes:
M-5045 yards, par 70.
W-4634 yards, par 72.

Seattle Golf Club (private, 18 hole course)

210 NW 145th; Seattle, WA 98177

Phone: (206) 363-8811. Fax: (206) 363-6658. Internet: www.seattlegolfclub.com

Pro: Doug Doxsie, PGA. Superintendent: Peter Wilson.

Rating/Slope: T 72.2/136; C 71.3/130; M 69.8/125; W 72.1/124. **Record:** 63.

Green fees: private course, members only; no credit cards.

Power cart: private club. **Pull cart:** complimentary. **Trail fee:** not allowed.

Reservation policy: private club members only. No outside public is allowed.

Winter condition: the golf course is open year round. Dry conditions.

Terrain: very hilly. **Tees:** all grass. **Spikes:** no policy.

Services: lessons, snack bar, lounge, restaurant, beer, wine, liquor, pro shop, showers, putting green, driving range. **Comments:** a beautiful, stately old golf course. Mature trees line the fairways and are a major factor off the tee. Greens are large and well trapped. Water holes can play extremely difficult. From the back tees the golf course plays long, putting emphasis on accuracy.

Directions: from I-5 N&S take exit # 175 to NE 145th. Turn west and travel 1.4 miles to the golf course entrance. The golf course is on your right hand side. Look for a small sign.

Course Yardage & Par:
C-6806yards, par 72.
M-6013 yards, par 72.
W-5418 yards, par 72.

Semiahmoo Golf & Country Club (semi-private, 18 holes)

8720 Semiahmoo Parkway; Blaine, WA 98230 Internet: www.semiahmoo.com
Phone: (360) 371-7005, 800-231-4425. **Fax:** (360) 371-7012.
Pro: Michael Anderson, PGA. **Superintendent:** Vance Much.
Rating/Slope: T 73.9/137; C 71.0/132; M 69.2/123; W 70.6/124. **Record:** 63.
Green fees: peak golfing season rates: $90 all week long; twilite rates $65 after
4pm; winter rates $55 all week long (Nov.-Feb.); VISA, M/C, AMEX, DIS.
Power cart: included in fee. **Pull cart:** $5. **Trail fee:** not allowed.
Reservation policy: the public may call up to 30 days in advance for tee times.
Winter condition: the golf course is open all year long. Dry conditions.
Terrain: flat, some hills. **Tees:** grass. **Spikes:** no metal spikes in summer.
Services: club rentals, lessons, snack bar, wine, beer, pro shop, driving range.
Comments: Arnold Palmer designed layout with numerous bunkers and ponds.
Voted in 1992 as the 18th **Best Resort Course** in the nation by *Golf Digest*.
It was also voted the #1 Resort Course in America by *Golf Digest* when it
opened in 1987. This course is truely one of the finest facilities in the entire NW.

Directions: from I-5 N take exit
274 to Bell Road. Turn left. The
road becomes Blaine Road. Travel 1
mile to Drayton Harbor Road. Turn
right and follow to the fork, stay left it
becomes Harbor View Road. Proceed
.5 miles to Lincoln Road. Follow the
signs to the golf course.

Course Yardage & Par:

T-7005 yards, par 72.
C-6435 yards, par 72.
M-6003 yards, par 72.
W-5288 yards, par 72.

Serendipity Golf Club (semi-private, 9 hole course)
North 31171 Le Clerc Road; Ione, WA 99139
Phone: (509) 442-3313. Fax: (509) 442-3621. Internet: www.bedngolf.com
Owner: Karin Cox. Manager/Superintendent: David Cox.
Rating/Slope: the golf course is not rated. **Course record:** 29.
Green fees: $25/$15 all week long; call for special rates; no credit cards.
Power cart: available. **Pull cart:** not available. **Trail fee:** not available.
Reservation policy: call ahead for tee-times on the weekend only.
Winter condition: the golf course is closed November 1st until thaw.
Terrain: flat, easy walking. **Tees:** grass. **Spikes:** metal spikes permitted.
Services: basically a self serve golf course, but rental clubs are available for
free. Golf course can be available for rental on special occasions. A large gazebo
is available for parties. **Comments:** this unique 5 green, 9 fairway, 9 hole
course is nestled along the banks of the Pend Oreille River. The surrounding
beauty and friendly atmosphere provides the golfer with a enjoyable round.

Directions: from the Spokane area,
travel on Hwy 2 approx. 30 miles to
Ione/Metaline Falls left turn-off onto
Hwy 211. Travel 15 miles north to Hwy
31, turn left. Travel approx. 30 miles.
Turn right approx. 2 miles south of the
town of Ione for direction of Sullivan
Lake (see GC sign). After crossing the
orange bridge (Pend Oreille River) take
immediate right (sign) and travel 1 1/2
miles. The course is on the right.

Course Yardage & Par:

M-2169 yards, par 34.
W-1979 yards, par 34.

Shelton Bayshore Golf Club (public, 9 hole course)
3800 E Highway 3; Shelton, WA 98584
Phone: (360) 426-1271. **Fax:** (360) 427-6327. **Internet:** none.
Pro: Brian Davis, PGA. **Superintendent:** Mark Wigren.
Rating/Slope: M 68.6/117; W 71.8/117. **Course record:** 63.
Green fees: W/D $16/$11; W/E $18/$13; Sr. rates Mon. & Thur. $12/$8.
Power cart: $22/$13. **Pull cart:** $3.50. **Trail fee:** $5 for personal carts.
Reservation policy: yes, call 14 days in advance for weekends and holidays.
Winter condition: the golf course is open all year long. Dry (drains very well).
Terrain: flat, some hills. **Tees:** all grass. **Spikes:** soft spikes preferred.
Services: club rentals, lessons, pro shop, club memberships, snack bar, wine,
beer, putting & chipping greens. **Comments:** this golf course is very tight,
tricky, and well maintained. Greens are small and can be hard to hold. Two sets
of tees are available for a full 18 hole round. Good test for any level of player.

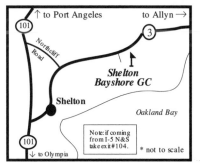

Directions: from I-5 N&S take exit #104
to Hwy 101 toward Shelton. Take the exit
for Hwy 3 (toward Allyn). The golf
course is located 4 miles north of Shelton,
going towards Bremerton.

Course Yardage & Par:
M-2946 yards, par 36.
W-2752 yards, par 36.
Dual tees for 18 holes:
M-6004 yards, par 72.
W-5698 yards, par 73.

Sheridan Greens Golf Course (public, 9 hole course)
P.O. Box 454; 380 Sheridan Road; Republic, WA 99166
Phone: (509) 775-2767. Fax: none. Internet: none.
Manager: Ron Tatlow. Superintendent: none.
Rating/Slope: the golf course is not rated. **Course record:** 68.
Green fees: $8 all week long; $10 all day rate; no credit cards.
Power cart: $10. **Pull cart:** $1. **Trail fee:** not allowed.
Reservation policy: no advance reservations are required or needed.
Winter condition: the golf course is closed from October to mid-March.
Terrain: flat, some hills. **Tees:** grass. **Spikes:** soft spikes preferred.
Services: club rentals, snacks, pro shop, lounge. **Comments:** the course is often
on the honor system. The golf course is very easy to walk. It now has expanded
to 9 holes so you now can play a somewhat rustic but regulation golf course.

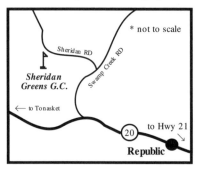

Directions: the golf course is located
2 miles west of Republic off Hwy 20.
Turn right on Swamp Creek Road and
proceed for 1.5 miles to the golf course.
Note the sign for the golf course cut-off
on Sheridan Road.

Course Yardage & Par:
M-2185 yards, par 32.
W-2185 yards, par 32.

Shuksan Golf Club (public, 18 hole course)

1500 East Axton; Bellingham, WA 98226

Phone: (360) 398-8888. **Fax:** (360) 398-8272. **Internet:** www.cybergolf.com/shuks
Pro: Ben Harvey, PGA. **Superintendent:** Reg Riddle.
Rating/Slope: C 72.2/135; M 70.1/125; W 71.0/123. **Course record:** 72.
Green fees: course has asked that you call for rates and any specials.
Power cart: $12+tax, per person. **Pull cart:** N/A. **Trail fee:** not allowed.
Reservation policy: please call 7 days in advance for a tee time.
Winter condition: the golf course is open all year long. Weather permitting.
Terrain: flat, some steep hills. **Tees:** grass. **Spikes:** soft spikes required.
Services: club rentals, lessons, snack bar, restaurant, beer, wine, pro shop,
driving range, putting green, tournaments always welcome, banquet facilities.
Comments: excellent newer course that offers the golfer fantastic golf on every
hole. Magestic views of the mountains and surrounding countryside can be seen
from nearly every tee. The facility was recently ranked FOUR STAR by *Golf
Digest* Places to Play. This course is a must play for any northwest golfer.

Directions: from I-5 southbound take exit
#262 (Main St-City Center) eastbound.
Travel east on Main which will become
Axton Rd. The course is located approxi-
mately 7.8 miles ahead on the left. From
I-5 northbound take exit #256. Follow
Meridian to Axton Rd. and turn right.
The golf course will be on your left.
Look for signs to the golf course.

Course Yardage & Par:

C-6733 yards, par 72.
M-6235 yards, par 72.
W-5271 yards, par 72.

Similk Beach Golf Course (public, 18 hole course)
12518 Christianson Road; Anacortes, WA 98221
Phone: (360) 293-3444. Fax: (360) 293-2327. Internet: none.
Pro: Dick Freier. Superintendent: John Yandle.
Rating/Slope: M 68.4/110; W 72.3/112. Course record: 65.
Green fees: W/D $19/$13; W/E $22/$16; all day rates; M/C, VISA.
Power cart: $22/$11. **Pull cart:** $2.50. **Trail fee:** no charge for personal carts.
Reservation policy: you may call up 2 weeks in advance for tee times.
Winter condition: the course is open all year. Damp conditions.
Terrain: flat, some hills. **Tees:** all grass. **Spikes:** soft spikes preferred.
Services: club rentals, lessons, snack bar, pop, driving range, putting green.
Comments: the layout of this course is fairly open with a few water hazards.
Greens are medium in size and are usually open in the front. The golf course has
a well stocked pro shop and excellent driving range to serve you. Good public
track that is very popular with the local golfer. Worth a trip if on the area.

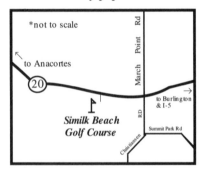

Directions: from I-5 northbound take
exit # 230 to Hwy 20 W (Burlington-
Anacortes). The golf course is located
5 miles east of Anacortes, just off of
Hwy 20. You will be able to see the golf
course from the highway.

Course Yardage & Par:
M-6177 yards, par 72.
W-5788 yards, par 74.

Skagit Golf & Country Club (private, 18 hole course)

16701 Country Club Drive; Burlington, WA 98233
Phone: (360) 757-0530. Fax: (360) 757-0154. Internet: none.
Pro: David Bobillot, PGA. Superintendent: Gregory Miller.
Rating/Slope: M 68.7/118; W 70.6/115. Course record: 65.
Green fees: private club members & guests only; reciprocates.
Power cart: private club. **Pull cart:** private club. **Trail fee:** not allowed.
Reservation policy: summer only 48 hours in advance. No outside play.
Winter condition: the golf course is open all year long. Damp conditions.
Terrain: flat. **Tees:** all grass. **Spikes:** no metal spikes in the summer.
Services: club rentals, lessons, snack bar, lounge, restaurant, beer, wine, liquor, pro shop, lockers, showers, club memberships, putting green, driving range.
Comments: the golf course is a combination of tree-lined and open fairways. Many bunkers front the large greens. Four ponds come into play off the tee and are a major factor on your approach shots. Excellent private golf course.

Direction: from I-5 N&S take exit # 230 to Hwy 20 W. Travel west for 2.1 miles to Avon-Allen Road (the flashing light). Turn right. Proceed .5 miles to the golf course. Look for a small sign.

Course Yardage & Par:
M-6019 yards, par 71.
W-5439 yards, par 73.

Skamania Lodge Golf Course (public, resort, 18 hole course)

P.O. Box 189; 1131 Skamania Lodge Way; Stevenson, WA 98648
Phone: 1-800-293-0418 or (509) 427-2541. Fax: (509) 427-2546.
Pro: Guy Puddefoot, PGA. Superintendent: James Medler.
Rating/Slope: C 68.9/127; M 66.7/122; W 65.2/115. **Course record:** 66.
Green fees: $40/$20 all week long; Jr. and twilight rates; winter rates.
Power cart: $26/$14. **Pull cart:** $5/$3. **Trail fee:** not allowed.
Reservation policy: yes, please call up to 2 weeks in advance for tee times.
Winter condition: the golf course is open all year. Weather permitting.
Terrain: flat, some hills. **Tees:** all grass. **Spikes:** soft spikes only.
Services: pro shop, restaurant, wine, liquor, driving range, lodge facilities.
Comments: This well kept golf course offers great views of the Columbia
River Gorge and surrounding countryside. If you plan on vacationing for a few
days stay at the Skamania Lodge. The course itself is narrow in spots and its
greens are well bunkered. Shot placement is a must from the tee if you want to
score well. This full service facility is worth a special trip if you are in the area.

Directions: From Portland take I-84
eastbound to the Bridge of the Gods.
Turn eastbound to Hwy 14 and proceed
1.1 miles eastbound to Stevenson. The
golf course is located on the north side
of Hwy 14. From I-205 exit at Hwy 14
and proceed eastbound to Stevenson and
to the golf course. Look for signs.

Course Yardage & Par:
C-5776 yards, par 70.
M-5351 yards, par 70.
W-4362 yards, par 69.

Skyline Golf Course (public, 9 hole course)
20 Randall Drive; Cathlamet, WA 98612
Phone: (360) 795-8785. **Fax:** none. **Internet:** none.
Manager: Wayne Cochran. **Superintendent:** Wayne Cochran.
Rating/Slope: M 62.7/106; W 66.7/111. **Course record:** 59.
Green fees: $15/$8 all week long; no credit cards.
Power cart: $20/$10. **Pull cart:** $1. **Trail fee:** $5.
Reservation policy: please call 1 day in advance for tee-times.
Winter condition: the golf course is open all year long, dry.
Terrain: very hilly. **Tees:** grass & mats. **Spikes:** metal spikes permitted.
Services: limited services, club memberships.
Comments: the course is short and tight with a friendly atmosphere. Family
run and owned. The golf course can play much tougher than it appears.

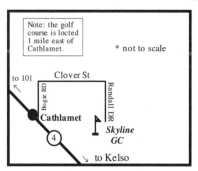

Directions: from I-5 N&S take the exit to
Hwy 4 westbound at Kelso to Cathlamet.
Turn right on Bogie Road. The road turns
right on Clover Street. Turn right at the
sign pointing to the golf course. The way
is well marked.

Course Yardage & Par:
M-2255 yards, par 35.
W-2012 yards, par 35.
Dual tees for 18 holes:
M-4774 yards, par 70.
W-4205 yards, par 70.

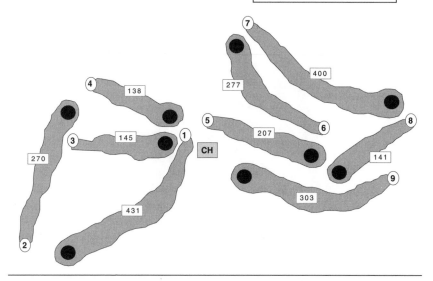

Snohomish Public Golf Course (public, 18 hole course)
7805 147th SE; P.O. Box 1188; Snohomish, WA 98290
Phone: (360) 568-2676 or 1- 800-560-2676. Internet: **www.snohomishgolf.com**
Dir. of Golf: Fred Jacobson, PGA. Pro: J. Brandvold, PGA. Supt.: M. Harping.
Rating/Slope: C 71.7/122; M 69.8/117; W 73.3/125. **Course record:** 63.
Green fees: Monday-Thursday $22/$16; Friday-Sunday & holidays $28/$17;
Jr. & Sr. and active military rates (Monday-Friday); M/C, VISA.
Power cart: $22/$13 **Pull cart:** $3/$2. **Trail fee:** $9. **(add tax to all fees).**
Reservation policy: yes, call up to 1 week in advance for your tee times.
Winter condition: the golf course is open all year long. Dry conditions.
Terrain: relatively hilly. **Tees:** grass & mats. **Spikes:** soft spikes preferred.
Services: club rentals, lessons, snack bar, restaurant, beer, wine, pro shop, club
memberships, driving range, putting & chipping greens. **Comments:** beautiful
rural course. Located on a hill the course is surrounded by trees. The greens are
very large and well bunkered. Great public golf course that is a must play.

Directions: From I-5 N&S take exit
#194 to Hwy 2 going eastbound for 8
miles. Follow Hwy 2 east to Snohomish.
Take the Snohomish exit (look for a sign)
to 88th St. SE. Go east on 88th to 131st
Ave. SE. Turn left on 131st. Proceed to
84th Ave. SE and turn right. 84th
becomes 139th Ave. SE as you must turn
left. At the T in the road turn right on
80th St. SE. Proceed on 80th to 147th
Ave. SE. Turn left. Course is on right.

Course Yardage & Par:
C-6858 yards, par 72. M-6315 yards, par 72. W-5980 yards, par 74.

LinksTime.com
a division of Book4golf.com

Snoqualmie Falls Golf Course (public, 18 hole course)

35109 SE Fish Hatchery Road; P.O. Box 790; Fall City, WA 98024
Phone: (425) 222-5244 or 392-1276. Fax: (425) 222-5666. Internet: none.
Dir. of Golf: John Groshell, PGA. Pro: David Doty, PGA. Supt.: Lee Baldwin.
Rating/Slope: M 64.9/102; W 68.1/111. **Course record:** 60.
Green fees: W/D $26/$16; W/E $28/$18; Jr /Sr (M-F) $21/$13; VISA, M/C.
Power cart: $22/$12, single rider $15/$8. **Pull cart:** $3/$2. **Trail fee:** no.
Reservation policy: yes, call up to 6 days in advance for your tee times.
Winter condition: the golf course is open all year long. Drains well.
Terrain: very flat. **Tees:** grass & mats. **Spikes:** metal spikes permitted.
Services: club rentals, lessons, snack bar, restaurant, beer, pro shop, driving range. **Comments:** situated in the foothills of the Cascade Mountain Range, Snoqualmie Falls is easy to walk and fun to play. The golf course has a well stocked pro shop and great on course restaurant. Good public golf course.

Directions: from I-90 eastbound take exit # 22 to Preston. Turn left over the freeway, then right to the Preston-Fall City Road for 6.2 miles to Hwy 202E. Turn right and proceed approximately .8 miles to SE Fish Hatchery Road (look for a sign at the turn). Turn right to the golf course.

Course Yardage & Par:
M-5452 yards, par 71.
W-5224 yards, par 71.

Snoqualmie Ridge TPC Golf Club (private, 18 hole course)

36005 SE Ridge Street; Snoqualmie, WA 98065   www.tpcsnoqualmieridge.com
Director of Golf: Lindsey Taft, PGA. Superintendent: Tom Wolff.
Head Golf Professional: Mark Granberg, PGA
Phone: (425) 396-GOLF; 800-982-2290. Fax: (425) 888-2849.
Rating/Slope: T 75.5/142; C 73.5/140; M 72.0/135; W 71.4/127. **Record:** 67.
Green fees: private club members & guests only; reciprocates.
Power cart: private club. **Pull cart:** private club. **Trail fee:** private club.
Reservation policy: private club members & guests only.
Winter condition: the golf course is open year round, weather permitting.
Terrain: flat, some big hills. **Tees:** all grass. **Spikes:** soft spikes only.
Services: lessons, lounge, beer, wine, liquor, driving range, club memberships.
Comments: this newer golf course is nothing short of spectacular. Reaching
over 7200 yards from the back tees Snoqualmie Ridge features extensive
mounding, generous landing areas from the tees and large undualting greens.
Bunkers, ponds and native growth areas will gobble up any errant tee shot.
This is will soon become one of the premier private courses in the Northwest.

<u>Directions:</u> from I-90 east & west take
exit #25 (Hwy 18) turn northbound onto
Snoqualmie Ridge Parkway which is
about .4 miles ahead. From Hwy 202
turn southbound onto Snoqualmie Ridge
Parkway. Look for signs posted.

Course Yardage & Par:

T-7264 yards, par 72.
C-6880 yards, par 72.
M-6522 yards, par 72.
M-6111 yards. par 72.
W-5384 yards, par 72.

Spokane Country Club (private, 18 hole course)

W 2010 Waikiki Road; P.O. Box 18750; Spokane, WA 99218;
Phone: (509) 466-9813. Fax: (509) 466-8044. Internet: none.
Pro: Les Blakley, PGA. Superintendent: Jeff Gullikson.
Rating/Slope: C 71.2/126; M 69.6/122; W 74.0/129. **Course record:** 61.
Green fees: private club members & guests only; reciprocates; no credit cards.
Power cart: private club. **Pull cart:** private club. **Trail fee:** private club.
Reservation policy: members only club, reciprocates call for policy.
Winter condition: the golf course is open all year, weather permitting.
Terrain: flat, some hills. **Tees:** all grass. **Spikes:** soft spikes only.
Services: club rentals, lessons, snack bar, restaurant, lounge, beer, wine, liquor, showers, driving range, putting green. **Comments:** this golf course was remodeled in 1988 by Robert Muir Graves. A very difficult layout that puts a premium on accuracy off the tee. Excellent private track that is very demanding.

Directions: from I-90 E&W exit #281 (Division Street). Travel northbound on Division Street to Francis Avenue and turn left. Proceed on Francis Avenue to Wall Street and turn right. Then follow Wall Street to Waikiki Road which will lead to the golf course.

Course Yardage & Par:
C-6634 yards, par 72.
M-6301 yards, par 72.
W-5858 yards, par 73.
W-5549 yards, par 73.

Sudden Valley Golf & Country Club (semi-private, 18 holes)
2145 Lake Whatcom Boulevard; Bellingham, WA 98226
Phone: (360) 734-6435. **Fax:**(360) 734-1915. **Internet:** www.suddenvalleygolf.com
Pro: Greg Paul, PGA. **Superintendent:** Bryan Newman.
Rating/Slope: C 71.8/126; M 70.0/123; W 72.8/124. **Course record:** 64.
Green fees: M-Thur. $30+tax; Fri-Sun. $45+tax; Jr. rates.; M/C, VISA, AMEX.
Power cart: $24/$14+tax. **Pull cart:** $3. **Trail fee:** personal carts not allowed.
Reservation policy: yes, call up to 1 week in advance for your tee times.
Winter condition: the golf course is open all year long. Good conditions.
Terrain: relatively hilly. **Tees:** grass. **Spikes:** soft spikes required in summer.
Services: club rentals, lessons, snack bar, lounge, restaurant, beer, wine, liquor,
pro shop, golf packages, range. **Comments:** Designed by Ted Robinson this
championship caliber course is considered a true masterpiece, stressing finesse
and accuracy with water hazards in play on 14 holes and some 47 sand bunkers
sprinkled throughout the layout. It's a golfing experience that you will not forget.

Directions: from I-5 S take exit #253
(Lakeway Dr.). Take left at the stop light
onto Lakeway Dr. Proceed on Lakeway Dr.
(which turns into Lake Whatcom Blvd. for
10.2 miles then you will run right into
Sudden Valley. From I-5 N take exit # 240
(Alger). Turn right at the stop sign and
proceed 1 mile to the next stop sign (Alger
Tavern on left). Go straight through
intersection onto Cain Lake Rd. Proceed
for 8 miles. Turn left onto Lake Whatcom
Blvd. Proceed for 3.5 miles to entrance.

Course Yardage & Par:

C-6553 yards, par 72.
M-6143 yards, par 72.
W-5627 yards, par 72.

LinksTime.com
a division of Bookgolf.com

Sumner Meadows Golf Links (public, 18 hole course)

14802 8th Street E; Sumner, WA 98390. Internet: www.cybergolf.com/sumnermeadows
Phone: (253) 863-8198; T-Times: 1-888-258-3348. Fax: (253) 863-8341
Dir. of Golf: Ron Hagen, PGA. Pro: Charles Clinton. Supt.: Lee Anderson.
Rating/Slope: T 72.2/124; C 71.4/123; M 69.2/120; W 70.0/123. **Record:** 66.
Green fees: Monday thru Thursday $22.50/$15.75; Friday thru Sunday &
Holidays $29/$20; early bird specials, Jr. & Sr. rates, twilight rates & punch
cards; VISA, M/C, AMEX; all rates that are listed are subject to change.
Power cart: $23.85/$16.80. **Pull cart:** $3.75/$2.50. **Trail fee:** $10/$5 seasonal.
Reservation policy: please call 2 weeks in advance for tee times (can get busy).
Winter condition: the golf course is open all year long. Good conditions.
Terrain: flat, very walkable. **Tees:** all grass. **Spikes:** soft spikes preferred.
Services: club rentals, pro shop, lessons, deli, driving range, putting green.
Comments: This excellent newer facility is one of the finest courses in the
Northwest. This links style track has many challenging holes with approach
shots that carry over the water. Greens are large and bunkered. Golf tournaments
are welcome. This is a City of Sumner facility managed by Golf Resources NW.

Directions: from Hwy 167 north and south
bound exit in Sumner on the 8th Street E/
Milton exit. Proceed eastbound on 8th
Street E for 1 mile to the golf course on
your right hand side. Look for signs from
Hwy 167 marking your exit to the course.

↑ to Auburn
* not to scale
East Valley Hwy
8th St. E
8th Street E/Milton exit
Sumner Meadows Golf Links
167
↓ to Sumner

Course Yardage & Par:
T-6801 yards, par 72/73.
C-6630 yards, par 72.
M-6196 yards, par 72.
M-5705 yards, par 72.
W-5295 yards, par 72.

Sun Country Golf Resort (public, 9 hole course)

841 St. Andrews Drive; P.O. Box 364; Cle Elum, WA 98922
Phone: (509) 674-2226. Fax: none. Internet: none.
Manager: Ella Riach. Superintendent: Ken or Bryan Riach.
Rating/Slope: M 68.8/119; W 70.9/124. **Course record:** 33 for 9 holes.
Green fees: W/D $15/$10; W/E $20/$13; no credit cards.
Power cart: $18/$10. **Pull cart:** $1. **Trail fee:** $5 for 18 holes.
Reservation policy: yes, call ahead 7 days for your tee times.
Winter condition: the golf course is closed from mid October to mid April.
Terrain: flat, one hill. **Tees:** grass. **Spikes:** soft spikes only please.
Services: club rentals, snack bar, RV park.
Comments: beautiful setting in the eastern Cascade Mountain foothills. RV park adjacent to the clubhouse for those traveling. Two sets of tees for a full 18 holes of golf. Good course with medium to large greens with few hazards.

Directions: from I-90 E&W take exit #78 Golf Course Road. Follow signs to the RV park. The golf course is located on the south side of I-90 in the Sun Country Resort. Signs are posted.

Course Yardage & Par:
M-2861 yards, par 36.
W-2742 yards, par 37.
<u>**Dual tees for 18 holes:**</u>
M-5715 yards, par 72.
W-5466 yards, par 74.

Sun Dance Golf Course (public, 18 hole course)

9725 Nine Mile Road; Nine Mile Falls, WA 99026
Phone: (509) 466-4040. Fax: (509) 466-6143. Internet: www.sundancegc.com
Director: Ken Johnston, PGA. **Pro:** Denny Johnston.
Rating/Slope: M 67.9/112; W 72.6/ 119. **Course record:** 63.
Green fees: $18/$9 all week long Sr. rates $13 (M-F) Jr. rates $9.
Power cart: $20/$12 all week long. **Pull cart:** $3. **Trail fee:** $6.
Reservation policy: please call ahead 1 week for your tee times.
Winter condition: the golf course is closed from November to March.
Terrain: flat, some hills. **Tees:** grass. **Spikes:** no metal spikes permitted.
Services: club rentals, lessons, snack bar, restaurant, lounge, beer, wine, pro shop, driving range, putting green & chipping green, club memberships.
Comments: this public course sports tree-lined fairways and small greens. The golf course can get very busy during the summer so call ahead. Well conditioned track that plays much longer than the yardage may indicate. Good golf course.

Directions: from I-90 take exit # 280A to Walnut St. Turn north for 1.5 miles to Northwest Blvd. Turn left. Travel 5 miles to Hwy 291. Turn left and proceed 3 miles to the golf course. Look for a sign.

Course Yardage & Par:
C-6208 yards, par 70.
M-5965 yards, par 70.
W-5452 yards, par 72.

Sun Willows (public, 18 hole course)

2035 20th Avenue; Pasco, WA 99301
Phone: (509) 545-3440. Fax: (509) 545-6758. Internet: none.
Director of Golf: Joe Dubsky, PGA. Pro: Jeff Kent, PGA. Supt.: Pete Tice.
Rating/Slope: C 72.0/120; M 69.8116; W 71.6/119. **Course record:** 63.
Green fees: $18/$13 all week long; Jr. rates (Monday-Friday); VISA, M/C.
Power cart: $24/$12. **Pull cart:** $3. **Trail fee:** $8 for personal carts.
Reservation policy: yes, call up to 1 week in advance for tee times.
Winter condition: usually open all year long depending on the weather, dry.
Terrain: flat, walking course. **Tees:** grass. **Spikes:** soft spikes only.
Services: club rentals, lessons, restaurant, lounge, beer, wine, pro shop, driving range, putting & chipping greens. **Comments:** this excellent public facility has well-trapped greens and gentle rolling terrain. The tree-lined fairways are very wide with large landing areas. Water comes into play on several holes.

Directions: from I-182/Hwy12 take the 20th St. exit #128 and travel northbound to the course. The golf course is located across from the Red Lion Inn in Pasco. Look for signs indicating your turn.

Course Yardage & Par:
C-6715 yards, par 72.
M-6325 yards, par 72.
W-5665 yards, par 72.

SunLand Golf & Country Club (private, 18 hole course)
109 Hilltop Drive; Sequim, WA 98382
Phone: (360) 683-6800. **Fax:** (360) 683-4989. **Internet:** none.
Pro: Kelly O'Mera, PGA. **Superintendent:** Daniel Ratcliff.
Rating/Slope: C 70.7/123; M 69.7/121; W 71.6/123. **Course record:** 64.
Green fees: members club, weekend tournaments, reciprocals encouraged.
Power cart: private. **Pull cart:** private. **Trail fee:** personal carts not allowed.
Reservation policy: call the pro shop as outside play is restricted.
Winter condition: the golf course is open all year long. Dry conditions.
Terrain: flat, some hills. **Tees:** all grass. **Spikes:** soft spikes preferred.
Services: club rentals, lessons, snack bar, pro shop, driving range, putting green.
Comments: the course winds through a variety of forest and homesites. Greens are well-trapped and water comes into play on 3 holes. Great golf course located in the banana belt of Washington State. Very limited outside play available.

Directions: from Hwy 101 as you enter Sequim turn right on Sequim Avenue proceed 2.1 miles to Taylor Blvd. Turn right and follow to Fairway Dr. Turn left on Fairway Dr. to the clubhouse. Look for signs marking your turn to the complex.

Course Yardage & Par:

C-6313 yards, par 72.
M-6051 yards, par 72.
W-5554 yards, par 73.

Suntides Golf Course (public, 18 hole course)

231 Pence Road; Yakima, WA 98908
Phone: (509) 966-9065. **Fax:** (509) 966-2742. **Internet:** none.
Pro: Paul Cobleigh, PGA. **Superintendent:** Alex Imrie.
Rating/Slope: C 68.4/113; M 66.9/111; W 68.3/109. **Course record:** 62.
Green fees: $22/$13 all week long; winter rates; Jr. rates; VISA, M/C.
Power cart: $22/$11. **Pull cart:** $2/$1. **Trail fee:** $5 for personal carts.
Reservation policy: call Tuesday for Friday, Wednesday for the weekend
and Monday to book your Tuesday through Thursday tee-times.
Winter condition: the golf course is open all year long. Weather permitting.
Terrain: flat easy walking. **Tees:** grass. **Spikes:** soft spikes required.
Services: club rentals, lessons, snack bar, restaurant, lounge, beer, wine, liquor,
pro shop, driving range, putting course, RV park. **Comments:** a small creek
winds through the course which comes into play on numerous holes. A very
pleasant course to walk. New putting course opened in June of 1998.

Directions: the golf course is located 3
miles west of Yakima off of Hwy 12.
You will find the golf course on the north
side of the highway with the exit .5 miles
west of the Naches River. At traffic light
turn right, then quick right on Pence Rd.

Course Yardage & Par:
C-6232 yards, par 70.
M-5941 yards, par 70.
W-5509 yards, par 70.

Surfside Golf Course (public, 9 hole course)

31508 "J" Place; Ocean Park, WA 98640
Phone: (360) 665-4148. Fax: none. Internet: none.
Pros: Louis Runge, PGA, Mike Davidson, PGA. Superintendent: none.
Rating/Slope: M 68.6/119; W 72.5/124. **Course record:** 65.
Green fees: $20/$12 all week long; Jr /Sr, winter rates (M-F); VISA, M/C, DIS.
Power cart: $20/$12. **Pull cart:** $2.50/$1.50. **Trail fee:** $10/$5.
Reservation policy: yes, recommended. Call 7 days in advance for tee times.
Winter condition: dry, the golf course is open all year long weather permitting.
Terrain: flat (easy walking). **Tees:** all grass. **Spikes:** metal spikes permitted.
Services: club rentals, snack bar, pro shop, club memberships, lessons, driving range, putting & chipping greens. **Comments:** the course is very easy to walk. Water comes into play on four of the nine holes. The wind plays a major factor from the tee and on your approach shots. Greens are on the small size and can be hard to hold. Good place to play when visiting the Washington coast.

Directions: from I-5 N&S take exit # 104 to Hwy 101 south to Long Beach to Hwy 103. Go north to Ocean Park, following signs to Surfside. The course is located 2 miles north of Ocean Park. Look for signs marking your turn to the golf course. The way is well marked.

Course Yardage & Par:

M-2960 yards, par 36.
W-2788 yards, par 36.
Dual tees for 18 holes:
M-6060 yards, par 72.
W-5647 yards, par 72.

Tacoma Country & Golf Club (private, 18 hole course)

Gravelly Lake Drive SW; Tacoma, WA 98498

Phone: (253) 588-0404. **Fax:** (253) 588-2164. **Internet:** none.

Pro: Rich Friend, PGA. **Superintendent:** Paul Joel Kachmarek.

Rating/Slope: C 71.6/124; M 70.1/121; W 72.7/124. **Course record:** 62.

Green fees: members only & guests only; very limited reciprocation.

Power cart: private club. **Pull cart:** private club. **Trail fee:** not allowed.

Reservation policy: private club members & guests of members only.

Winter condition: the golf course is open all year long. Dry conditions.

Terrain: flat, some slight hills. **Tees:** grass. **Spikes:** soft spikes preferred.

Services: club rentals, lessons, snack bar, lounge, beer, wine, liquor, pro shop, lockers, showers, club memberships, driving range, putting & chipping greens.

Comments: the course was built in 1894, the oldest private golf club west of the Mississippi. Greens are large with bunkers coming into play on nearly every hole. Fairways are tree-lined and play tight in certain area's of the course.

Directions: from I-5 N&S take exit # 124 to Gravelly Lake Dr. Travel west for .5 miles to Country Club Dr. SW. Turn south to the course.

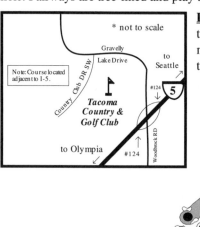

Course Yardage & Par:

C-6590 yards, par 72.
M-6282 yards, par 72.
W-5768 yards, par 73.

Tall Chief Golf Course (public, 18 hole course)

1313 West Snoqualmie River Road SE; Fall City, WA 98024
Phone: (425) 222-5911. Fax: (425) 222-5054. Internet: www.tallchiefgolf.com
Pro: Rick Larson, PGA. Superintendent: Craig Labelle.
Rating/Slope: C 65.0/108; M 64.1/106; W 62.9/103. **Course record:** 61.
Green fees: W/D $22/$15; W/E $25/$16; Jr. & Sr. rates are available
(Monday thru Friday only); outside tournaments are welcome. VISA, M/C.
Power cart: $23/$15. **Pull cart:** $3. **Trail fee:** not available.
Reservation policy: call up to 6 days in advance by phone, 7 days in person.
Winter condition: damp conditions. The golf course is open all year long.
Terrain: flat, some hills. **Tees:** all grass. **Spikes:** metal spikes permitted.
Services: club rentals, lessons, cafe, beer, wine, practice area, driving net.
Comments: this golf course is set in the foothills of the scenic Cascade Mountain Range. An excellent facility for tournaments and private functions. There is a Campground adjacent to the golf course. Friendly course that is worth the trip if you want a fun casual day of golfing with the whole family. Good golf course.

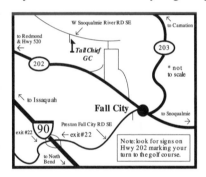

Directions: from I-5 N&S take exit # 168B to Hwy 520 eastbound. Travel east to Hwy 202 E (Redmond-Fall City Road). Turn right and travel 10.5 miles to 308th SE. Turn left and proceed .8 miles, follow the arterial to West Snoqualmie River Road. Go left and proceed .9 miles to the golf course. There are signs on Hwy 202 marking your turn to the golf course.

Course Yardage & Par:
C-5422 yards, par 70.
M-5218 yards, par 70.
W-4945 yards, par 71.

Practice Green

Tam O' Shanter Golf & Country Club (private, 18 hole course)
1313 183rd Avenue NE; Bellevue, WA 98008
Phone: (425) 746-3502. Fax: (425) 746-4667. Internet: tamoshanter.net.
Pro: Steve Englund, PGA. Superintendent: Tom Corlett.
Rating/Slope: C 70.1/127; M 68.7/123; W 70.7/123. **Course record:** 62.
Green fees: private, members & guests of members only, limited reciprocation.
Power cart: private club members only. **Pull cart:** private. **Trail fee:** private.
Reservation policy: private club members only. Limited reciprocation.
Winter condition: the golf course is open all year long. Wet conditions.
Terrain: relatively hilly. **Tees:** grass. **Spikes:** soft spikes preferred.
Services: club rentals, lessons, snack bar and grill, lounge, restaurant, beer,
wine, liquor, large pro shop, putting/chipping green, driving range (irons only).
Comments: must be a homeowner to gain membership in the golf club. Dual
tees and dual flags are provided for a full 18 hole round. The greens are large,
well bunkered and fast. Well kept private facility that was opened in 1964.

Directions: from I-5 N&S take exit
#168B to Hwy 520 eastbound. Exit at
148th SE. Turn south (right) and make
the first available left which is NE 24th.
Travel east on NE 24th for 2.1 miles to
182nd Ave. NE. Turn south for .7 miles
to the golf course.

Course Yardage & Par:
C-3072 yards, par 36.
M-2984 yards, par 36.
W-2704 yards, par 36.
Dual tees for 18 holes:
C-6168 yards, par 71.
M-5854 yards, par 71.
W-5383 yards, par 72.

Tanwax Greens (public, 9 hole course)

36510 Mountain Hwy East; Eatonville, WA 98328
Phone: (360) 832-8400. Fax: (360) 832-4498. Internet: none.
Manager: Ray Henricksen. Superintendent: Mark Henricksen.
Rating/Slope: the golf course has yet to be rated. **Course record:** 66.
Green fees: $25/$14 all week long; Sr rates $20/$10; M/C, VISA.
Power cart: $20/$12. **Pull cart:** $5. **Trail fee:** $5 for personal carts.
Reservation policy: yes, call up to 1 week in advance for reservations.
Winter condition: the golf course is open all year long. Dry conditions.
Terrain: flat, some hills. **Tees:** all grass. **Spikes:** soft spikes preferred.
Services: club rentals, pro shop, putting green, driving range.
Comments: this new layout set in Pierce County is finally ready for public play. The new course has water coming into play on four holes. Greens are huge with bumps, swales and tricky ridges. Not overly long Tanwax does challenge any level of golfer. The track sports dual tees for 18 hole play.

Directions: from Hwy 512 E&W exit southbound to Hwy 7. Follow Hwy 7 southbound through Spanaway and beyond for approximately 16 miles. The golf course is located on Hwy 7 just south of the junction of Hwy 702. The course is on the west side of the Hwy.

Course Yardage & Par:
C-3056 yards, par 36.
M-2908 yards, par 36.
W-2686 yards, par 36.
Dual tees for 18 holes:
C-5970 yards, par 72.
M-5697 yards, par 72.
W-5277 yards, par 72.

Tapps Island Golf Course (public, 9 hole course)
20818 Island Parkway East; Sumner, WA 98390
Phone: (253) 862-7011. Fax: (253) 862-3310. Internet: www.cybergolf.com
Pro: Bob Gelinas, PGA. Superintendent: Jeff Furrenes.
Rating/Slope: M 66.5/117; W 68.1/120. **Course record:** 62.
Green fees: M-Th $21/$14; Fri.-Sun $24/$16; Jr/Sr rates (M-Th); M/C, VISA.
Power cart: $22/$15. **Pull cart:** $3. **Trail fee:** $9 for personal carts.
Reservation policy: yes, call up to 1 week in advance for tee time reservations.
Winter condition: the golf course is open all year long. Dry conditions.
Terrain: flat, some hills. **Tees:** all grass. **Spikes:** soft spikes optional.
Services: club rentals, lessons, coffee shop, beer, wine, pro shop, putting green.
Comments: water comes into play on five holes. Well bunkered greens and narrow tree-lined fairways make this course a real challenge. Do not let the lack of distance fool you this course is very demanding. Rated as the #1 nine hole course in Washington Tapps Island offers good food and challenging golf. Some of the greatest greens around make Tapps Island G. C. worth a special trip.

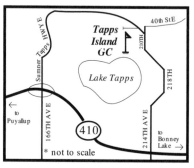

Directions: from I-5S take Hwy 512 to Hwy 410 into Bonney Lake. Turn left at 214th Ave. and proceed 4 miles to stop sign. Go left 3/4 mile and turn left on to Tapps Island. From I-5N take Hwy 18 east to Auburn/Enumclaw exit. Proceed 1 mile and veer right onto Howard St. Then in 1/4 mile turn right on "R" St. Follow "R" St. for 3 miles to 9th/214th Ave. Turn left on 214th Ave. Course located 3 miles ahead on your right.

Course Yardage & Par:
M-2643 yards, par 35.
W-2424 yards, par 35.
Dual tees for 18 holes:
M-5342 yards, par 70.
W-4848 yards, par 70.

Tekoa Golf Club (public, 9 hole course)
off of Hwy 27; P. O. Box 809; Tekoa, WA 99033
Phone: (509) 284-5607. **Fax:** none. **Internet:** none.
Pro: none available. **Manager:** none available.
Rating/Slope: M 64.2/105; W 68.2/113. **Course record:** 30.
Green fees: W/D $10; W/E & holidays $12; no credit cards.
Power cart: $12. **Pull cart:** none available. **Trail fee:** $3.
Reservation policy: none required play is on a first come first serve basis.
Winter condition: depending on the weather, but the course is generally closed.
Terrain: flat, some rolling hills. **Tees:** grass. **Spikes:** metal spikes permitted.
Services: the golf course has very limited services, putting green, league play.
Comments: this course features wide open rolling terrain and a few trees. The golf course plays very short with no hole over 500 yards. Great walking course for the first time or senior golfer. This course is rustic in design and grooming.

Directions: the golf course is located 1/2 mile south of Tekoa off of Hwy 27. Look for Farmington Road for your turn to the golf course. When you get to Golf Course Road you will turn left. Proceed on Golf Course Road to the clubhouse. Look for signs marking your turn to the clubhouse.

Course Yardage & Par:
M-2550 yards, par 35.   **W-2550 yards, par 35.**

The Golf Club at Newcastle (semi-private, 36 hole course)

15500 Six Penny Lane; Newcastle, WA 98059
Phone: (425) 793-GOLF. **Fax:** (425) 793-4643. **Internet:** www.newcastlegolf.com
Director of Golf: Jeff Minton, PGA. **Superintendent:** Phil Neiderbremer.
General Manager: Michael Abbott. **Dir. of Golf School:** Brian Lally, PGA.
Rating/Slope: T 73.7/133; C 71.6/128; M 68.5/122; W 69.4/119. **Record:** 67.
Green fees: January 1st to April 30th $125 all week; May 1st to June 30th
$145 all week; July 1st-December 31st $150 all week; M/C, VISA, AMEX.
Power cart: included in fee. **Pull cart:** not allowed. **Trail fee:** not allowed.
Reservation policy: you may call 7 days in advance for your tee times.
Winter condition: the golf course is open all year long. Weather permitting.
Terrain: some hills. **Tees:** all grass. **Spikes:** soft spikes required.
Services: club rentals, lessons, snack bar, pro shop, driving range, putting &
chipping greens, club memberships available, state of the art practice facility.
Comments: this is a unique new course built atop the old Newcastle landfill.
The course is already gaining notariety. The course has received the "Excellence
in Environmental Health" award from the National Association of County and
City Health Officials. The basic design is by the renowned architect Robert E.
Cupp of Atlanta with Fred Couples of PGA Tour fame acting as design consult-
ant. Spectacular views of the surrounding countryside and the Bellevue area
abound from nearly every tee. Championship caliber golf awaits you when you
step up to the first tee. The first 18 holes opened in the spring of 1999 with
another 18 holes to follow in the spring of 2001.

Directions: from I-405 N&S take exit
#10 Coal Creek Parkway. At the signal
light head east on Coal Creek Parkway.
Follow for 2.6 miles to Coal Creek
Marketplace Shopping Center. Turn left
at the signal on SE 72nd Place. Follow
up the hill to the next stop sign. Turn
left on SE Newcastle/Coal Creek Road.
Continue for 1.4 miles. Turn right at
155th. Proceed to Six Penny Lane where
you will turn right to the golf course.

Course Yardage & Par:
Coal Creek North Course
Gold: 7024 yards, par 72.
Blue: 6534 yards, par 72.
White: 6011 yards, par 72.
Red: 5153 yards, par 72.

Course Yardage & Par:
China Creek South Course
Gold: 6940 yards, par 72.
Blue: 6440 yards, par 72.
White: 6030 yards, par 72.
Red: 5120 yards, par 72.

Coal Creek
North Course

China Creek
South Course

Three Lakes Golf Course (public, 18 hole course)

2695 Golf Drive; Malaga, WA 98828

Phone: (509) 663-5448. **Fax:** (509) 662-5355. **Internet:** none.

Pro: John Christensen, PGA. **Superintendent:** Casey Creighton.

Rating/Slope: M 65.2/104; W 70.1/121. **Course record:** 61.

Green fees: Mon.-Thur. $20/$12; Friday-Sunday $25/$15; Jr. rates available.

Power cart: $22/$13. **Pull cart:** $3/$2. **Trail fee:** $10 (annual pass available).

Reservation policy: yes, please call 7 days in advance for a tee time.

Winter condition: closed December to February depending on the weather.

Terrain: relatively hilly. **Tees:** grass. **Spikes:** soft spikes required.

Services: club rentals, lessons, restaurant, beer, wine, pro shop, driving range, putting green. **Comments:** narrow tree-lined fairways make this course a real challenge. The golf course is well-kept and offers scenic views of the Columbia River and the surrounding countryside of the Wenatchee Valley.

Directions: from Hwy 97 take the Wenatchee exit. Go through the city center (on Wenatchee Ave). Travel 4 miles to the golf course turnoff which is southeast of the city. Turn right at West Malaga Road. The golf course will be on your left hand side. Look for signs.

Course Yardage & Par:

M-5327 yards, par 69.
W-5233 yards, par 72.

Three Rivers Golf Course (public, 18 hole course)
2222 South River Road; Kelso, WA 98626
Phone: (360) 423-4653, 800-286-7765. Fax: (360) 423-4653. Internet: none.
Pro: Chris Smith, PGA. Superintendent: Walt Stender.
Rating/Slope: C 70.8/118; M 68.3/113; M 67.2/110; W 70.0/111. **Record:** 64.
Green fees: W/D $20/$13; W/E $22/$16; Jr & Sr rates (M-F); M/C, VISA.
Power cart: $24/$13. **Pull cart:** $2. **Trail fee:**$10 (annual pass available).
Reservation policy: yes, call up to 1 week in advance for tee time reservations.
Winter condition: the golf course is open all year long, dry (drains very well).
Terrain: flat, some slight hills. **Tees:** grass. **Spikes:** metal spikes permitted.
Services: club rentals, lessons, snack bar, lounge, restaurant, beer, wine, lockers,
pro shop, club memberships, covered driving range, putting & chipping greens.
Comments: the course is built upon the Mt. St. Helens ash that filled the area, it
therefore has excellent drainage. The course is wide open and has large greens.

Directions: from I-5 take exit #36 and go
west on Hwy 432, turn north on Talley
Way which becomes Colorado Street and
then S. Pacific Avenue. Turn left on to
South River Road and follow signs to the
golf course.

Course Yardage & Par:
C-6694 yards, par 72.
M-6143 yards, par 72.
M-5800 yards, par 72.
W-5456 yards, par 72.

Touchet Valley Golf Course (public, 9 hole course)
209 North Pine Street; P.O. Box 54; Dayton, WA 99328
Phone: (509) 382-4851. **Fax:** none. **Internet:** none.
Manager: Sean Casseday. **Pro:** none. **Superintendent:** none.
Rating/Slope: C 67.8/114; M 66.8/115; W 72/122. **Course record:** 30.
Green fees: W/D $14/$10; W/E $16/$12; no special rates.
Power cart: $18/$10. **Pull cart:** $2.50. **Trail fee:** $5 for personal carts.
Reservation policy: please call ahead for weekend tee times. 1 day in advance.
Winter condition: the golf course is closed from October 16th to March 15th.
Terrain: flat (easy walking). **Tees:** all grass. **Spikes:** soft spikes only.
Services: club rentals, snack bar, restaurant. **Comments:** a unique setting within
the grounds of a horse racing track (Columbia Co. Fairgrounds Racing Track).
The golf course is flat and is very easy to walk. Greens are large and very flat.

Directions: the golf course is located
in Dayton on the north side of Hwy 12.
You will turn westbound on Main Street.
Then turn right at the Dayton Mercantile
store. Follow street north for 2 blocks.

Course Yardage & Par:
C-2931 yards, par 36.
M-2841 yards, par 36.
W-2745 yards, par 36.
<u>**Dual tees for 18 holes:**</u>
C-5862 yards, par 72.
M-5682 yards, par 72.
W-5490 yards, par 72.

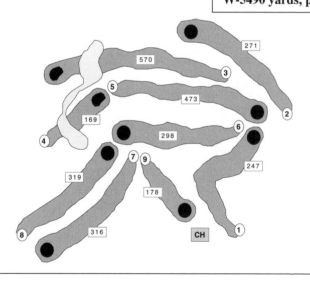

Tri City Country Club (semi-private, 18 hole course)

314 North Underwood Street; Kennewick, WA 99336
Phone: (509) 783-6014. Fax: (509) 783-1773. Internet: none.
Pro: Chris Isaacson, PGA. Superintendent: LeAnn Brosseau.
Rating/Slope: C 64.2/114; M 62.5/112; W 65.2/115. **Course record:** 57.
Green fees: Monday-Thursday $22; Friday-Sunday $30; no credit cards.
Power cart: $24/$12. **Pull cart:** $2.50. **Trail fee:** $15 for personal carts.
Reservation policy: yes, you may call 2 days ahead for your tee time.
Winter condition: the golf course is open all year long, weather permitting.
Terrain: relatively hilly. **Tees:** all grass. **Spikes:** soft spikes only.
Services: club rentals, lessons, pro shop, restaurant and lounge (members only).
Comments: the course sports tree-lined fairways and many well-trapped greens.
Water comes into play on three holes. In order to score well you must be able to
place your tee shot in the proper position. Excellent course that can play tough.

Directions: from Hwy 12 take the exit
Hwy 14 and continue to Yelm St. Turn
left. Travel to Clearwater. Left on
Clearwater and proceed to Underwood
where you turn into the golf course.

Course Yardage & Par:
C-5010 yards, par 65.
M-4693 yards, par 65.
W-4400 yards, par 65.

Tri-Mountain Golf Course (public, 18 hole course)

1701 NW 299th Street; Ridgefield, WA 98642
Phone: (888) TRI-MNTN. **Fax:** (360) 887-0516. **Internet:** www.cybergolf.com/tri-mtn
Pro: Chuck DaSilva, PGA. **Superintendent:** Dan Bierscheid.
Rating/Slope: C 71.4/124; M 69.1/116; W 70.9/123. **Course record:** 66.
Green fees: W/D $26/$15.50; W/E & Hol. $32/$18.50; winter, twilight rates.
Power cart: $24/$14. **Pull cart:** $3.50/$2.25. **Trail fee:** not allowed.
Reservation policy: please call 7 days in advance for a tee time reservation.
Winter condition: the golf course is open all year long. Good conditions.
Terrain: flat, with rolling hills. **Tees:** all grass. **Spikes:** soft spikes Apr.-Oct.
Services: club rentals, lessons, coffee shop, liquor, pro shop, aquatic driving
range, putting green, putting course, banquet room, on course beverage cart.
Comments: the course offers a number of challenges such as 74 sand traps,
11 lakes and award winning greens. This links-stlye golf course offers a new
clubhouse, restaurant and new drainage for 2000. Golf Groups are welcome.
This is a Clark County facility professionally managed by Golf Resources NW.

Directions: from I-5 northbound and
southbound take exit #14. Travel
eastbound on Hwy 501 to 11th Ave.
Turn left on 11th. Proceed to 299th.
Turn left on 299th to the golf course.
Look for signs to the golf course.

Course Yardage & Par:
C-6850 yards, par 72.
M-6091 yards, par 72.
W-5284 yards, par 72.

Trophy Lake Golf & Casting (public, 18 hole course)
3900 SW Lake Flora Road; Port Orchard, WA 98367
Phone: (360) 874-8337. Fax: (360) 876-6197. Internet: www.trophylakegolf .com
Pro: Mark Knowles, PGA. Superintendent: Eric Boley.
Rating/Slope: T 74.3/137; C 72.0/133; M 69.5/129; W 70.3/125. **Record:** 66.
Green fees: $34-$89, rates higher during peak months; M/C, VISA, AMEX.
Power cart: complimentary. **Pull cart:** complimentary. **Trail fee:** not allowed.
Reservation policy: please call 30 days in advance for a tee time reservation.
Winter condition: the golf course is open all year long. Dry conditions.
Terrain: flat, some hills. **Tees:** all grass.   **Spikes:** soft spikes April-October.
Services: club rentals, lessons, restaurant, snack bar, pro shop, beer, wine,
liquor, driving range. **Comments:** this championship layout opened on May
15th 1999 and offers something for both the golfing and fishing enthusiast.
Gentle rolling terrian, well manicured fairways and excellent putting surfaces
provide for an excellent round of golf. Spectacular views of Mt. Rainier and the
Olympic Mountains. The tournament pavillion and clubhouse oversee action on
the 18th green. Golf and fishing packages available. Worth a special trip.

Directions: from Hwy 16 exit at the
Sedgwick Road exit. Head westbound on
Sedgwick Road (which will become
Lake Flora Road) for 3.8 miles. The golf
course entrance will be on your left.

Course Yardage & Par:
T-7206 yards, par 72.
C-6756 yards, par 72.
M-6162 yards, par 72.
M-5654 yards, par 72.
W-5342 yards, par 72.

Tumwater Valley Golf Club (public, 18 hole course)
4611 Tumwater Valley Drive; Tumwater, WA 98501
Phone: (360) 943-9500. **Fax:** (360) 943-4378. **Internet:** www.olywa.net/tumwater/golf.html
Pro: Stu Adden, PGA. Superintendent: Skip Wirtz.
Rating/Slope: T 73.1/120; C 70.7/115; M 68.8/111; W 70.4/114. **Record:** 60.
Green fees: Mon.-Thur. $16/$10; Fri.-Sunday & Holidays $22/$15 (+tax).
Power cart: $10/$8 per player. **Pull cart:** $4/$3. **Trail fee:** $10.
Reservation policy: yes, please call up to 7 days in advance for reservations.
Winter condition: dry, excellent drainage. Course is open all year long.
Terrain: flat, some slight hills. **Tees:** grass. **Spikes:** soft spikes preferred.
Services: club rentals, lessons, snack bar, beer, beverages, pro shop, driving range, putting & chipping green, golf schools available, club memberships.
Comments: the course sports quick, undulating greens, and numerous sand or water hazards on seemingly every hole. Fairways are wide giving you room to work the ball off the tee. An excellent facility that has a great learning program.

Directions: from I-5 N&S take exit #103. Proceed southbound for .3 miles to Custer Way. Turn left and proceed for .2 miles to Capitol Blvd. Turn right for .4 miles to "E" Street. Turn left and proceed for .4 miles to the golf course. Look for signs marking your way.

Course Yardage & Par:
T-7154 yards, par 72.
C-6523 yards, par 72.
M-6108 yards, par 72.
W-5428 yards, par 72.

Twin Lakes Golf & Country Club (private, 18 hole course)
3583 SW 320th; Federal Way, WA 98023
Phone: (253) 838-0345. Fax: (253) 927-4441. Internet: none.
Pro: Joe Trembly, PGA. Superintendent: Dennis Campbell.
Rating/Slope: C 70.6/122; M 68.7/119 W 69.7/118. **Course record:** 62.
Green fees: private club member and guests only; reciprocates (very limited).
Power cart: private club members only. **Pull cart:** private. **Trail fee:** private.
Reservation policy: private club members only & guests of members only.
Winter condition: the golf course is open all year long. Dry conditions.
Terrain: flat, some hills. **Tees:** all grass. **Spikes:** soft spikes only.
Services: club rentals, lessons, lounge, restaurant, snack bar, beer, wine, liquor, lockers, showers, pro shop, putting & chipping greens, club memberships.
Comments: sweeping views of Puget Sound are seen from some fairways. A very tight, tree-lined track. Greens are large, fast and firm. Bunkers come into play throughout the golf course and are a major factor. Excellent private course.

Directions: from I-5 N&S take exit #143 to SW 320th. Travel west for 2.8 miles to the golf course which will be on your left hand side. The golf course can be seen from SW 320th Street which is a main road in Federal Way. Look for a small sign indicating your turn into the parking lot.

Course Yardage & Par:
C-6221 yards, par 72.
M-5852 yards, par 72.
W-5123 yards, par 72.

Twin Rivers Golf Course (public, 18 hole course)

4446 Preston-Fall City Road SE; Fall City, WA 98024
Phone: (425) 222-7575. **Fax:** (425) 222-6924. **Internet:** none.
Pro: Curt Roddewig, PGA. **Superintendent:** Doug Rutledge.
Manager/Owner: Richard Rutledge.
Rating/Slope: C 66.0/101; M 61.8/93; W 66.1/102. **Course record:** 63.
Green fees: $28/$18 everyday; Jr. & Sr. rates $20/$12 (Monday thru Friday).
Power cart: $22/$12. **Pull cart:** $4/$2. **Trail fee:** $3 for personal carts.
Reservation policy: you may call 7 days in advance for your tee-times.
Winter condition: the golf course open all year long. Good conditions.
Terrain: flat, easy to walk. **Tees:** all grass. **Spikes:** soft spikes only.
Services: club rentals, snack bar, beer, driving range, putting green, lessons.
Comments: The layout is fairly wide open featuring medium to small greens that are in excellent condition and can be hard to hold in the summer months. Twin Rivers is a very friendly golf course that is a pleasure to play.

Directions: from I-90 take exit #22. Follow the Preston-Fall City Road approximately 4.5 miles to the course which will be on your right. From Redmond travel east on Hwy 202 to Fall City. Turn right (south) on the Preston-Fall City Rd. approximately .5 miles to the course on your left. Look for sign.

Course Yardage & Par:

M-5760 yards, par 70.
W-4862 yards, par 70.

Tyee Valley Golf Course (public, 18 hole course)
2401 South 192nd; Seattle, WA 98188
Phone: (206) 878-3540. Fax: none. Internet: none.
Pro: Mark Olson, PGA. Superintendent: to be determined.
Rating/Slope: C 64.3/106; M 63.1/104; W 69.2/114. **Course record:** 60.
Green fees: W/D $18/$12; W/E $20; Sr./Jr. rates (M-F); VISA.
Power cart: $18/$10. **Pull cart:** $3.50/$2.50. **Trail fee:** $7.
Reservation policy: yes, call up to 1 week in advance for tee time reservations.
Winter condition: the golf course is open all year long, dry (drains very well).
Terrain: relatively hilly. **Tees:** grass. **Spikes:** metal spikes permitted.
Services: club rentals lessons, restaurant, beer, wine, pop, putting green.
Comments: fairly easy walking course. Greens are guarded by green side bunkers. The course is fairly wide open giving the golfer room off the tee. Water comes into play on a few holes and can be a factor. Fair conditioned golf course.

Directions: from I-5 N&S take exit #152 to S 188th. Proceed west for 1.1 miles to Pacific Hwy S. (Hwy 99S). Turn south for 2 miles to S 192nd. Turn west for .3 miles to the golf course. Look for signs marking your way to the golf course.

Course Yardage & Par:
C-5845 yards, par 71.
M-5812 yards, par 71.
W-5414 yards, par 73.

University Golf Club (public, 9 hole course)
754 124th South; Tacoma, WA 98444
Phone: (253) 535-7393. **Fax:** none. **Internet:** none.
Pro: Gary L. Cinotto. **Superintendent:** Benjamin Cinotto.
Rating/Slope: M 64.7/101; W 69.7/108. **Course record:** 60.
Green fees: $15/$9; Jr & Sr rates $12/$7 (weekdays only); M/C, VISA.
Power cart: $14/$7. **Pull cart:** $2. **Trail fee:** $3/$2 for personal carts.
Reservation policy: strictly open play, times are on a first come first play basis.
Winter condition: dry, drains well. The course is open all year long.
Terrain: very flat. **Tees:** all grass. **Spikes:** soft spikes preferred.
Services: club rentals, lessons, snack bar, pro shop, club memberships, putting
& chipping greens. **Comments:** the course is easy to walk and has excellent
greens. The track stays very dry during the winter months due to its excellent
drainage. Greens are medium in size with some guarded by bunkers.

Directions: from I-5 N&S take exit
127 to Hwy 512 E. Travel east for 2.1
miles to Highway 7 south. Proceed
southbound on Highway 7 for 1 mile to
125th Street S. Turn west and proceed to
Yakima Avenue, then turn right to the
golf course. Look for signs.

Course Yardage & Par:
M-2732 yards, par 35.
W-2732 yards, par 36.
Dual tees for 18 holes:
M-5391 yards, par 70.
W-5391 yards, par 71.

Useless Bay Golf & Country Club (private, 18 hole course)

5725 South Country Club Drive; Langley, WA 98260
Phone: (360) 321-5958. Fax: (360) 321-7636. Internet: none.
Pro: Bill Davis, PGA. Superintendent: Fred Vanbenschoten.
Rating/Slope: C 70.1/119; M 69.0/116; W 70.9/121. **Course record:** 65.
Green fees: private club members & guests only; reciprocates.
Power cart: private club members only. **Pull cart:** private. **Trail fee:** private.
Reservation policy: private club members & guests of members only.
Winter condition: damp conditions. The golf course is open all year long.
Terrain: flat, some hills. **Tees:** all grass. **Spikes:** soft spikes only.
Services: club rentals, lessons, snack bar, lounge, restaurant, beer, wine, liquor,
pro shop, putting green, club memberships. **Comments:** there are many water
hazards to contend with, along with a number of holes defined by out-of-bounds.
Greens are large in size and have some undulations. Great private golf course
that is set in a beautiful area of Washington State. No outside play allowed.

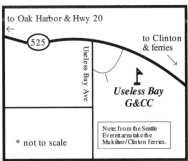

Directions: from the Mukilteo-Clinton
ferry take Hwy 525 for approximately 7
miles to Useless Bay Road. Turn left to
the golf course. Look for signs.

Course Yardage & Par:
C-6389 yards, par 72.
M-6134/6040 yards, par 72.
W-5493 yards, par 74.

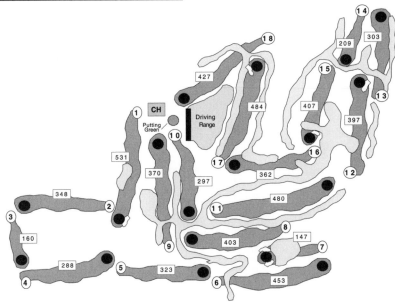

Valley View Golf Course (public, 9 hole course)

Liberty Lake Road; P. O. Box 326; Liberty Lake, WA 99019
Phone: (509) 928-3484. Fax: none. Internet: none
Pro: Dennis Reger, PGA. Superintendent: Dennis Reger.
Rating/Slope: M 58/no slope; W 62/no slope. **Course record:** 28.
Green fees: W/D $11/$7; W/E $14/$9; Jr/Sr rates (M-F); no credit cards.
Power cart: $12/$7. **Pull cart:** $2.50. **Trail fee:** no charge.
Reservation policy: not required. Times are on a first come first served basis.
Winter condition: the golf course is closed from December to March.
Terrain: flat (easy walking). **Tees:** all grass. **Spikes:** soft spikes only.
Services: club rentals, lessons, restaurant, lounge, beer, wine, driving range.
Comments: Spokane's only executive course. The course is well maintained
and easy to walk. Water comes into play on two holes. Two sets of tees.

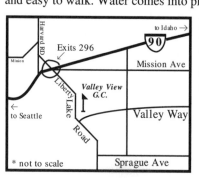

Directions: from I-90 eastbound and
westbound take exit # 296 (Liberty Lake).
The golf course is located two blocks to
the south on Liberty Lake Road. Look for
signs marking your way to the course.

Course Yardage & Par:
M-2072 yards, par 32.
W-2072 yards, par 32.
<u>Dual tees for 18 holes:</u>
M-4095 yards, par 62.
W-4095 yards, par 62.

Vashon Island Golf & Country Club (private, 9 hole course)

24615 75th Avenue SW; Vashon, WA 98070
Phone: (206) 463-2006. Fax: (206) 463-6489. Internet: none.
Pro: Steve Stensland, PGA. Superintendent: Ron Krieger.
Rating/Slope: M 68.0/119; W 70.2/118. **Course record:** 63.
Green fees: private club members only; reciprocates.
Power cart: private club. **Pull cart:** private. **Trail fee:** private.
Reservation policy: private club with limited outside play. Call pro shop.
Winter condition: the golf course is open all year long. Dry conditions.
Terrain: very hilly. **Tees:** all grass. **Spikes:** no metal spikes in summer.
Services: lessons, lounge, restaurant, beer, wine, liquor, pro shop, putting
green, covered driving range. **Comments:** dual tees available for a full 18 hole
round. Few hazards to contend with. The course is tree lined with bunkers
guarding the greens. Excellent track that plays much longer than the yardage.

Directions: from the West Seattle ferry
follow Vashon Island Hwy for 6.1 miles
to SW 204th. To east for 1 mile to
George Edwards Road. Turn south for
12 miles to SW 228th. Turn east for .1
mile to Portage-Dockton Road. Turn
south and proceed 1 mile to the course.

Course Yardage & Par:
M-3006 yards, par 35.
W-2618 yards, par 36.
Dual tees for 18 holes:
M-5890 yards, par 70.
W-5195 yards, par 72.

Veterans Memorial Golf Course (public, 18 hole course)
201 East Rees; P.O. Box 70; Walla Walla, WA 99362
Phone: (509) 527-4507. Fax: (509) 529-7586. Internet: weman@wwwics.com
Pro: Pat Welch, PGA, Nick Manolopoulos, PGA. 18 hole course, range.
Rating/Slope: C 70.7/115; M 69.2/111; W 70.0/114. **Course record:** 63.
Green fees: $19/$13 all week long; Jr. & Sr. rates; M/C, VISA.
Power cart: $24/$13. **Pull cart:** $3. **Trail fee:** $6 for personal carts.
Reservation policy: please call in advance for all your tee times.
Winter condition: the golf course is open all year long weather permitting, dry.
Terrain: flat, some hills. **Tees:** all grass. **Spikes:** metal spikes permitted.
Services: club rentals, lessons, snack bar, resturant, lounge, beer, wine, liquor,
pro shop, lockers, putting green, driving range. **Comments:** Veterans Memorial
is well-kept with tree-lined fairways and great greens. If you are looking for a
good course in eastern Washington, try Veterans Memorial. You will enjoy it.

Directions: the golf course is located east
of the city of Walla Walla off of Hwy 12.
Take the Rees Rd. exit to the golf course.
Go westbound for 1 block and turn right
on Rees Rd. Proceed and turn left to the
golf course. Look for signs at your turn.

Course Yardage & Par:
C-6646 yards, par 72.
M-6304 yards, par 72.
W-5403 yards, par 72.

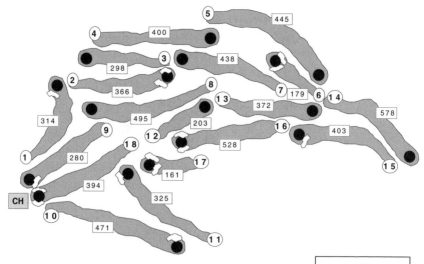

Vic Meyer's Golf Course (public, 9 hole course)

34228 Park Lake Road NE; Box 141; Coulee City, WA 99115
Phone: (509) 632-5738. Fax: none. Internet: none.
Manager: Ken Osborne. Superintendent: John Johanson.
Rating/Slope: C 70.9/105; M 67.9/102; W 70.8/108. **Course record:** 69.
Green fees: W/D $14/$10; W/E $16/$11; no special rates; VISA, M/C.
Power cart: $20/$12. **Pull cart:** $2. **Trail fee:** none for personal carts.
Reservation policy: yes, call ahead for a tee time, (especially in summer).
Winter condition: the golf course is closed from mid-October to mid-March.
Terrain: relatively hilly. **Tees:** grass. **Spikes:** soft spikes preferred.
Services: club rentals, snack bar, pro shop, showers, putting green, RV parking.
Comments: the course is a part the the Sun Lakes recreation area. The golf course is set atop the cliffs over looking Sun Lakes. Fairways are bordered by desert and is a major factor off the tee. This is a fair conditioned golf course.

Directions: the golf course is located off Hwy 17 north of Ephrata and Soap Lake at the Sun Lakes State Park Resort. From Hwy 17 turn at the park entrance and follow signs to the golf course.

Course Yardage & Par:
C-3123 yards, par 35.
M-2897 yards, par 35.
W-2702 yards, par 35.

Vicwood Golf Links (public, 18 hole course)
8383 Vicwood Lane; Lacey, WA 98516
Phone: (360) 455-8383 or 1-800-55-TEE-IT. **Internet:** www.cybergolf.com/vicwood
Pro: Kevin Meyers, PGA. **Superintendent:** Scott Brooke.
Rating/Slope: T 72.8/123; C 71.7/120; M 69.6/118; W 69.5/112; . **Record:** 65.
Green fees: Monday-Thursday $35; Friday-Sunday $41; M/C, VISA, AMEX.
Power cart: $12 per player. **Pull cart:** $3.50. **Trail fee:** not allowed.
Reservation policy: please call up to 7 days in advance for tee times.
Winter condition: the golf course is open all year long. Drains very well.
Terrain: relatively flat, walkable. **Tees:** grass. **Spikes:** soft spikes April-Sept.
Services: full service clubhouse featuring Two-Woods Eatery, beverage cart services, club rentals, lessons, pro shop, driving range, putting green & course.
Comments: this links-style course features commanding views of Mt. Rainier and Puget Sound. Large greens and wide fairways make this golf course very playable for every level of golfer. Golf groups are welcome any time of year. The facility is professionally managed by Golf Resources Northwest.

Directions: from the north take exit #111 from I-5. Turn right at the light. Go approximately 125 yards and turn right on Hogum Bay Rd. Go .3 miles to Meridian Campus Entrance at Willamette Dr., go 2.2 miles to the golf course. From the south take exit #111 from I-5. Turn left at the light and go over the freeway. Proceed through stop light and follow the above directions.

Course Yardage & Par:
T-6887 yards, par 72.
C-6774 yards, par 72.
M-6338 yards, par 72.
F-5722 yards, par 72.
W-5202 yards, par 72.

Village Greens Golf Course (public, 18 hole course)
2298 Fircrest Drive SE; Port Orchard, WA 98366
Phone: (360) 871-1222. **Fax: same as phone #. Internet: none.**
Pro: Doug Hathaway, PGA. **Superintendent:** Al Kim.
Rating/Slope: M 55.7/87; W 58.4/90. **Course record:** 51.
Green fees: $14/$12 all week long; Jr. $8; Sr. rates and military rates $10.
Power cart: $15/$10. **Pull cart:** $2. **Trail fee:** no trail fee.
Reservation policy: yes, please call ahead for a tee time.
Winter condition: the golf course is open all year long. Dry conditions.
Terrain: flat, some hills. **Tees:** all grass. **Spikes:** soft spikes preferred.
Services: club rentals, lessons, snack bar, pro shop, club memberships, putting & chipping greens, driving range. **Comments:** narrow tree-lined fairways and small greens make this short golf course very difficult. Varied terrain gives the golfer a wide variety of lies from the fairway. Worth a trip if you want a change of pace from the back breaker 6500 yard course. The new course record at Village Greens was just posted by 12 year old Brady Sharp.

Directions: from I-5 N&S take the exit for Hwy 16 W. Exit Hwy 16 at the 2nd Port Orchard exit, (sign will read Tremont and old Clifton Rd.). Stay on Tremont through five stop lights and continue until you reach a stop sign. Turn right and proceed for 1 1/2 blocks and then turn left on Fircrest. The course should be ahead.

Course Yardage & Par:
M-3255 yards, par 58.
W-3255 yards, par 62.

Walla Walla Country Club (private, 18 hole course)
1390 Country Club Road; Box 2246; Walla Walla, WA 99362
Phone: (509) 525-1562. **Fax:** (509) 525-1257. **Internet:** none.
Pro: John Thorsnes, PGA. **Superintendent:** Jeff Blanc.
Rating/Slope: M 71.0/123; W 71.1/119. **Course record:** 63.
Green fees: private club members only; reciprocates; M/C, VISA.
Power cart: private club. **Pull cart:** private club. **Trail fee:** private club.
Reservation policy: private club members only & guests only.
Winter condition: varies on the weather. Generally open during the winter.
Terrain: relatively hilly. **Tees:** all grass. **Spikes:** soft spikes only.
Services: club rentals, lessons, restaurant, lounge, beer, wine, liquor, pro shop, lockers, showers, driving range, putting & chipping greens, club memberships.
Comments: The course features sand and grass bunkers, narrow tree-lined fairways, and water. The fairways are plush during the summer and the views from this course are great. This well kept facility is one of the state's finest.

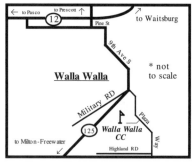

Directions: from Hwy 12 follow the Pendleton signs off of Hwy 12 to Plaza & 9th. Turn south on Plaza to Country Club Rd. Turn right and proceed to the golf course. Look for small sign.

Course Yardage & Par:
M-6429 yards, par 72.
W-5809 yards, par 74.

Walter E. Hall Memorial Golf Course (public, 18 hole course)
1226 West Casino Road; Everett, WA 98204
Phone: (425) 353-4653. **Fax:** (425) 423-9134. **Internet:** www.cybergolf.com/walterhall
Dir. of Golf: Mike Coury. **Pro:** Tyrone Hardy, PGA. **Supt.:** Barry Galde.
Rating/Slope: C 69.6/117; M 68.6/115; W 71.6/118. **Course record:** 63.
Green fees: Everett resident: Mon.-Thur. $17/$12.50; Fri.-Sun. & Hol. $21/$14.
Non resident Monday-Thur. $23/$17; Fri.-Sun. & Hol. $27/$19; Jr. & Sr. rates.
Power cart: $22/$14. **Pull cart:** $3. **Trail fee:** $5 for private carts.
Reservation policy: please call up to 1 week in advance for weekday tee times.
Please call on Monday morning at 9am for your weekend tee times.
Winter condition: the golf course is open all year long. Drains fairly well.
Terrain: flat, some hills. **Tees:** all grass. **Spikes:** soft spikes preferred.
Services: club rentals, lessons, restaurant, beer, wine, pro shop, club member-
ships, putting green, practice area. **Comments:** the course is very busy during
the summer. An easy walking golf course that only has a few elevation changes.
Walter E. Hall hosts a creek which winds through most of the back nine. This is
a City of Everett Parks facility, professionally managed by Golf Resources NW.

Directions: from I-5 N&S take exit
189 to Hwy 526 W. Turn west and
travel .6 miles to Evergreen Way. Turn
south. Proceed 1/10 of a mile to West
Casino Road. On W Casino Road turn
west and travel 1 mile to the golf course.

Course Yardage & Par:
C-6450 yards, par 72.
M-6209 yards, par 72.
W-5657 yards, par 73.

Wandermere Golf Course (public, 18 hole course)

North 13700 Division Street; Spokane, WA 99208
Phone: (509) 466-8023. Fax: (509) 468-0718. Internet: none.
Pros: Bob Ross, PGA, Bill Ross, PGA. Superintendent: Herb Brown.
Rating/Slope: C 68.4/108; M 66.7/105; W 69.4/107. **Course record:** 62.
Green fees: W/D $18/$14; W/E $20; Jr. & Sr. rates (M-F); VISA, M/C.
Power cart: $22/$11. **Pull cart:** $5/$3. **Trail fee:** $6 for personal carts.
Reservation policy: please call 7 days in advance for weekend and holiday
tee times. You may call 1 day in advance for weekday tee times.
Winter condition: the course is closed from December 23rd to late February.
Terrain: flat, some hills. **Tees:** all grass. **Spikes:** soft spikes preferred.
Services: club rentals, lessons, restaurant, lounge, beer, wine, pro shop, driving
range, putting green, club memberships. **Comments:** the course features rolling
fairways in which a creek comes into play on two holes. The fairways have
generous landing area's giving you room off the tee. Greens are small, firm and
hard to hold. This public play course can get very busy so be sure call ahead.

Directions: the golf course is located 10
miles north of Spokane off of Hwy 395.
Take the Division St exit off of I-90
eastbound and westbound. This will
turn into Hwy 395. Proceed on Hwy 395
northbound. Turn right on Wandermere
Road, the course will on your right.

Course Yardage & Par:
C-6050 yards, par 70.
M-5625 yards, par 70.
W-5625 yards, par 72.
W-5202 yards, par 71.

Washington National Golf Club (public, 18 hole course)
14330 SE Husky Way; Auburn, WA 98092

Phone: (253) 333-5000. **Fax:** (253) 333-2222. **Internet:** www.wngolf.com
Pro: Alan Plusquellec, PGA. **Superintendent:** Tom Christy.
Rating/Slope: H 75.6/141; S 72.7/134; J 71.1/133; S 68.2/120. **Record:** N/A.
Green fees: $34-$99; prices vary depending upon season, day and time of day.
Power cart: included in fee. **Pull cart:** N/A. **Trail fee:** not allowed.
Reservation policy: yes, call up to 30 days in advance for tee time reservations.
Winter condition: the golf course is open all year long. Dry conditions.
Terrain: flat, rolling terrain. **Tees:** all grass. **Spikes:** soft spikes only.
Services: club rentals, lessons, lounge, restaurant, snack bar, beverages, pro
shop, putting green & chipping green, driving range will open in June 2001.
Comments: phase one of this (1st 18) 36 hole complex opened in August of
2000. The golf course has quickly become recognized as one of the top golf
facilities on the west coast. The golf course theme is based on the U of W, and
is home to the Husky golf teams. Great golf course that is worth a special trip.

Directions: from Hwy 18 take the Auburn -
Black Diamond Hwy exit. Travel east bound
for 2.5 miles to 148th Way. Turn right and
proceed for 1 mile. The golf course will be
located on the right hand side.

Course Yardage & Par:
Husky-7304 yards, par 72. **Senior-6782 yards, par 72.** **Junior-6424 yards, par 72.** **Sophomore-5794 yards, par 72.** **Freshman-5117 yards, par 72.**

Washington State University Golf Course (public, 9 hole course)

North Fairway Drive; Pullman, WA 99164
Phone: (509) 335-4342. **Fax:** (509) 335-3837. **Internet:** none.
Manager: Les Davies. **Superintendent:** Steve Poole.
Rating/Slope: M 65.4/110; W 69.8/119. **Course record:** 29.
Green fees: $18/$13 (public) $14/$11 (student) all week long; VISA, M/C.
Power cart: $22/$13. **Pull cart:** $3. **Trail fee:** $3 for personal carts.
Reservation policy: yes, you may call 14 days in advance for a tee time.
Winter condition: the golf course is closed from November to mid-March.
Terrain: relatively hilly. **Tees:** all grass. **Spikes:** soft spikes recommended.
Services: club rentals, lessons, pro shop, driving range, putting & chipping
greens. **Comments:** this is a well-conditioned, scenic course located in the
heart of the Palouse on the campus of Washington State University. The terrain
varies from being flat on the first few holes then becoming very steep on the
inward holes. Greens are medium in size and fronted by sand bunkers.

Directions: from Hwy 270, turn into
the main WSU campus entrance. Follow
Stadium Way to Fairway Drive. Turn
right on Fairway Drive to the course.
The golf course is located on the
Washington State University campus.
Look for signs marking your way.

Course Yardage & Par:

M-2955 yards, par 36.
W-2642 yards, par 36.
Dual tees for 18 holes:
M-5891 yards, par 72.
W-5314 yards, par 72.

Wayne Golf Course (public, 18 hole course)
16721 96th NE; Bothell, WA 98011
Phone: (425) 486-4714 or 485-6237. **Fax:** none.
Pro: Steve Richards, PGA. **Superintendent:** John Amble.
Rating/Slope: M 60.6/97; W 64.5/105. **Course record:** 55.
Green fees: W/D $17/$14; W/E $20/$15; Jr & Sr rates (Monday thru Friday).
Power cart: $20/$14. **Pull cart:** $3. **Trail fee:** no charge (summer only).
Reservation policy: yes, call up to 1 week in advance for tee time reservations.
Winter condition: the golf course is open all year long. Wet conditions.
Terrain: relatively hilly. **Tees:** grass & mats. **Spikes:** metal spikes permitted.
Services: club rentals, lessons, snack bar, beer, pro shop, club memberships, putting green, practice net. **Comments:** the course is split by the Lake Washington-Sammamish Slough which winds through the golf course. A unique layout that sports eight par three holes including one of the shortest par fours on record. The 172 yard 12th hole. Greens are very small and can be hard to hold. The metropolitan location of this course makes it very popular with the local crowd.

Directions: from I-5 southbound take exit # 177 to Hwy 104E. Travel east for 2.5 miles to Hwy 522E. Travel east for 3.1 miles to 96th NE. Turn south to the course entrance on your right. From I-5 northbound take exit # 175 to NE 145th. Proceed east on NE 145th to for 1.5 miles to Bothell Way NE. Turn north and proceed 4.8 miles to 96th NE and to the course entrance on your right.

Course Yardage & Par:

M-4326 yards, par 65.
W-4237 yards, par 66.

Wellington Hills Golf Course (public, 9 hole course)
7026 240th Street SE; Woodinville, WA 98072
Phone: (425) 485-5589. Fax: (425) 483-1981. Internet: none.
Managers: Mimi Racicot, Jan Japar. Superintendent: Bob Japar.
Rating/Slope: M 63.2/102; W 67.8/107. **Course record:** 30 for 9 holes.
Green fees: W/D $16/$10; W/E $17/$11; Jr. & Sr. rates (M-F) $9; M/C, VISA.
Power cart: $25/$12.50. **Pull cart:** $2.50. **Trail fee:** no charge.
Reservation policy: reservations are taken daily. Please call in advance.
Winter condition: the golf course is open all year long, with damp conditions.
Terrain: relatively hilly. **Tees:** mats. **Spikes:** metal spikes permitted.
Services: club rentals, snack bar, restaurant, beer, wine, pro shop, putting green.
Comments: course is under new management. While the long-term range is
uncertain, the "Golf Options Company" has made many improvements over the
last five years, including a new irrigation system for putting greens and five new
grass tees. The pro shop has been expanded, to include discounted golf merchandise and apparel. At present time the course plans to operate indefinitely. This
track has rolling terrain, one pond and tree-lined fairways.

Directions: from I-405 N&S take exit
23 to Hwy 522 eastbound. Travel east
to Hwy 9S. Turn south. At 240th Street
SE turn east to the course. Look for signs
to the course from the exit from Hwy 522.

Course Yardage & Par:
M-2567 yards, par 34.
W-2557 yards, par 34.
Dual tees for 18 holes:
M-5175 yards, par 68.
W-5055 yards, par 68.

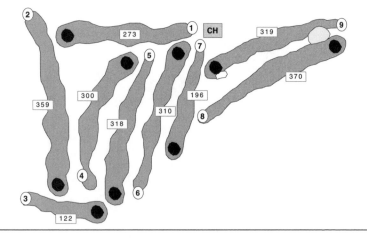

Wenatchee Golf & Country Club (private, 18 hole course)

1600 Country Club Drive; East Wenatchee, WA 98802
Phone: (509) 884-7050. Fax: (509) 884-6513. Internet: wenatcheegolfclub.org
Pro: Patrick Welch, PGA. Superintendent: Larry Farwell.
Rating/Slope: C 71.0/126; M 69.6/124; W 71.8/123. **Course record:** 62.
Green fees: private club members only; reciprocates; no credit cards.
Power cart: private club members only. **Pull cart:** private. **Trail fee:** private.
Reservation policy: private club members & guests of members only.
Winter condition: the golf course is open all year long weather permitting.
Terrain: relatively hilly. **Tees:** all grass. **Spikes:** soft spikes only.
Services: club rentals, lessons, lounge, restaurant, beer, wine, showers, grass
driving range, locker room, putting & chipping greens, club memberships.
Comments: narrow fairways and quick greens characterize this course. Greens
are well fronted by bunkers. Great private golf course that is a challenge to all.

Directions: from Hwy 2, after crossing
the Columbia River traveling toward East
Wenatchee, turn right at the Sunset Hwy
to 19th Street. Turn left. Follow to
Country Club Drive and the golf course.

Course Yardage & Par:
C-6405 yards, par 72.
M-6119 yards, par 72.
W-5519 yards, par 73.

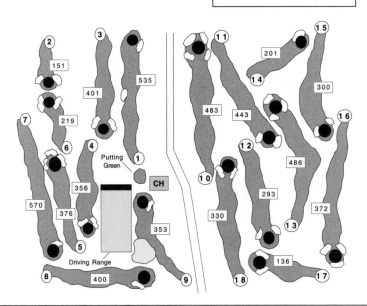

West Richland Municipal Golf Course (public, 18 holes)

4000 Fallon Drive (P.O. Box 41); West Richland, WA 99352
Phone: (509) 967-2165. Fax: (509) 967-5353. Internet: none
Pro: Rod Marcum, PGA. Superintendent: Dan Miksch.
Rating/Slope: M 67.7/114; W 70.3/114. **Course record:** 61.
Green fees: $12.50/$9.35; Jr & Sr rates (all week long); VISA, M/C.
Power cart: $20/$10. **Pull cart:** $2. **Trail fee:** $5 for personal carts.
Reservation policy: please call in 7 days advance for a tee time.
Winter condition: the golf course is open all year long. Dry conditions.
Terrain: very flat. **Tees:** grass & mats. **Spikes:** metal spikes permitted.
Services: club rentals, lessons, restaurant, pro shop, putting green, driving range, club memberships. **Comments:** this is a good course to walk due to its flat terrain and few elevation changes. The Yakima River borders the golf course and comes into play on numerous holes. Greens are large in size and have few hazards fronting them. Fairways are wide giving you lots of room.

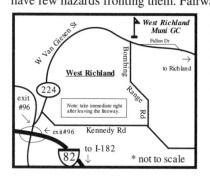

Directions: from I-82 take the West Richland exit #96 and enter town. Turn left on Fallon Road (by the Yakima River) to the golf course. From the Hwy 240 Bypass take the Van Gliesen exit, turn right onto 38th Street and follow this to the golf course. Look for signs.

Course Yardage & Par:
M-6103 yards, par 70.
W-5516 yards, par 71.

West Seattle Golf Club (public, 18 hole course)
4470 35th SW; Seattle, WA 98126
Phone: (206) 935-5187; Fax: (206) 937-7946. Internet: www.westseattlegolf.com
Director of Golf: Matt Amundsen, PGA.
Superintendent: Vern Rollin. Pro: Colin Gants, PGA.
Rating/Slope: C 70.8/118; M 68.8/116; W 71.6/120. **Records:** M 63; W 69.
Green fees: W/D $24; W/E $27; winter rates , Jr. & Sr. rates; M/C, VISA.
Power cart: $20/$13. **Pull cart:** $4. **Trail fee:** $10 for personal carts.
Reservation policy: up to 7 days ahead in person. 30 days via the internet.
Winter condition: the golf course is open all year long. Damp conditions.
Terrain: relatively hilly. **Tees:** all grass. **Spikes:** soft spikes preferred.
Services: club rentals, lessons, snack bar, lounge, restaurant, beer, wine, liquor, beverages, pro shop, lockers, putting & chipping green, club memberships.
Comments: the course sports a terrific view of the Seattle skyline. Fairways are tree-lined with a creek meandering throughout. Greens are large with bunkers guarding the front. Good track that plays much longer than the yardage indicates.

Directions: from I-5 N&S take exit # 163 to the West Seattle Freeway. Travel west for 2.5 miles to Fauntleroy Way. At 35th SW (the first light), turn left to the golf course. The golf course is next to the West Seattle Stadium.

Course Yardage & Par:
C-6623 yards, par 72.
M-6175 yards, par 72.
W-5611 yards, par 72.

Westwood West Golf Course (public, 9 hole course)
6408 Tieton Drive; Yakima, WA 98908
Phone: (509) 966-0890. Fax: none. Internet: none.
Manager: Bob Cyr. Superintendent: Bob Cyr.
Rating/Slope: M 64.3/104; W 69.1/110. **Course record:** 29.
Green fees: W/D $20/$12.50 (+ tax); W/E $22/$14 (+ tax); no credit cards.
Power cart: $22/$11 (+ tax). **Pull cart:** $2. **Trail fee:** $5/$3.
Reservation policy: call 7 days in advance for a tee time reservations.
Winter condition: the course is closed from mid-November to mid-February.
Terrain: flat, some slight hills. **Tees:** grass. **Spikes:** metal spikes permitted.
Services: club rentals, lessons, pro shop, putting green, covered driving range.
Comments: course is built in a unique setting, within an old apple orchard. The course offers rolling terrain and small greens to challenge your play. For those wanting to practice the course features a covered driving range with grass tees. Be sure to visit the fruit stand at the course when its apple picking time.

Directions: from I-82 take the exit at Nob Hill Road #34. Travel west to S 64th Avenue. Turn right and follow to Tieton Drive and the golf course. From Hwy 12 exit onto 40th Avenue S for 2.3 miles. Proceed to Tieton Drive and turn right to the golf course. Look for signs.

Course Yardage & Par:

M-2691 yards, par 35.
W-2607 yards, par 36.
Dual tees for 18 holes:
M-5378 yards, par 70.
W-5252 yards, par 72.

Whidbey Golf & Country Club (private, some outside play)

2430 SW Fairway Lane; Oak Harbor, WA 98277   (18 hole Course)
Phone: (360) 675-4546. Fax: (360) 679-9395. Internet: none.
Pro: Chuck West, PGA. Superintendent: Kurt Noonan.
Rating/Slope: C 71.2/120; M 69.6/117; W 70.6/120. **Course record:** 61.
Green fees: private club members and guests only; reciprocates. The course
does allow outside play in the afternoon. Monday to Thursday $40/$25.
Power cart: $24/$14. **Pull cart:** $2.50. **Trail fee:** $10 for personal carts.
Reservation policy: yes, call up to 7 days in advance for tee time reservations.
Winter condition: the golf course is open all year long. Drains very well.
Terrain: flat, some hills. **Tees:** grass. **Spikes:** soft spikes April-October.
Services: lessons, snack bar, restaurant, driving range, putting & chipping
greens, club memberships. **Comments:** the course has excellent greens all year
long. A very demanding layout with numerous sand traps and ponds to contend
with. Good private golf course that will challenge you at every turn.

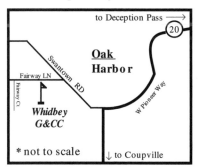

Directions: from I-5 N&S take exit 230
to Highway 20 West. Travel through
Oak Harbor. Turn right at Swan Town
Road to the golf course. Look for a sign
at the turn.

Course Yardage & Par:
C-6464 yards, par 72.
M-6096 yards, par 72.
W-5399 yards, par 73.

Whispering Firs Golf Club (private, 18 hole course)
NAFFMB Box 4369; McChord AFB 98438
Phone: (253) 984-2053 w/pin #; (253) 984-4927 w/out pin #.
Manager: James Tompkins. Superintendent: Terry Beck.
Rating/Slope: C 71.8/122; M 70.5/119; W 73.3/120. **Course record:** 63.
Green fees: private military club; All military ID holders, call for rates.
Power cart: private club. **Pull cart:** military only. **Trail fee:** not allowed.
Reservation policy: please call 7 days in advance for your tee times.
Winter condition: the golf course is open all year long. Dry conditions.
Terrain: flat, some hills. **Tees:** grass. **Spikes:** no metal spikes permitted.
Services: club rentals, lessons, snack bar, pop, beer, wine, pro shop, lockers,
showers, club memberships, covered driving range, putting & chipping greens.
Comments: the course is well-kept all year long. Narrow tree-lined fairways
and numerous sand traps make this a very difficult course. Water comes into
play on several holes and is a major factor off the tee. Great military golf course.

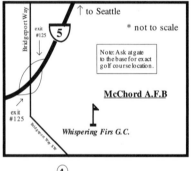

Directions: from I-5 southbound take
the exit at Lakewood/McChord. Turn
left at Bridgeport and travel straight to
the AFB where the golf course is
located. You will take exit #125 and
head toward the main gate. Ask at the
Main gate for exact directions to the golf
course once you are inside the base.

Course Yardage & Par:
C-6646 yards, par 72.
M-6345 yards, par 72.
W-5818 yards, par 73.

Willapa Harbor Golf Club (public, 9 hole course)
Route 3, Box 441; 2424 Fowler Street; Raymond, WA 98577
Phone: (360) 942-2392. Fax: (360) 942-5715. Internet: www.willapaharborgolf&rv.com
Pro: Louis Runge, PGA. Superintendent: Louis Runge.
Rating/Slope: M 68.8/119; W 72.7/123. **Course record:** 64.
Green fees: $14/$12 (peak season) $15/$10 (winter); M/C, VISA.
Power cart: $20/$12. **Pull cart:** $2.50/$1.50. **Trail fee:** $10/$7.
Reservation policy: call 7 days in advance for tee times during the summer.
Winter condition: the course is open all year long. Good playing conditions.
Terrain: flat, some hills. **Tees:** all grass. **Spikes:** metal spikes permitted.
Services: club rentals, lessons, snack bar, coffee shop, beer, beverages,
club memberships, pro shop, driving range, putting green, chipping area.
Comments: this golf course plays rather difficult with tree-lined, narrow
fairways. There are also pot bunkers in which to contend with. RV hook-ups on
site for those wanting to play golf and spend the night. Good walking course.

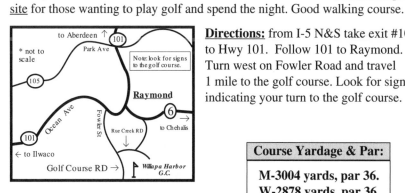

Directions: from I-5 N&S take exit #104
to Hwy 101. Follow 101 to Raymond.
Turn west on Fowler Road and travel
1 mile to the golf course. Look for signs
indicating your turn to the golf course.

Course Yardage & Par:
M-3004 yards, par 36.
W-2878 yards, par 36.

Willows Run Golf Club (public, 36 hole regulation course, 9 hole par 3)

10442 Willows Road NE; Redmond, WA 98052
Phone: (425) 883-1200 . Fax: (425) 869-7607. Internet: www.willowsrun.com
Pro: Ken Wooten, PGA. Superintendent: Ben Nelson.
Rating/Slope: Eagles Tallon C 72.4/122; M 69.8/117; W 72.3/119.
Rating/Slope: Coyote Creek C 69.5/118; M 67.3/114; W 69.3/113.
Course records: 64, Coyote Creek, 66 Eagle's Talon.
Green fees: Monday to Thursday $40; Friday to Sunday $55 (April-Oct. 15th).
Green fees Heron Links: W/D $11 adults; W/E $13 adults; $9 Jr. & Sr. rates.
Power cart: $25/$12.50. **Pull cart:** $5. **Trail fee:** not allowed.
Reservation policy: up to 1 week in advance all year long. A must in summer.
Winter condition: the golf course is open all year long. Dry conditions.
Terrain: flat, some hills. **Tees:** all grass. **Spikes:** soft spikes preferred.
Services: club rentals, pro shop, covered/heated practice range, practice putting and chipping greens, practice bunker, lessons, instructional program and clinics, restaurant, bar, beer, wine, spirits, club memberships, 18 hole putting course.
Comments: This excellent newer facility has a metropolitan location and is fast becoming one of the finest newer courses in the entire Northwest. This links style track has few trees, rolling terrain, and numerous bunkers. Greens are large and feature swales and undulations. With 45 holes and a brand new putting course, Willows Run is the most complete golf facility in the Pacific Northwest. This eastside golf complex is a must play.

Directions: from I-405 N&S take the 124th St. exit (Totem Lake). Travel eastbound on 124th Street for 1.4 miles to Willows Road NE. Turn right on Willows Road NE. Proceed on Willows Road NE for 1 mile to the golf course which will be on your left hand side.

Coyote Creek

Course Yardage & Par:
C-6337 yards, par 72.
M-5836 yards, par 72.
W-5194 yards, par 72.

Eagle's Talon

Course Yardage & Par:
C-6876 yards, par 72.
M-6340 yards, par 72.
W-5545 yards, par 72.

Heron Links

Course Yardage & Par:
M-1122 yards, par 27.
W-1122 yards, par 27.

Eagle's Talon & Coyote Creek Courses

Driving Range

CH

Heron Links Golf Course

Wing Point Golf & Country Club (private, 18 hole course)

811 Cherry Avenue; P.O. Box 10460; Bainbridge Island, WA 98110
Phone: (206) 842-7933. Fax: (206) 842-5088. Internet: none.
Pro: David Tunkkari. Supt.: Bill Schilling. Manager: Tom Zahaba.
Rating/Slope: C 69.2/127; M 67.6/123; W 71.8/124. **Course record:** 63.
Green fees: private club, members & guests of members only; reciprocates.
Power cart: private club members only. **Pull cart:** private. **Trail fee:** private.
Reservation policy: private club, members & guests of members only.
Winter condition: the golf course is open all year weather permitting, damp.
Terrain: flat, some hills. **Tees:** grass. **Spikes:** soft spikes May 1st to October.
Services: club rentals, lessons, lounge restaurant, beer, wine, liquor, pro shop,
lockers, putting & chipping greens, practice area, club memberships available.
Comments: the front nine is fairly open with numerous traps coming into play.
The back nine winds through tree lined fairways and plays short. In order to
score well you must place the ball in the right position off the tee. The layout
is designed to be a challenging target style golf course. Good private track.

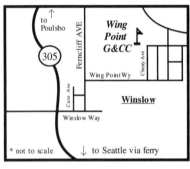

Directions: from the Seattle-Winslow
ferry terminal travel north for .2 miles to
Winslow Way. Turn right and proceed .5
miles to Ferncliff. Turn left. Continue .3
miles to Wing Point Way. Turn right and
travel another .5 miles to Cherry NE.
Turn left on Cherry NE to the golf course
clubhouse which will be on your left.

Course Yardage & Par:

C-6017 yards, par 71.
M-5613 yards, par 71.
W-5311 yards, par 72.

Yakima Country Club (private, 18 hole course)

500 Country Club Drive; Yakima, WA 98901
Phone: (509) 452-2266. Fax: (509) 575-8527. Internet: none.
Pro: Jim Gilbert, PGA. Supt.: Rob Robillard. Manager: John Thomas.
Rating/Slope: C 70.7/122; M 69.3/120; W 72.6/126. **Course record:** 64.
Green fees: private club members & guests only; reciprocates; no credit cards.
Power cart: available. **Pull cart:** available. **Trail fee:** $25 for personal carts.
Reservation policy: private club, members & guests only. The golf club does
reciprocate with other Northwest private clubs with established accounts.
Winter condition: the golf course is open all year long, weather permitting.
Terrain: flat, some hills. **Tees:** all grass. **Spikes:** no metal spikes permitted.
Services: lessons, restaurant, lounge, beer, wine, liquor, showers, driving range.
Comments: nicely treed well kept private course. Back nine plays very tight in
places making it tough to score on. Good course that is very demanding from
tee to green. Greens are large with bunkers and water coming into play.

Directions: from I-82 take exit #33 and travel eastbound. Turn north on Terrace Heights Drive to Country Club Drive. Turn right on Country Club Drive. Proceed on Country Club Drive to the golf course which will be located on your right hand side.

Course Yardage & Par:

C-6494 yards, par 71.
M-6181 yards, par 72.
W-5654 yards, par 72.

Yakima Elks Golf & Country Club (private, 18 hole course)

Golf Course Road; Selah, WA 98942

Phone: (509) 697-7177. Fax: (509) 697-3662. Internet: none.

Pro: Stuart Kitzmiller, PGA. Superintendent: N/A.

Rating/Slope: C 71.0/120; M 69.8/118; M 67.2/113; W 72.7/117. **Record:** 64.

Green fees: private club, members & guests only; reciprocates.

Power cart: private club. **Pull cart:** private club. **Trail fee:** private club.

Reservation policy: private club members & guests of members only.

Winter condition: the golf course is open all year, weather permitting.

Terrain: flat (easy walking). **Tees:** all grass. **Spikes:** no metal spikes permitted.

Services: club rentals, lessons, restaurant, lounge, beer, wine, liquor, lockers, showers, driving range, putting green, club memberships. **Comments:** this is a well conditioned, easy walking course with tree lined fairways and a number of water hazards to contend with. All the bunkers have been reconditioned and four bunkers have been added to improve play of the golf course.

Directions: from I-82 take the Selah exit (#30A) proceed eastbound to Golf Course Loop (the first right). Turn right and follow this to the golf course.

Course Yardage & Par:
C-6640 yards, par 71.
M-6360 yards, par 71.
M-5796 yards, par 71.
W-5844 yards, par 74.

Al's Cariboo Trail Driving Range
1 Morris Road; Okanogan, WA 98840
(509) 422-0618. Pro: no pro available.
Hours: range hours vary depending on the season.
Lights: no. **Covered:** no. **Putting & chipping:** yes.
Services: limited services. **Directions:** the range is located in Okanogan WA just off of Hwy 20. Turn right on Morris Road the range will be located on the left hand side of the street. Look for signs that are posted.

All Golf @ Tacoma
708 122th Street East; Tacoma, WA 98445
(253) 537-3037. Pro: Keith Sanden, PGA.
Hours: 9am to 9pm all week long.
Lights: yes. **Covered:** yes, heated, target greens. **Putting & chipping:** no.
Services: club repair, lessons, video lessons, pro shop. **Directions:** from Highway 512 take the Pacific Avenue exit. Turn left on 112th Street. The range is located 1/2 mile on the right hand side of the street.

Batstone Hill Driving Range
321 Mason Lake Road; Shelton, WA 98584
(360) 426-4276. Pro: none.
Hours: 9am to dusk. **Lights:** no. **Covered:** yes. **Putting & chipping:** putting & chipping. **Services:** lessons, vending machines. **Directions:** 5 miles north of Shelton on Hwy 3 to Mason Lake Road. The range is located .25 miles up Mason Lake Road on the left.

Beacon Hill Golf Center
4848 Valley Spring Road; Spokane, WA 99207
(509) 427-5730. Pro: unavailable.
Hours: 8am-dark. **Lights:** no. **Covered:** yes. **Putting & chipping:** 18 hole course, chipping area. **Services:** club repair, lessons, small pro shop, beverages.
Directions: from I-90 E&W take the Freya/Thor exit. Go north for 3 miles to Euclid Avenue. At Euclid Avenue go right for 3 blocks to Freya. When you get to Freya turn left to the range.

Columbia Super Range
511 128th SE; Everett, WA 98208
(425) 742-5790, (425) 338-2424. Pros: Kevin Mackay, PGA, Steve Rehul, PGA.
Hours: 7am to 11pm. **Lights:** yes. **Covered:** 50 stalls (heated).
Putting & chipping: 18 hole par 2 scramble course, putting green.
Services: club repair, lessons, video lessons, Nevada Bobs Retail Golf Store, snack bar, custom clubs.
Directions: I-5 N&S take exit 186. Go east for 1/2 mile to the range.

Emerald Links Driving Range
22719 Highway 410; Bonney Lake, WA 98390
(253) 891-8300. Pro: unavailable.
Hours: W/D 11am-7pm; W/E 9am-7pm (winter); (summer) 9am-8pm daily.
Lights: yes. **Covered:** yes. **Putting & chipping:** no.
Services: lessons, club repair, custom clubs, club fitting, discount pro shop.
Directions: the range is located on the north side of State Hwy 410.

Evergreen Golf Center
16703 SE 1st; Vancouver, WA 98684
(360) 253-3184. Pro: unavailable.
Hours: 9am to 9pm (winter), 9am to 10pm (summer).
Lights: yes. **Covered:** yes. **Putting & chipping:** putting only.
Services: lessons, club repair, custom clubs, pro shop, heated tee line.
Directions: from I-205 take the Mill Plain E exit to 164th. Turn north on 164th
to the stoplight which is 1st. Turn right on 1st to the driving range.

Family Golf Center @ Kent
9116 212th Street; Kent, WA 98032
(253) 850-8300. Pros: 5 PGA pros on staff.
Hours: 7:30am to 10pm (summer). Winter hours vary.
Lights: yes. **Covered:** most stalls are covered. **Putting & chipping:** putting.
Services: full service pro shop, PGA golf instruction, video teaching, deli,
beverages, 48 heated stalls. **Directions:** range is located at the intersections of
Highway 167 & 212th St. Take the exit for 212th off Hwy 167 go east to the
range. The range is located right off the highway.

Family Golf @ Tacoma Firs
4504 South Tyler Street; Tacoma, WA 98409
(253) 472- 6899. Pro: Craig Kennedy, PGA
Hours: 8am-10pm (summer); 9am-9pm (winter).
Lights: yes. **Covered:** yes. **Putting & chipping:** yes.
Services: club repair, lessons, restaurant, pro shop.
Directions: from I-5 N&S take exit #130 (56th St.). Go west for 1.3 miles to
Tyler. Turn right. Go 0.7 miles the range. From Hwy 16 take Fir-crest/Center St.

Gateway Golf Center
725 Port Way; Clarkston, WA 99403
(509) 758-4366. Pro: Chad Laird, PGA
Hours: 7am to 10pm (daily).
Lights: yes. **Covered:** yes. **Putting & chipping:** 18 hole putting course.
Services: lessons, club repair, pro shop, snack bar.
Directions: the range is located next to the Quality Inn on Port Drive, just off
Hwy 12. Look for signs.

Gold Creek Tennis & Sports Club
15327 140th PL NE; Woodinville, WA 98072
(425) 487-1090. Pro: Juanita Reinhardt, PGA.
Hours: Monday thru Friday 6am to 10pm, Saturday and Sunday 8am to 9pm.
Lights: yes. **Covered:** yes. **Putting & chipping:** yes.
Services: lessons, vending machines.
Directions: the range is located off of Hwy 202 in Woodinville. Look for the signs to the tennis & sports club.

Golf Club, The
6311 W Clearwater Ave.; Kennewick, WA 99336
(509) 735-6072. Pro: John Ostrander, PGA.
Hours: Monday-Thursday 10am-7pm; Friday- Saturday 10am-8pm; Sunday 10am-5pm, the range has longer hours during the summer months.
Lights: yes. **Covered:** yes & heated. **Putting & chipping:** no.
Services: lessons, discount pro shop, mini golf.
Directions: from Hwy 395 turn right on Clearwater Avenue. Proceed on Clearwater Avenue. 2.5 miles to the driving range is on the left hand side.

Grand Mound Driving Range
20525 Old Highway 9; Centralia, WA 98531
(360) 273-9335. Pro: none available.
Hours: 8am to dusk, 7 days a week (summer).
Lights: no. **Covered:** yes. **Putting & chipping:** yes.
Services: custom clubs, used clubs, practice bunker. **Directions:** from I-5 N&S take exit #88 (Hwy 12). Proceed west for 1 block to Old Hwy 99 and turn south. Proceed to Old Hwy 9 and turn left to the range.

Hickory Stick Driving Range
2831 Marvin Road NE; Olympia, WA 98502
(360) 438-2299. Manager: Ben Clement.
Hours: hours vary depending on season. Summer hours are extended.
Lights: yes. **Covered:** yes. **Putting & chipping:** yes, practice bunker.
Services: lessons, club repair, pro shop.
Directions: I-5 N&S take exit #111. Turn northbound on Marvin Road. The range is located 1/2 mile ahead on your left hand side of the road.

Iron Eagle Sports Center
16651 Currie Road; Monroe, WA 98272
(360) 794-0933. Pro: none.
Hours: 10am-8:30pm (M-Sat.) 10am-7:30pm (Sun.); extended summer hours.
Lights: yes. **Covered:** yes. **Putting & chipping:** putting only.
Services: pro shop, lessons, heated stalls. **Directions:** from Hwy 522 take 164th St. exit. Left off exit. Right on Curry Road to the driving range.

Kaddyshack Golf Center
4003 204th SW; Lynnwood, WA 98036
(425) 775-8911. Pros: Bill Jones PGA, Doug Lee, KPGA, app. John Spencer.
Hours: Sunday-Thursday 8am-11pm; Friday-Saturday 8am-12am.
Lights: yes. **Covered:** yes & heated. **Putting & chipping:** yes.
Services: club repair, lessons, discount pro shop. **Directions:** I-5 N take 44th
St. (Lynnwood) exit #181A. Straight through light at the bottom of hill and
follow to range.

Ken's Golf
1899 S Burlington Boulevard; Burlington, WA 98233
Phone: (360) 757-4653. Pro: Ken Harrsch, PGA.
Hours: 9am to dusk. The range has extended summer hours.
Lights: no. **Covered:** yes. **Putting & chipping:** no.
Services: pro shop, club repair, lessons. **Directions:** I-5S take exit 229 to stop
sign. Turn right, the range is located100 yards ahead.

Kitsap Country Green's
8400 NE W Kingston Road; Kingston, WA 98436
(360) 297-4653. Pro: none available.
Hours: 9am-9pm summer; 9am-7pm winter.
Lights: yes. **Covered:** yes. **Putting & chipping:** no.
Services: lessons, custom clubs, retail pro shop.
Directions: from Kingston turn left at Country Corners (Millers Bay Suquamish
Rd.). Proceed for 1 mile to the first left (West Kingston Rd.) turn left. Range 1/4
mile on your left.

Longshots Driving Range
1215 80th Street SW; Everett, WA 98203
(425) 355-2133. Pro: Bob Osgood, PGA.
Hours: summer 9am-9pm; winter hours vary.
Lights: yes. **Covered:** yes. **Putting & chipping:** no. **Services:** lessons.
Directions: From Hwy 99 go west on Casino Road to 5th Ave. North on 5th.
Take first left on 80th. The driving range is located on the right side of the street.

Marine Golf Driving Range
401 Parkway Drive; Rock Island, WA 98850
Phone: none. Pro: none.
Hours: 9am to dusk; extended summer hrs.
Lights: no. **Covered:** yes. **Putting & chipping:** no.
Services: pro shop, basic club repair, lessons.
Directions: range is off of Hwy 28 in Rock Island. Turn north on Akron
Avenue then right on Parkway drive.

North West Golf Range
368 NE Bucklin Hill Road; Bremerton, WA 98311
(360) 692-6828. Pro: Devin Loudon, PGA.
Hours: Monday through Sunday 9am-10pm.
Lights: yes. **Covered:** yes, 6 heated. **Putting & chipping:** no.
Services: lessons, club fitting, pro shop, 18 hole putting course, espresso, snack bar. **Directions:** range is located between Bremerton and Silverdale just off Wagga Way. Take the Schold Road exit.

ParFect Driving Range
91 S. Boyce Road; Sequim, WA 98382
Phone: (360) 681-5228. Owner: Randy Simmons.
Hours: 9am to 9pm daily.
Lights: yes. **Covered:** yes & heated. **Putting & chipping:** yes.
Services: club repair, lessons, pro shop. **Directions:** The range is located at the intersections of Boyce Rd. and State Hwy 101 west of the the city of Sequim.

Performance Golf Center
2416 14th Ave. NW; Gig Harbor, WA 98335
(253) 853-4653. Pro: Todd Erwin, PGA.
Hours: 7am to 11pm (summer) 9am-9pm (winter).
Lights: yes. **Covered:** yes. **Putting & chipping:** yes.
Services: discount pro shop, lessons, club repair, club fitting, 74 covered, heated tees, food service, grass tees, 18 hole miniature golf course.
Directions: the range is located right off of Hwy 16 in Gig Harbor.

Puetz Golf Range
11762 Aurora North; Seattle, WA 98133
(206) 362-2272. Pro: Jeff Zentner, PGA.
Hours: Monday to Saturday 9am-10pm; Sunday 9am-7pm; summer hours.
Lights: yes. **Covered:** yes. **Putting & chipping:** yes. **Services:** club repair, lessons, video lessons, soft mats, large discount pro shop, heated tee line.
Directions: I-5 N&S take exit #173 to NE Northgate Way W. West for .7 mi to Aurora Ave. Right on Aurora. Range is on the right.

Rainbow Golf Driving Range
2723 Harrison Avenue; Centralia, WA 98531
(360) 330-0585. Pro: none available.
Hours: Monday through Sunday 7am-8pm.
Lights: yes. **Covered:** yes. **Putting & chipping:** yes.
Services: pro shop, lessons, espresso, mini golf.
Directions: from I-5 N&S take exit #82 to Harrison Avenue. Proceed westbound on Harrison for 2.3 miles. The range is on your left.

Red Wood Golf Center
13029 Redmond Woodinville Road NE; Redmond, WA 98052
(425) 869-8814. Pros: Rodney Burruel, PGA, Keith Puetz, PGA.
Hours: 9:30am-9pm all week long.
Lights: yes. **Covered:** yes & heated. **Putting & chipping:** yes.
Services: full service pro shop, private, group, video & Jr. lessons, custom
clubs, and club repair. **Directions:** from I-405 N&S take exit 20B (NE 124th
St). Follow 124th east 3 miles to Hwy 202, turn left.

Rodarco Golf Range
8020 Kickerville Road; Blaine, WA 98230
(360) 332-2665. Pro: Roger D. Cook, PGA.
Hours: summer 8am-8pm daily.
Lights: no. **Covered:** 3 stalls with mats, 20 grass tees. **Putting & chipping:**
yes, practice bunker. **Services:** club repair, lessons, pro shop, snack bar.
Directions: I-5 N&S take exit #270 to Birch Bay-Lynden Road. West for 2
miles to Kickerville Road, turn south to range.

Ross's Driving Range
11405 NE 72nd Avenue; Vancouver, WA 98661
(360) 573-3315. Pro: none.
Hours: 10am-8pm (Monday through Friday), 9am-8pm (weekends).
Lights: yes. **Covered:** yes. **Putting & chipping:** no.
Services: lessons, custom clubs, club repair, pro shop.
Directions: from I-5 take exit #4 and proceed east on NE 78th to NE Andresen
Road. Turn left on Andresen and proceed to the range.

Southcenter Golf
18791 Southcenter Pkwy; Tukwila, WA 98188
(206) 575-7797. Pro: Jim Bennett, PGA.
Hours: 9am to 9pm (daily summer hours).
Lights: yes. **Covered:** yes. **Putting & chipping:** yes.
Services: club repair, lessons, pro shop, video studio, custom clubs.
Directions: proceed straight on Southcenter Pkwy. beyond the Pavillion thru the
intersection to the range located 2 blocks ahead.

Steamboat Golf
3605 Steamboat Is. Road; Olympia, WA 98502
(360) 867-0562. Pro: none.
Hours: 7am to 10pm, 7 days a week (summer). Winter hours vary.
Lights: yes. **Covered:** yes, grass tees. **Putting & chipping:** yes.
Services: soda pop, club rentals.
Directions: from Hwy 101 exit for Steamboat Island Road. The driving range
located 1/4 mile east on the left.

Studio Fore Golf
13434 16th Street; Bellevue, WA 98005
(425) 957-9810, 1-877-857-7733.
Pros: Lesley Holbert, LPGA. Ken Lawrence, PGA.
Hours: please call the indoor range for hours.
Lights: indoor. **Covered:** indoor. **Putting & chipping:** yes, indoor.
Services: club repair, lessons, custom clubs, golfers gym. **Directions:** the range is located on 16th street just off Bel-Red Road.

Tour Fairways Golf Center
1150 Abadie; Walla Walla, WA 99362
(509) 529-5810. Pro: Mike Rostollan, PGA
Hours: 8am-10pm summer. Winter hours vary.
Lights: yes. **Covered:** 12 covered, 75 grass tees. **Putting & chipping:** yes.
Services: pro shop, lessons, custom clubs, club repair, batting cages.
Directions: Hwy 12 exit at 2nd Ave. South to Rose St. Turn right on Rose. Go to 13th. Right on 13th. Left on Abadie.

University of Washington Driving Range
1/2 mi north of stadium; Seattle, WA 98195
(206) 543-8759. Pro: none.
Hours: 10am-7pm (winter) 9am-10pm (summer).
Lights: yes. **Covered:** yes. **Putting & chipping:** yes.
Services: lessons. **Directions:** I-5 N&S take exit 169 to NE 45th. Go east for 1.8 miles to Union Bay Pl NE. E for .1 mile to Clark Road. West to range. The range is located off Montlake Blvd.

Vanco Golf Range
703 N Devine; Vancouver, WA 98661
(360) 693-8811. Pros: Scott Blake, PGA. Chuck Milne, PGA.
Hours: 9am to 10pm (summer). 9am to 9pm (winter).
Lights: yes. **Covered:** yes. **Putting & chipping:** yes.
Services: club repair, custom clubs, lessons, pro shop.
Directions: from I-5 N&S take exit 1C to Mill Plain Road E for 4.1 miles to Devine Road. Range is on the left hand side of the road.

Westside Golf Range
106 NW 139th Street; Vancouver, WA 98685
(360) 573-2565. Manager: Kent Schmidt. Pro: Molly Miller, LPGA
Hours: hours vary depending upon the season.
Lights: yes. **Covered:** yes. **Putting & chipping:** yes.
Services: club repair, lessons, pro shop.
Directions: take 134th street exit off of I-5. Turn west bound on 134th street it will become Tenny Road. Range on the right.

Bogart Golf
10843 NE 8th Suite 110; Bellevue, Wa. (425) 646-9445
Services: lessons.

Caddy Shack Golf Shop
2614 A West Nob Hill Boulevard; Yakima, Wa. (509) 575-6461
Services: club repair, indoor driving range, sport tech swing analyzer, lessons.

Cart Service Euipment
10625 Pacific Avenue S.; Tacoma, Wa.; 1-800-344-0987
Services: golf cart sales and service.

Farwest Golf Cars of Washington, INC
7916 Pacific Highway East; Tacoma, Wa. 1-800-924-9424
Services: golf carts, golf cart repair.

Gals Golf Gear
11006 Pacific Avenue South; Tacoma, Wa. (253) 531-2773
Services: womens golf apparel and golf merchandise.

Golf Club Co., The
2423 Harrison Avenue NW; Olympia, Wa. (360) 352-1331
Services: custom-fitted clubs, full service repairs, accessories.

Golf USA
1210 N. Wenatchee Avenue; Wenatchee, Wa. (509) 662-7714
Services: club regripping, retail store, apparel, indoor range.

Golf Universe
7422 West Clearwater Avenue; Kennewick, Wa. (509) 783-1112
Services: golf retail store.

Golf Zone Training Studio
2603 151st Place NE; Redmond, Wa. (425) 556-9313
Services: lessons, swing analysis.

Golfing Gallery
1969 SW Hillcrest; Seattle, Wa. (206) 242-PUTT
Services: collectable golf art, prints, limited editions.

Guy Hyatt's Golf
8701 N Division Street; Spokane, Wa. (509) 465-9464
Services: discount golf merchandise.

Hagen Custom Golf
24826 164th SE; Covington, Wa. (206) 631-7754
Services: custom clubs, club repair, club refinishing.

Harris Conley Golf, INC
12700 NE 124th Street; Kirkland, Wa. (425) 814-2254
Services: custom clubs, club repair, club refinishing.

Jorgensen Golf *Julius Jorgensen, Owner/Pro, PGA*   **1-800-218-2373**
11700 Mukilteo Spdwy; STE 407; Mukilteo, Wa. (425) 349-1347, 787-9186
Services: indoor video lessons, club repair, upscale pro shop, USGA GHIN G.C.

Moe's Custom Golf
9616 Roosevelt Way NE; Seattle, Wa. (206) 523-7533
Services: club repair, custom clubs, club refinishing, club regrips.

National Golf
5114 Dartmouth Road; Spokane,Wa. (509) 927-GOLF
Services: discount golf merchandise, club repair.

National Golf
8701 N Division; Spokane, Wa. (509) 468-0660
Services: discount golf merchandise, club repair.

Nevada Bob's Discount Golf
14603 NE 20th; Bellevue Wa. (425) 641-6399
Services: large discount pro shop, club regripping and repairs.

Nevada Bob's Discount Golf
511 128th St. SE (Columbia Super Range); Everett, Wa. (425) 316-9202
Services: large discount pro shop, club regripping and repairs.

Nevada Bob's Discount Golf
31513 Pacific Hwy S; Federal Way, Wa. (253) 529-4023
Services: large discount pro shop, club regripping and repairs.

Nevada Bob's Discount Golf
4926A 196th SW; Lynnwood, Wa. (425) 774-1892
Services: large discount pro shop, club regripping and repairs.

Nevada Bob's Discount Golf
7223 170th Avenue; Redmond Wa. (425)497-9554
Services: large discount pro shop, club regripping and repairs.

Nevada Bob's Discount Golf
2020 W. Meeker (Riverbend Golf Complex); Kent, Wa. (253) 859-4000
Services: large discount pro shop, club regripping and repairs.

Northwest Golf Cart Service
22740 Hwy 99; Edmonds, Wa. (206) 240-7140
Services: golf cart sales and service.

Northwest Yamaha Golf Cars
7220 River Road E; Puyallup, Wa. (253) 445-1069 or 800-659-7843
Services: golf cart sales and service.

Olsen's Golf Shop
7612 Beverly Boulevard; Everett, Wa. (425) 355-9241
Services: club repair, club refinishing.

Pacific Discount Golf
31840 Pacific Highway S; Federal Way, Wa. (253) 839-6488
Services: club repair, club refinishing, lessons.

Pro Golf Discount
14121 NE 20th; Bellevue, Wa. (425) 641-6766
Services: club repair, club refinishing, discount pro shop.

Pro Golf Discount
1680 NW Mall Street; Issaquah, Wa. (425) 392-2333
Services: club repair, club refinishing, discount pro shop

Pro Golf Discount
301 Tukwila Parkway (Southcenter); Tukwila, Wa. (206) 431-0100
Services: club repair, club refinishing, discount pro shop.

Pro Golf Discount
10409 Aurora Avenue North; Seattle, Wa. (206) 527-7770
Services: club repair, club refinishing, discount pro shop.

Pro Golf Discount
18905 33rd Avenue West; Lynnwood, Wa. (206) 525-5518 or (425) 771-2131
Services: club repair, club refinishing, discount pro shop.

Pro Golf Discount
5015 Tacoma Mall Boulevard, Suite C; Tacoma, Wa. (253) 473-4290
Services: club repair, club refinishing, discount pro shop.

Pro Golf Discount
4225 Meridian Street; Bellingham, Wa. (360) 738-7101
Services: club repair, club refinishing, discount pro shop.

Pro Golf Discount
905 S 1rst Street; Yakima, Wa. (509) 248-0800
Services: club repair, club refinishing, discount pro shop.

Puetz Golf Superstore
1645 140th Avenue NE; Bellevue, Wa. (425) 747-0664
Services: club repair, club refinishing, discount pro shop, brand name clubs.

Puetz Golf Superstore
11762 Aurora Avenue N.; Seattle, Wa. (206) 362-2272
Services: club repair, refinishing, discount pro shop, lessons, video lessons.

Puetz Golf Superstore
6409 Tacoma Mall Boulevard; Tacoma, Wa. (253) 474-8288
Services: club repair, club refinishing, discount pro shop, brand name clubs.

Puetz Golf Superstore
402 Strander Blvd.; Tukwila, Wa. (206) 439-1740
Services: club repair, club refinishing, discount pro shop, brand name clubs.

Redbird Sports
4868 Beacon Avenue S.; Seattle, Wa. (206) 725-7872
Services: custom clubs.

Swingwerk Golf Instruction
1626 S 341st Place; #A2; Federal Way, Wa. (253) 661-9303
Services: lessons.

Tom Wells Golf Company
7806 Aurora Avenue North; Seattle, Wa. (206) 523-7124
Services: club repair, club refinishing, custom clubs, lessons.

Von's Golf Plus   *Jim Von Lossow owner*
7419 48th Avenue NE; Seattle, Wa. (206) 524-6716
Services: custom clubs, club repair, used clubs, putter collector & sales.

Wide World of Golf
N. 4921 Division; Spokane, Wa. (509) 489-4653
Services: club repair, custom clubs.

Washington State Regional Map

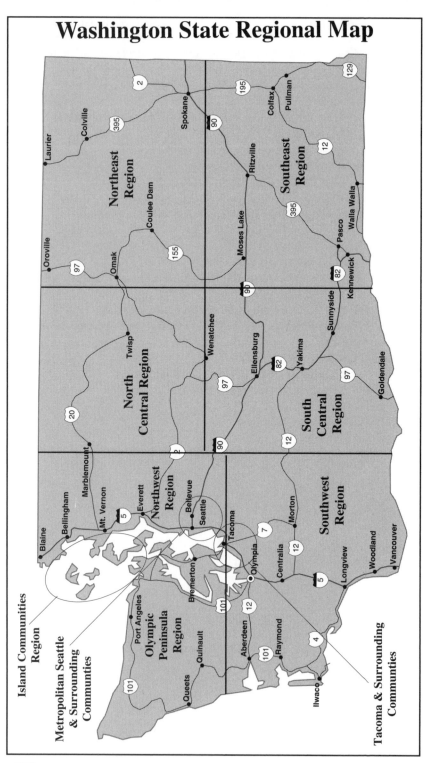

Island Communities Region

Gallery Golf Course
Holmes Harbor Golf Club
Island Greens
Lams Golf Links
Lopez Island Golf Course
Orcas Island Golf Course
Riviera Golf & Country Club
San Juan Golf & Country Club
Similk Beach Golf Course
Useless Bay Golf & Country Club
Vashon Island Golf & Country Club
Whidbey Island Golf & Country Club

Metropolitan Seattle & Surrounding Communities

Ballinger Lakes Golf Course
Bear Creek Country Club
Bellevue Municipal Golf Course
Brae Burn Golf & Country Club
Broadmoor Golf Club
Carnation Golf Course
Cascade Golf Course
Course at Taylor Creek, The
Crossroads Park Golf Course
Druids Glen Golf Club
Elk Run Golf Course
Fairwood Golf & Country Club
Family Golf Center at Kent
Foster Golf Links
Glen Acres Golf & Country Club
Glendale Golf & Country Club
Gold Creek Tennis & Sports Club
Green Lake Golf Course
Harbour Pointe Golf Club
Inglewood Golf & Country Club
Interbay Family Golf Center
Jackson Golf Club
Jefferson Golf Club
Kaddyshack Golf Center
Lynnwood Municipal Golf Course
Maplewood Golf Course
Members Club at Aldarra, The
Meridian Valley Golf & Country Club
Mill Creek Golf & Country Club

Mount Si Golf Course
Nile Golf & Country Club
Overlake Golf & Country Club
Plateau Club, The
Puetz Golf Center
Rainier Golf & Country Club
Red Wood Golf Center
Riverbend Golf Complex
Sahalee Country Club
Sand Point Golf Club
Seattle Golf Club
Snoqualmie Falls Golf Course
Snoqualmie Ridge TPC Golf Club
Southcenter Golf
Studio Fore Golf
Tall Chief Golf Course
Tam O' Shanter Golf & Country Club
The Golf Club at Newcastle
Twin Rivers Golf Course
Tyee Valley Golf Course
University of Washington Driving Range
Wayne Golf Course
Wellington Hills Golf Course
West Seattle Golf Course
Willows Run Golf Club

North Central Region
Alta Lake Golf Course
Bear Creek Golf Course
Crescent Bar Resort
Desert Canyon Golf Resort
Fairways at West Terrace
Kahler Glen Golf Course
Lake Chelan Golf Course
Lake Woods Golf Course
Leavenworth Golf Club
M A 8 Golf
Marine Golf Driving Range
Mount Cashmere Golf Course
Oasis Park Par 3
Quincy Valley Golf Course
Rock Island Golf Club
Three Lakes Golf Course
Wenatchee Golf & Country Club

Northeast Region

Al's Cariboo Trail Driving Range
Banks Lake Golf Club
Beacon Hill Golf Center
Big Bend Golf & Country Club
Chewelah Golf & Country Club
Colville Elks Golf Course
Creek at Qualchan, The
Deer Meadows Golf Course
Deer Park Golf Club
Downriver Golf Course
Esmeralda Golf Course
Hangman Valley Golf Club
Harrington Golf & Country Club
Indian Canyon Golf Course
Latah Short Course
Liberty Lake Golf Course
Manito Golf & Country Club
MeadowWood Golf Course
Odessa Golf Club
Okanogan Valley Golf Club
Oroville Golf Club
Painted Hills Golf Club
Pend Oreille Golf & Country Club
Pine Acres Par 3 Golf Course
Serendipity Golf Course
Sheridan Greens Golf Course
Spokane Country Club
Sun Dance Golf Course
Valley View Golf Course
Vic Meyer's Golf Course
Wandermere Golf Course

Northwest Region

Avalon Golf Club
Baker's Edge Golf Course
Battle Creek Golf Course
Bellingham Golf & Country Club
Birch Bay Golf Club
Birch Bay Village Golf Course
Blue Boy West
Camaloch Golf Club
Cedarcrest Golf Course
Columbia Super Range

Dakota Creek Golf & Country Club
Eaglemont
Echo Falls Golf Club
Everett Golf & Country Club
Evergreen Golf Course
Flowing Lake Golf Course
Gleneagle Golf Course
Grandview Golf Course
Hat Island Golf Course
Homestead Farms & Golf Resort
Iron Eagle Sports Center
Kayak Point Golf Course
Ken's Golf
Kenwanda Golf Course
Lake Padden Golf Course
Legion Memorial Golf Course
Lobo Country Club
Longshots Driving Range
Loomis Trail Golf Club
Monroe Golf Course
Mulligan's Driving Range
New World Pro Golf Center
North Bellingham Public Golf Course
Overlook Golf Course
Raspberry Ridge Golf Community
Riverside Golf Course
Rodarco Golf Range
Sandy Point Golf Course
Sauk Mountain View Golf Course
Semiahmoo Golf & Country Club
Shuksan Golf Club
Skagit Golf & Country Club
Snohomish Public Golf Course
Sudden Valley Golf & Country Club
SunLand Golf & Country Club
Walter E. Hall Memorial Golf Course

Olympic Peninsula Region
Alderbrook Golf & Yacht Club
Batstone Hill Driving Range
Canterwood Golf & Country Club
Chevy Chase Golf Club
Dungeness Golf & Country Club
Gig Harbor Golf & Country Club

Gold Mountain Golf Complex
Grow's Vineyard Greens
Horseshoe Lake Golf Course
Kitsap Country Green's
Kitsap Golf & Country Club
Lake Cushman Golf Course
Lake Limerick Golf Course
Lakeland Village Golf & Country Club
Madrona Links Golf Course
McCormick Woods
Meadowmeer Golf & Country Club
Northwest Golf Range
ParFect Driving Range
Performance Golf Center
Peninsula Golf Club
Port Ludlow Golf Course
Port Townsend Golf Course
Rolling Hills Golf Course
Shelton Bayshore Golf Course
Trophy Lake Golf & Casting
Village Greens Golf Course
Wing Point Golf & Country Club

South Central Region
Apple Tree Golf Course
Carey Lakes Golf Course
Cherry Hill Golf Club
Ellensburg Golf Club
Fisher Park Golf Course
Goldendale Country Club
Hot Springs Golf Course
Husum Hills Golf Course
Lower Valley Golf Club
Mount Adams Country Club
Royal City Golf Course
Sun Country Golf Resort
Suntides Golf Course
Westwood West Golf Course
Yakima Country Club
Yakima Elks Golf & Country Club

Evergreen Golf Center
Fairway Village Golf Course
Family Golf Center @ Tumwater
First Tee of Olympia, The
Golfgreen Golf Center
Grand Mound Driving Range
Gray's Harbor Country Club
Green Mountain Resort
Hartwood Golf Course
Hickory Stick Driving Range
High Valley Golf Course
Highland Golf Course
Indian Summer Golf & Country Club
Ironwood Green Public Golf Course
Lakeview Golf Challenge
Lewis River Golf Course
Longview Country Club
Maple Grove Golf
Meriwood Golf Course
Mint Valley Golf Course
Newaukum Valley Golf Course
Nisqually Valley Golf Course
Oaksridge Golf Course
Ocean Shores Golf Course
Olympia Country & Golf Club
Orchard Hills Golf & Country Club
Peninsula Golf Course
Pine Crest Golf Course
Rainbow Golf Driving Range
Riverside Golf Club
Ross's Driving Range
Royal Oaks Country Club
Scott Lake Golf Course
Skamania Lodge Golf Course
Skyline Golf Course
Surfside Golf Course
Tanwax Greens
Three Rivers Golf Course
Tri-Mountain Golf Course
Tumwater Valley Golf Club
Vanco Golf Range
Vicwood Golf Links
Westside Golf Range
Willapa Harbor Golf Club

Tacoma & Surrounding Communities

All Golf @ Tacoma
Allenmore Golf Course
American Lake VA Golf Course
Auburn Golf Course
Brookdale Golf Course
Christy's Range & Par 3
Classic Country Club
Druids Glen Golf Club
Elk Run Golf Course
Emerald Links Driving Range
Enumclaw Golf Course
Fircrest Golf Club
Fort Lewis Golf Club
Fort Steilacoom Golf Course
High Cedars Golf Club
Highlands Golf Course
Jade Greens Golf Course
Lake Spanaway Golf Course
Lake Wilderness Golf Course
Linden Golf & Country Club
Lipoma Firs Golf Course
Meadow Park Golf Course
Meridian Greens Golf Course & Driving Range
North Shore Golf Course
Oakbrook Golf & Country Club
Steamboat Golf
Sumner Meadows Golf Links
Tacoma Country & Golf Club
Tacoma Firs Golf Center
Tapps Island Golf Course
Twin Lakes Golf & Country Club
University Golf Club
Washington National
Whispering Firs Golf Club

In the sixteen years of writing golf books and doing golf research I have played golf with some very interesting people along the way but no one as fun and interesting as my friend Warren. You may know him better from ski world fame and his fifty plus years of producing ski films and making us laugh. Warrens love for skiing is only surpassed by his love for golf these days. This story is about one of our mis-adventures.

"THREE INCHES OF RAIN IS PAR"

The slap, slap, of the windshield wipers emphasized that it was going to be a really miserable day to be playing golf. It further substantiated my personal belief that golf is as dumb as skiing, but is for older people. I had made the arrangements a month ago and the two people I was going to play with had set the day aside in their busy schedule of corporate life. Since both of them are good golfers, I felt I could learn something if I hacked my way around 18 holes with them. What I learned is that the more I play golf the dumber I am when I try and play 18 holes while it is raining a half inch of cold rain an hour and the snow level is down to 2,000 feet and I am playing at about fifteen hundred feet above sea level.

My friends assured me when they made the reservation that the course is never crowded on Tuesday. It turned out that we were the only three people in this part of the world who were insane enough today, to wade around this particular golf course.

Several times, the slowly flowing water was up over the floorboards of our golf cart, but by that time I didn't even bother lifting my feet out of the muddy water, because on the first hole I was walking toward where my ball stuck a little way up out of a large puddle. This is where the clay topsoil has the tenacity of a five-foot octopus and it sucked my right shoe right off. By the time I got it back on, my sock was the color of the muddy clay and I started to doubt my theory that if a scratch golfer will play in this kind of weather, there must be something I can learn from him.

I learned that we laughed at how hard it is to try and hit a golf ball that is always half under water, no matter where it stops rolling on the fairway. Winter rules notwithstanding, we had to move the ball as much as a hundred feet from what would be considered the drop zone to get a spot dry enough where we could put the ball on grass and have enough room to get some sort of a hold with our spikes in the deep sticky clay.

I forgot to mention that before I left the clubhouse I got nailed for the price of a pair of waterproof pants and a waterproof windbreaker. What I really should have bought was a facemask, a snorkel and a pair of swim fins. When the club pro loaned me his waterproof hat and his waterproof glove I sort of realized that he knew something I didn't know. The hat worked the best because when I stood over the ball, the rain was really pouring off of the hat brim and all I had to do was to figure out where to line up the flowing water in relation to the ball. Maybe Golf Magazine could offer a tip of the month about lining up your hat-brim, rain-drippings with the ball.

Most of the sand traps were two thirds full of water so we played winter rules and took a drop on the sandy edge of the miniature lake. When we sloshed into the clubhouse to thaw out before starting the back nine holes I almost bought my own pair of Northwestern golf goulashes. These are fourteen-inch high rubber boots with golf spikes on the bottom. I can see how they might normally really work on rainy day like this, but some of the running water today would have come right over the top of them.

Bob, Dan, and I were laughing so much at the dumbness of our first nine holes that we decided to keep right on playing. However, Dan knew the course a lot better than either of us and he magically skipped a hole and in the driving rain and the low-lying clouds, Bob and I had no idea where we were. As we approached the green on what we thought was the third hole of the back nine, it turned out to be the green for the ninth hole. We had been sloshing around in this rain for two and a half hours so far so when our tour conductor, Dan said, "how does a cup of coffee sound to the two of you" we didn't even bother finishing that ninth hole for the second time.

The clubhouse restaurant was closed for the day because of lack of customers. However we did play on our own private golf course that day and the green fee was only $18.00 a person. Oh, and I have to add to that my cost of a waterproof windbreaker, a pair of waterproof pants, and a pair of goulashes with golf spikes in the doubtful chance that some other time in my life, I just might be dumb enough to get into a situation where I can't phone in sick when it's raining a half an inch an hour.

By: Warren Miller ©

"Can I Play Through"
by:

ꙡARREN MILLER ™

Coming *"SOON"* to your local pro shop or book store.

"Change is inevitable.
Except from vending machines."

What happens when a
golf book guy meets
up with a ski film guy?
They decide to do a
book together what
else! Coming to a book
store or pro-shop
near you!

"Can I Play Through" by:

WARREN MILLER

"The object is to hit a ball
approximately 13/4 inches in
diameter that is resting on one
eight thousand miles in diameter
and not hit the larger of the two."

"Three out of four golfers account
for seventy five percent of the
golfers in the world."

We all need to laugh at ourselves as golfers and at the rules of
golf. Warren takes a look at the lighter side of golf only the
way he can in this new hardbound book filled with humor and
featuring Warren's original hand drawn color illustrations. Look
for this upcoming book at your local book store or golf pro shop
or on line at www.warrenmiller.net or mac.productions.com.

Book4golf.com – Tee Times Made Easy

I have been writing golf books since 1986 and watched how the golf industry has changed over these years. Titanium. Who had heard of it in 1986? Well...you know the story.

The internet is growing at an incredible rate. It is quickly becoming the medium of choice for purchasing everything from cars, toys, airline tickets, even groceries. In only the first four years it reached over 50 million users, something that took radio 38 years to achieve and 13 years for television. With this tremendous growth, access to information and many other services is growing daily. The technology is revolutionizing the way we live, and play. I am pleased to say that this new medium is bringing golf reservations into the 21st century. **MAC Productions** is dedicated to providing the most accurate, up to date information available for each and every book. When we go to press we go to great lengths to make sure that the information is the best available at that time. I take pride in my product and in the service I provide to my customers. In all my years of business **Book4golf.com** is the first service that has been presented to me that complimented my books. Like myself, **Book4golf.com** is also, truly dedicated to customer service to golfers and the golf industry alike. I am pleased to be a part of this emerging network.

Imagine....you are sitting in your office, it is Monday...lunchtime. Stale sandwich in hand, followed by a lukewarm soda, you are dreaming of Saturday afternoon at your favorite course. You know that getting a tee time can be tough if you don't call right away the first available day that the reservations are taken for the weekend tee times. You can't take 20 minutes to call course after course to find one that has the slot you want, nor can you make long distance calls from work. The only way for you to get that tee time is by booking your times on-line and in advance.

Solution! Book4golf.com

Book4golf.com is the leading Internet and wireless based, real-time, tee-time reservation network in North America. The Book4golf.com website allows golfers to instantly reserve a tee time anytime and anywhere with no additional service charges. Golfers can book a tee time and retrieve valuable information about the course including green fees, dress codes, amenities, type of payment accepted, and local weather conditions.

Booking online with **Book4golf.com** offers golfers several advantages over traditional "call-in" and "walk-in" tee time bookings. It provides a one-stop, convenient location to browse thousands of golf courses across North America. Golfers can search for tee times using one or a combination of several search criteria including city, golf course name, price range, slope and rating, and region and up to the second, real time availability of tee times are accessible 24 hours per day, 7 days per week and 365 days per year. When tee times are being booked outside of the local calling area, booking over the internet also saves long distance calling charges.

Membership to **Book4golf.com** is free and navigation is smooth and seamless. You can enter as a Guest and browse freely through the system to check tee time availability or log in as a member to reserve tee times and to take advantage of any club discounts you might be entitled to through your own special member-ships. **Book4golf.com** also offers wireless access so you can book a tee time at your favorite course even when you're on the move.

And if you're planning a golf vacation, **Book4golf.com** Travel Services can customize just the right individual or corporate package through American West

Golf Vacations and Continental Airlines Golf Vacations.

Find out for yourself why Book4golf.com is North America's most convenient and easy-to-use internet golf reservation system.

Remember to check on the Book4golf.com web-site frequently as they are adding new golf courses in your area on a daily basis.

Your tee time is just a <u>click</u> away.

Washington State Participating Golf Courses

Avalon Golf Club
Birch Bay Golf Club
Buckskin Golf Club
Carnation Golf Course
Course at Taylor Creek, The
Deer Park Golf Club
Druids Glen Golf Club
Eaglemont
Echo Falls Golf Club
Gold Mountain Golf Course
Harbour Pointe Golf Club
Homestead Farms Golf Resort
Horseshoe Lake Golf Course
Jackson Park Golf Course
Jefferson Park Golf Club
Kayak Point Golf Course
Lake Padden Golf Course
Lake Wilderness Golf Course
LakeLand Village Golf & Country Club

Lipoma Firs Golf Course
Meadowmeer Golf & Country Club
Monroe Golf Course
Moses Pointe Golf Resort
Newaukum Valley Golf Course
North Bellingham Public Golf Course
Port Ludlow Golf Course
Snohomish Public Golf Course
Sudden Valley Golf & Country Club
Tall Chief Golf Course
The Golf Club at Newcastle
Three Rivers Golf Course
Trophy Lake Golf & Casting
Veterans Memorial Park Golf Course
Washington National Golf Club
West Richland Municipal Golf Course
West Seattle Golf Club
Willows Run Golf Club